Short Courses

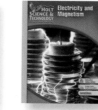

Teacher's Edition

WALK-THROUGH

Student Edition

CONTENTS IN BRIEF

HOLT, RINEHART AND WINSTON

A Harcourt Education Company

Orlando • **Austin** • New York • San Diego • Toronto • London

A program that gets EVERYONE pointed in the right direction.

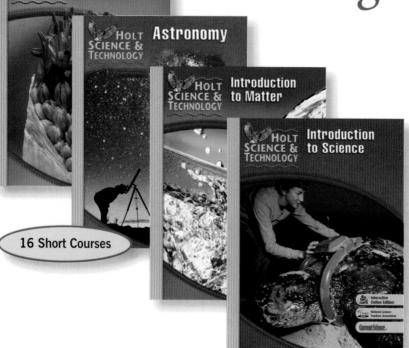

16 Short Courses

Every student, every class, every teacher is unique. Holt is here to help pave the way to success for each and every one.

MEETS THE INDIVIDUAL NEEDS OF YOUR STUDENTS

- Inclusion strategies and different learning styles are addressed to support all learners.
- Activities are labeled by ability level.
- Directed Reading worksheets and Chapter Tests are available that address different ability levels.
- English Language Learner support includes **ELL Strategies for Science**, a **Multilingual Glossary for Science**, and **Spanish Resources**.

FOSTERS READING FOR UNDERSTANDING

- The *Student Edition* is accessible with a clean, easy-to-follow design and highlighted vocabulary words that are defined in the margin at point of reference.
- Reading strategies are built into both the *Student Edition* and the *Teacher's Edition.*
- **Reading Comprehension Guide** and **Guided Reading Audio CDs** help students better understand the content.
- **Interactive Textbook** makes science content accessible to struggling readers and ELL students.
- **Live Ink**—exclusive to Holt—is a scientifically-researched tool that improves reading comprehension and raises test scores.
- **Student Edition on CD-ROM** provides students with the entire textbook on a CD-ROM so that they have less to carry home.

ASSESSMENT OPTIONS YOU CAN USE

- **Comprehensive Section** and **Chapter Reviews** and **Standardized Test Preparation** allow students to practice their test-taking skills.

- Customize your assessment with the **One-Stop Planner CD-ROM with Test Generator and State-Specific Resources.**

- **Science Tutor CD-ROM** serves as a personal tutor to help students practice what they learn.

- **Brain Food Video Quizzes** (on DVD and VHS) are game show-style quizzes that assess students' progress and help them prepare for tests.

BUILDS SCIENCE SKILLS THROUGH ACTIVITIES

- The laboratory program includes labs in each chapter, labs in the **LabBook** at the end of the *Student Edition,* six different lab books, and **Video Labs.**

- All labs are teacher-tested and rated by difficulty in the *Teacher's Edition,* so you can be sure that labs will be appropriate for your students.

- All of the program labs are provided on the **Holt Lab Generator CD-ROM.**

- **Virtual Investigations CD-ROM** provides a simulated lab experience in a safe environment with no clean up.

HOLT CIENCIAS Y TECNOLOGÍA — CIENCIAS DEL MEDIO AMBIENTE

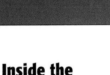

EcoLabs

HOLT SCIENCE & TECHNOLOGY

HOLT SCIENCE & TECHNOLOGY

Resource Disc Chapters 1-11

HOLT, RINEHART AND WINSTON

One-Stop Planner®
with Test Generator and State-Specific Resources
CD-ROM for Macintosh® and Windows®

HOLT SCIENCE & TECHNOLOGY

Chapter Resource Files for Short Course

F

Inside the Restless Earth

Skills Worksheets
Directed Reading A
Directed Reading B
Vocabulary and Section Summary
Section Reviews
Chapter Review
Reinforcement
Critical Thinking

Assessments
Section Quizzes
Chapter Test A
Chapter Test B
Chapter Test C
Performance-Based Assessment
Standardized Test Preparation

Labs and Activities
Datasheet for Chapter Lab
Datasheet for Quick Lab
Datasheet for LabBook
Vocabulary Activity
SciLinks® Activity

Answer Keys
Teacher Notes for Performance-Based Assessment
Lab Notes and Answers
Answer Key for Skills Worksheets, Assessments, and Activities

Teaching Transparency List
- L82 The Flow of Blood Through the Heart
- L83 The Flow of Blood Through the Body
- L84 The Role of Blood in Respiration
- P24 Exhaling, Pressure, and Fluid Flow
- Chapter Starter Transparencies
- Bellringer Transparencies
- Concept Mapping Transparencies

Programa de audio guiado en CD
Guided Reading Audio CD Program

HOLT CIENCIAS Y TECNOLOGÍA — LAS INTERACCIONES DE LA MATERIA

Direct Spanish read of the student text

L

Life Science

P INTRODUCTION TO SCIENCE

In addition to the short courses listed below, *Short Course P Introduction to Science* pro students with a sound foundation for their st science including topics such as careers in s scientific methods, models, and measureme

	A MICROORGANISMS, FUNGI, AND PLANTS	**B** ANIMALS
CHAPTER 1	**It's Alive!! Or, Is It?** • Characteristics of living things • Homeostasis • Heredity and DNA • Producers, consumers, and decomposers • Biomolecules	**Animals and Behavior** • Characteristics of animals • Classification of animals • Animal behavior • Hibernation and estivation • The biological clock • Animal communication • Living in groups
CHAPTER 2	**Bacteria and Viruses** • Binary fission • Characteristics of bacteria • Nitrogen-fixing bacteria • Antibiotics • Pathogenic bacteria • Characteristics of viruses • Lytic cycle	**Invertebrates** • General characteristics of invertebrates • Types of symmetry • Characteristics of sponges, cnidarians, arthropods, and echinoderms • Flatworms versus roundworms • Types of circulatory systems
CHAPTER 3	**Protists and Fungi** • Characteristics of protists • Types of algae • Types of protozoa • Protist reproduction • Characteristics of fungi and lichens	**Fishes, Amphibians, and Reptiles** • Characteristics of vertebrates • Structure and kinds of fishes • Development of lungs • Structure and kinds of amphibians and reptiles • Function of the amniotic egg
CHAPTER 4	**Introduction to Plants** • Characteristics of plants and seeds • Reproduction and classification • Angiosperms versus gymnosperms • Monocots versus dicots • Structure and functions of roots, stems, leaves, and flowers	**Birds and Mammals** • Structure and kinds of birds • Types of feathers • Adaptations for flight • Structure and kinds of mammals • Function of the placenta
CHAPTER 5	**Plant Processes** • Pollination and fertilization • Dormancy • Photosynthesis • Plant tropisms • Seasonal responses of plants	
CHAPTER 6		
CHAPTER 7		

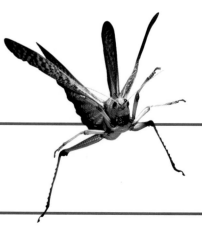

PROGRAM SCOPE AND SEQUENCE

Selecting the right books for your course is easy. Just review the topics presented in each book to determine the best match to your district curriculum.

C CELLS, HEREDITY, & CLASSIFICATION

Cells: The Basic Units of Life
- Cells, tissues, and organs
- Cell theory
- Surface-to-volume ratio
- Prokaryotic versus eukaryotic cells
- Cell organelles

The Cell in Action
- Diffusion and osmosis
- Passive versus active transport
- Endocytosis versus exocytosis
- Photosynthesis
- Cellular respiration and fermentation
- Cell cycle

Heredity
- Dominant versus recessive traits
- Genes and alleles
- Genotype, phenotype, the Punnett square and probability
- Meiosis
- Determination of sex

Genes and Gene Technology
- Structure of DNA
- Protein synthesis
- Mutations
- Heredity disorders and genetic counseling

The Evolution of Living Things
- Adaptations and species
- Evidence for evolution
- Darwin's work and natural selection
- Formation of new species

The History of Life on Earth
- Geologic time scale and extinctions
- Plate tectonics
- Human evolution

Classification
- Levels of classification
- Cladistic diagrams
- Dichotomous keys
- Characteristics of the six kingdoms

D HUMAN BODY SYSTEMS & HEALTH

Body Organization and Structure
- Homeostasis
- Types of tissue
- Organ systems
- Structure and function of the skeletal system, muscular system, and integumentary system

Circulation and Respiration
- Structure and function of the cardiovascular system, lymphatic system, and respiratory system
- Respiratory disorders

The Digestive and Urinary Systems
- Structure and function of the digestive system
- Structure and function of the urinary system

Communication and Control
- Structure and function of the nervous system and endocrine system
- The senses
- Structure and function of the eye and ear

Reproduction and Development
- Asexual versus sexual reproduction
- Internal versus external fertilization
- Structure and function of the human male and female reproductive systems
- Fertilization, placental development, and embryo growth
- Stages of human life

Body Defenses and Disease
- Types of diseases
- Vaccines and immunity
- Structure and function of the immune system
- Autoimmune diseases, cancer, and AIDS

Staying Healthy
- Nutrition and reading food labels
- Alcohol and drug effects on the body
- Hygiene, exercise, and first aid

E ENVIRONMENTAL SCIENCE

Interactions of Living Things
- Biotic versus abiotic parts of the environment
- Producers, consumers, and decomposers
- Food chains and food webs
- Factors limiting population growth
- Predator-prey relationships
- Symbiosis and coevolution

Cycles in Nature
- Water cycle
- Carbon cycle
- Nitrogen cycle
- Ecological succession

The Earth's Ecosystems
- Kinds of land and water biomes
- Marine ecosystems
- Freshwater ecosystems

Environmental Problems and Solutions
- Types of pollutants
- Types of resources
- Conservation practices
- Species protection

Energy Resources
- Types of resources
- Energy resources and pollution
- Alternative energy resources

Earth Science

	F INSIDE THE RESTLESS EARTH	**G** EARTH'S CHANGING SURFACE
CHAPTER 1	**Minerals of the Earth's Crust** • Mineral composition and structure • Types of minerals • Mineral identification • Mineral formation and mining	**Maps as Models of the Earth** • Structure of a map • Cardinal directions • Latitude, longitude, and the equator • Magnetic declination and true north • Types of projections • Aerial photographs • Remote sensing • Topographic maps
CHAPTER 2	**Rocks: Mineral Mixtures** • Rock cycle and types of rocks • Rock classification • Characteristics of igneous, sedimentary, and metamorphic rocks	**Weathering and Soil Formation** • Types of weathering • Factors affecting the rate of weathering • Composition of soil • Soil conservation and erosion prevention
CHAPTER 3	**The Rock and Fossil Record** • Uniformitarianism versus catastrophism • Superposition • The geologic column and unconformities • Absolute dating and radiometric dating • Characteristics and types of fossils • Geologic time scale	**Agents of Erosion and Deposition** • Shoreline erosion and deposition • Wind erosion and deposition • Erosion and deposition by ice • Gravity's effect on erosion and deposition
CHAPTER 4	**Plate Tectonics** • Structure of the Earth • Continental drifts and sea floor spreading • Plate tectonics theory • Types of boundaries • Types of crust deformities	
CHAPTER 5	**Earthquakes** • Seismology • Features of earthquakes • P and S waves • Gap hypothesis • Earthquake safety	
CHAPTER 6	**Volcanoes** • Types of volcanoes and eruptions • Types of lava and pyroclastic material • Craters versus calderas • Sites and conditions for volcano formation • Predicting eruptions	

WATER ON EARTH

 WEATHER AND CLIMATE

J ASTRONOMY

The Flow of Fresh Water
- Water cycle
- River systems
- Stream erosion
- Life cycle of rivers
- Deposition
- Aquifers, springs, and wells
- Ground water
- Water treatment and pollution

The Atmosphere
- Structure of the atmosphere
- Air pressure
- Radiation, convection, and conduction
- Greenhouse effect and global warming
- Characteristics of winds
- Types of winds
- Air pollution

Studying Space
- Astronomy
- Keeping time
- Types of telescope
- Radioastronomy
- Mapping the stars
- Scales of the universe

Exploring the Oceans
- Properties and characteristics of the oceans
- Features of the ocean floor
- Ocean ecology
- Ocean resources and pollution

Understanding Weather
- Water cycle
- Humidity
- Types of clouds
- Types of precipitation
- Air masses and fronts
- Storms, tornadoes, and hurricanes
- Weather forecasting
- Weather maps

Stars, Galaxies, and the Universe
- Composition of stars
- Classification of stars
- Star brightness, distance, and motions
- H-R diagram
- Life cycle of stars
- Types of galaxies
- Theories on the formation of the universe

The Movement of Ocean Water
- Types of currents
- Characteristics of waves
- Types of ocean waves
- Tides

Climate
- Weather versus climate
- Seasons and latitude
- Prevailing winds
- Earth's biomes
- Earth's climate zones
- Ice ages
- Global warming
- Greenhouse effect

Formation of the Solar System
- Birth of the solar system
- Structure of the sun
- Fusion
- Earth's structure and atmosphere
- Planetary motion
- Newton's Law of Universal Gravitation

A Family of Planets
- Properties and characteristics of the planets
- Properties and characteristics of moons
- Comets, asteroids, and meteoroids

Exploring Space
- Rocketry and artificial satellites
- Types of Earth orbit
- Space probes and space exploration

T7

Physical Science

K INTRODUCTION TO MATTER	**L** INTERACTIONS OF MATTER
CHAPTER 1	
The Properties of Matter • Definition of matter • Mass and weight • Physical and chemical properties • Physical and chemical change • Density	**Chemical Bonding** • Types of chemical bonds • Valence electrons • Ions versus molecules • Crystal lattice
CHAPTER 2	
States of Matter • States of matter and their properties • Boyle's and Charles's laws • Changes of state	**Chemical Reactions** • Writing chemical formulas and equations • Law of conservation of mass • Types of reactions • Endothermic versus exothermic reactions • Law of conservation of energy • Activation energy • Catalysts and inhibitors
CHAPTER 3	
Elements, Compounds, and Mixtures • Elements and compounds • Metals, nonmetals, and metalloids (semiconductors) • Properties of mixtures • Properties of solutions, suspensions, and colloids	**Chemical Compounds** • Ionic versus covalent compounds • Acids, bases, and salts • pH • Organic compounds • Biomolecules
CHAPTER 4	
Introduction to Atoms • Atomic theory • Atomic model and structure • Isotopes • Atomic mass and mass number	**Atomic Energy** • Properties of radioactive substances • Types of decay • Half-life • Fission, fusion, and chain reactions
CHAPTER 5	
The Periodic Table • Structure of the periodic table • Periodic law • Properties of alkali metals, alkaline-earth metals, halogens, and noble gases	
CHAPTER 6	

FORCES, MOTION, AND ENERGY

Matter in Motion
- Speed, velocity, and acceleration
- Measuring force
- Friction
- Mass versus weight

Forces in Motion
- Terminal velocity and free fall
- Projectile motion
- Inertia
- Momentum

Forces in Fluids
- Properties in fluids
- Atmospheric pressure
- Density
- Pascal's principle
- Buoyant force
- Archimedes' principle
- Bernoulli's principle

Work and Machines
- Measuring work
- Measuring power
- Types of machines
- Mechanical advantage
- Mechanical efficiency

Energy and Energy Resources
- Forms of energy
- Energy conversions
- Law of conservation of energy
- Energy resources

Heat and Heat Technology
- Heat versus temperature
- Thermal expansion
- Absolute zero
- Conduction, convection, radiation
- Conductors versus insulators
- Specific heat capacity
- Changes of state
- Heat engines
- Thermal pollution

ELECTRICITY AND MAGNETISM

Introduction to Electricity
- Law of electric charges
- Conduction versus induction
- Static electricity
- Potential difference
- Cells, batteries, and photocells
- Thermocouples
- Voltage, current, and resistance
- Electric power
- Types of circuits

Electromagnetism
- Properties of magnets
- Magnetic force
- Electromagnetism
- Solenoids and electric motors
- Electromagnetic induction
- Generators and transformers

Electronic Technology
- Properties of semiconductors
- Integrated circuits
- Diodes and transistors
- Analog versus digital signals
- Microprocessors
- Features of computers

O SOUND AND LIGHT

The Energy of Waves
- Properties of waves
- Types of waves
- Reflection and refraction
- Diffraction and interference
- Standing waves and resonance

The Nature of Sound
- Properties of sound waves
- Structure of the human ear
- Pitch and the Doppler effect
- Infrasonic versus ultrasonic sound
- Sound reflection and echolocation
- Sound barrier
- Interference, resonance, diffraction, and standing waves
- Sound quality of instruments

The Nature of Light
- Electromagnetic waves
- Electromagnetic spectrum
- Law of reflection
- Absorption and scattering
- Reflection and refraction
- Diffraction and interference

Light and Our World
- Luminosity
- Types of lighting
- Types of mirrors and lenses
- Focal point
- Structure of the human eye
- Lasers and holograms

Program resources make teaching and learning easier.

CHAPTER RESOURCES

A *Chapter Resources book* accompanies each of the 16 *Short Courses*. Here you'll find everything you need to make sure your students are getting the most out of learning science—all in one book.

Skills Worksheets
- Directed Reading A: Basic
- Directed Reading B: Special Needs
- Vocabulary and Chapter Summary
- Section Review
- Chapter Review
- Reinforcement
- Critical Thinking

Labs & Activities
- Datasheets for Chapter Labs
- Datasheets for Quick Labs
- Datasheets for LabBook Labs
- Vocabulary Activity
- SciLinks® Activity

Assessments
- Section Quizzes
- Chapter Test A: General
- Chapter Test B: Advanced
- Chapter Test C: Special Needs
- Performance-Based Assessment
- Standardized Test Preparation

Teacher Resources
- Lab Notes and Answers
- Teacher Notes for Performance-Based Assessment
- Answer Keys
- Lesson Plans
- Full-color **Teaching Transparencies**, plus section **Bellringers**, **Concept Mapping**, and **Chapter Starter Transparencies.**

ENGLISH-LANGUAGE LEARNER RESOURCES

- **Multilingual Glossary** provides simple definitions of key science terms in multiple languages.

Spanish materials are available for each *Short Course:*

- *Student Edition*
- **Spanish Resources** booklet contains worksheets and assessments translated into Spanish with an English **Answer Key.**
- **Guided Reading Audio CD Program**

ONLINE RESOURCES

- *Enhanced Online Editions* engage students and assist teachers with a host of interactive features that are available anytime and anywhere you can connect to the Internet.
- **Live Ink® Reading Help**—exclusive to Holt—is a scientifically-researched tool to improve students' reading comprehension and is proven to raise students' test scores.
- **SciLinks**—a Web service developed and maintained by the National Science Teachers Association—links you and your students to up-to-date online resources directly related to chapter topics.
- **go.hrw.com** links you and your students to online chapter activities and resources.
- **Current Science** articles relate to students' lives.

ADDITIONAL LAB AND SKILLS RESOURCES

- *Calculator-Based Labs* incorporates scientific instruments, offering students insight into modern scientific investigation.
- *EcoLabs & Field Activities* develops awareness of the natural world.
- *Holt Science Skills Workshop: Reading in the Content Area* contains exercises that target key reading skills.
- *Inquiry Labs* taps students' natural curiosity and creativity with a focus on the process of discovery.
- *Labs You Can Eat* safely incorporates edible items into the classroom.
- *Long-Term Projects & Research Ideas* extends and enriches lessons.
- *Math Skills for Science* provides additional explanations, examples, and math problems so students can develop their skills.
- *Science Skills Worksheets* helps your students hone important learning skills.
- *Whiz-Bang Demonstrations* gets your students' attention at the beginning of a lesson.

ADDITIONAL RESOURCES

- *Assessment Checklists & Rubrics* gives you guidelines for evaluating students' progress.
- *Holt Anthology of Science Fiction* sparks your students' imaginations with thought-provoking stories.
- *Holt Science Posters* visually reinforces scientific concepts and themes with seven colorful posters including **The Periodic Table of the Elements.**

- *Professional Reference for Teachers* contains professional articles that discuss a variety of topics, such as classroom management.
- *Program Introduction Resource File* explains the program and its features and provides several additional references, including lab safety, scoring rubrics, and more.
- *Science Fair Guide* gives teachers, students, and parents tips for planning and assisting in a science fair.
- *Science Puzzlers, Twisters & Teasers* activities challenge students to think about science concepts in different ways.

TECHNOLOGY RESOURCES

- *Guided Reading Audio CD Program,* available in English and Spanish, provides students with a direct read of each section.
- *HRW Earth Science Videotape* takes your students on a geology "field trip" with full-motion video.
- *Interactive Explorations CD-ROM Program* develops students' inquiry and decision-making skills as they investigate science phenomena in a virtual lab setting.
- *Holt Lab Generator CD-ROM* features all the labs from the *Holt Science & Technology* program and lab bank. Labs can be edited to fit classroom needs.
- *Virtual Investigations CD-ROM* makes it easy for students to practice science skills without the expense. Students perform lab activities in a safe, simulated environment.

- *One-Stop Planner CD-ROM®* organizes everything you need on one disc, including printable worksheets, customizable lesson plans, a powerful test generator, **PowerPoint® Resources, Lab Materials QuickList Software, Holt Calendar Planner, Interactive Teacher's Edition,** and more.
- *Science Tutor CD-ROMs* help students practice what they learn and provides immediate feedback.
- *Lab Videos* make it easier to integrate more experiments into your lessons without the preparation time and costs. Available on DVD and VHS.
- **Brain Food Video Quizzes** are game-show style quizzes that assess students' progress. Available on DVD and VHS.
- *Visual Concepts CD-ROMs* include graphics, animations, and movie clips that demonstrate key chapter concepts.

Science and Math Worksheets

The **Holt Science & Technology** program helps you meet the needs of a wide variety of students, regardless of their skill level. The following pages provide examples of the worksheets available to improve your students' science and math skills whether they already have a strong science and math background or are weak in these areas. Samples of assessment checklists and rubrics are also provided.

In addition to the skills worksheets represented here, **Holt Science & Technology** provides a variety of worksheets that are correlated directly with each chapter of the program. Representations of these worksheets are found at the beginning of each chapter in this *Teacher Edition*.

Many worksheets are also available on the Holt Web site. The address is **go.hrw.com**.

Science Skills Worksheets: Thinking Skills

BEING FLEXIBLE

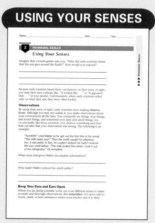

USING YOUR SENSES

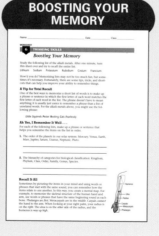

THINKING OBJECTIVELY

UNDERSTANDING BIAS

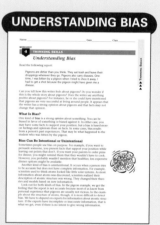

USING LOGIC

BOOSTING YOUR MEMORY

IMPROVING YOUR STUDY HABITS

READING A SCIENCE TEXTBOOK

Science Skills Worksheets: Experimenting Skills

SAFETY RULES!

DOING A LAB WRITE-UP
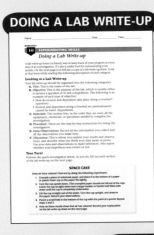

UNDERSTANDING VARIABLES
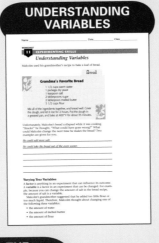

WORKING WITH HYPOTHESES
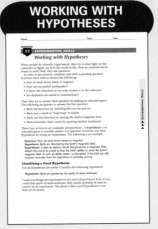

DESIGNING AN EXPERIMENT
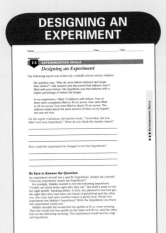

USING THE INTERNATIONAL SYSTEM OF UNITS (SI)

MEASURING
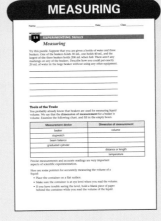

Science Skills Worksheets: Researching Skills

CHOOSING YOUR TOPIC
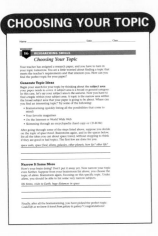

ORGANIZING YOUR RESEARCH
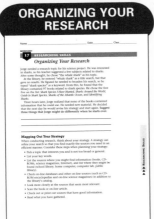

FINDING USEFUL SOURCES
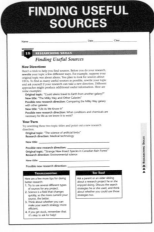

RESEARCHING ON THE WEB
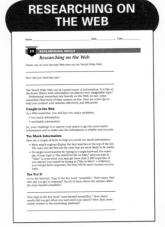

Science Skills Worksheets: Researching Skills (continued)

IDENTIFYING BIAS

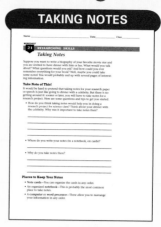

Identifying Bias

TAKING NOTES

Taking Notes

Science Skills Worksheets: Communicating Skills

SCIENCE WRITING

Science Writing

SCIENCE DRAWING

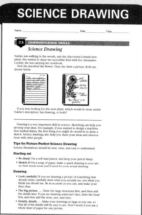

Science Drawing

USING MODELS TO COMMUNICATE

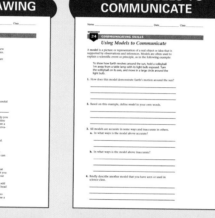

Using Models to Communicate

INTRODUCTION TO GRAPHS

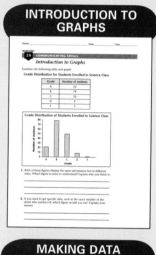

Introduction to Graphs

GRASPING GRAPHING

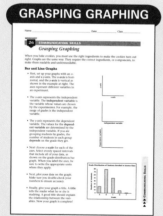

Grasping Graphing

INTERPRETING YOUR DATA

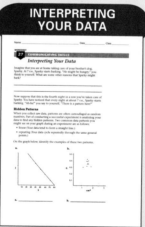

Interpreting Your Data

RECOGNIZING BIAS IN GRAPHS

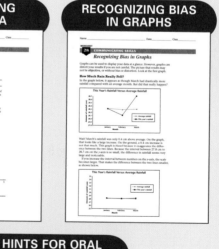

Recognizing Bias in Graphs

MAKING DATA MEANINGFUL

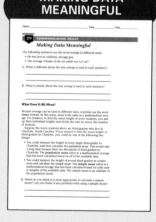

Making Data Meaningful

HINTS FOR ORAL PRESENTATIONS

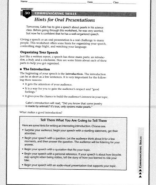

Hints for Oral Presentations

Math Skills for Science

ADDITION AND SUBTRACTION

Worksheet 1 — Addition Review

Addition is used to find the total of two or more quantities. The answer to an addition problem is known as the sum.

Worksheet 2 — Subtraction Review

Subtraction is used to take one number from another number. The answer to a subtraction problem is known as the difference.

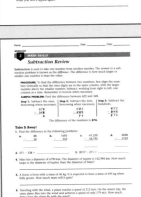

MULTIPLICATION

Worksheet 3 — Multiplying Whole Numbers

Worksheet 4 — A Shortcut for Multiplying Large Numbers

DIVISION

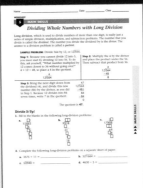

Worksheet 5 — Dividing Whole Numbers with Long Division

Worksheet 6 — Checking Division with Multiplication

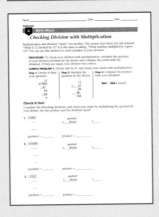

AVERAGES

Worksheet 7 — What Is an Average?

Worksheet 8 — Average, Mode, and Median

POSITIVE AND NEGATIVE NUMBERS

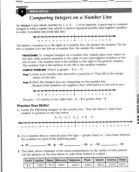

Worksheet 9 — Comparing Integers on a Number Line

Worksheet 10 — Arithmetic with Positive and Negative Numbers

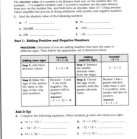

FRACTIONS

Worksheet 11 — What Is a Fraction?

Worksheet 12 — Reducing Fractions to Lowest Terms

Worksheet 13 — Improper Fractions and Mixed Numbers

Worksheet 14 — Adding and Subtracting Fractions

Worksheet 15 — Multiplying and Dividing Fractions

Math Skills for Science (continued)

RATIOS AND PROPORTIONS

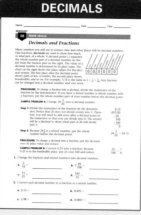

DECIMALS

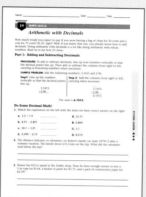

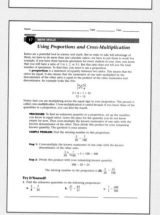

PERCENTAGES

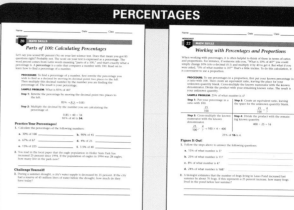

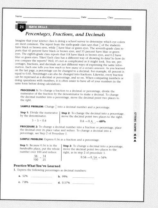

POWERS OF 10

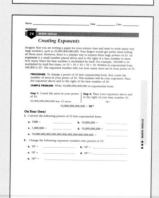

SCIENTIFIC NOTATION

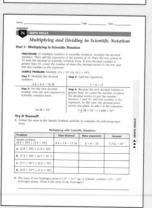

SI MEASUREMENT AND CONVERSION

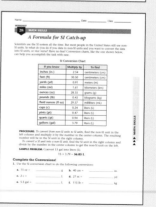

Math Skills for Science (continued)

GEOMETRY

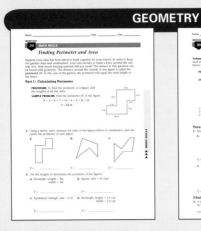

29 MATH SKILLS
Finding Perimeter and Area

Suppose your class has been asked to build a garden for your school. In order to keep the garden clean and undisturbed, your class decides to build a fence around the outside of it. How much fencing material will you need? The answer to this question can be found with geometry. The distance around the outside of a figure is called the perimeter (P). In the case of the garden, the perimeter will equal the total length of the fence.

Part 1: Calculating Perimeter

PROCEDURE: To find the perimeter of a figure, add the lengths of all the sides.

SAMPLE PROBLEM: Find the perimeter (P) of the figure.

9 + 5 + 4 + 7 + 10 + 4 + 5 + 8 = 52

P = **52 m**

1. Using a metric ruler, measure the sides of the figures below in centimeters, and calculate the perimeters of each figure.

2. Use the lengths to determine the perimeter of the figures.
   a. Rectangle: length = 4m, width = 2m
   b. Square: side = 45 mm
   c. Equilateral triangle: side = 6 m
   d. Rectangle: length = 3.5 cm, width = 2.4 cm

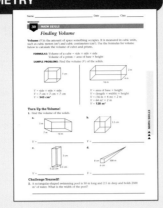

30 MATH SKILLS
Finding Volume

Volume (V) is the amount of space something occupies. It is measured in cubic units, such as cubic meters (m³) and cubic centimeters (cm³). Use the formulas for volume below to calculate the volume of cubes and prisms.

FORMULAS: Volume of a cube = side × side × side
Volume of a prism = area of base × height

SAMPLE PROBLEMS: Find the volume (V) of the solids.

V = side × side × side
V = 7 cm × 7 cm × 7 cm
V = **343 cm³**

V = area of base × height
V = (length × width) × height
V = (16 m × 4 m) × 2 m
V = 64 m² × 2 m
V = **128 m³**

Turn Up the Volume!

1. Find the volume of the solids.

Challenge Yourself!

2. A rectangular-shaped swimming pool is 50 m long and 2.5 m deep and holds 2500 m³ of water. What is the width of the pool?

THE UNIT FACTOR AND DIMENSIONAL ANALYSIS

31 MATH SKILLS
The Unit Factor and Dimensional Analysis

Part 1: Converting with a Unit Factor

SAMPLE PROBLEM A: Convert 3.5 km to millimeters.

On Your Own!

1. Convert the following measurements using a unit factor.

Conversion	Unit factor	Answer
a. 2.34 cm = ? mm		
b. 34.6 mL = ? L		
c. 12 kg = ? g		

MATH IN SCIENCE: INTEGRATED SCIENCE

32 MATH IN SCIENCE: INTEGRATED SCIENCE
Density

Calculate density, and identify substances using a density chart.

Density is a measure of the amount of mass in a certain volume. This physical property is often used to identify and classify substances. It is usually measured in grams per cubic centimeters, or g/cm³. The chart on the right lists the density of some common materials.

FORMULA: $density = \frac{mass}{volume}$

$D = \frac{m}{V}$

SAMPLE PROBLEM: What is the density of a billiard ball that has a volume of 100 cm³ and a mass of 250 g?

$D = \frac{250 \text{ g}}{100 \text{ cm}^3}$

$D = 2.5 \text{ g/cm}^3$

Densities of Substances

Substance	Density (g/cm³)
Gold	19.3
Mercury	13.5
Lead	11.4
Iron	7.87
Aluminum	2.7
Bone	1.7–2.0
Gasoline	0.66–0.69
Air (dry)	0.00119

Your Turn!

1. A loaf of bread has a volume of 2270 cm³ and a mass of 454 g. What is the density of the bread?

2. A liter of water has a mass of 1000 g. What is the density of water? (Hint: 1 mL = 1 cm³)

3. A block of wood has a density of 0.6 g/cm³ and a volume of 1.2 cm³. What is the mass of the block of wood? Be careful!

4. Use the data below to calculate the density of each unknown substance. Then use the density chart above to determine the identity of each substance.

Mass (g) Example: 4725	Volume (cm³) 350	Density (g/cm³) 4725 ÷ 350 = 13.5	Substance mercury
a. 171	15		
b. 148	40		
c. 475	250		
d. 680	1000		

33 MATH IN SCIENCE: INTEGRATED SCIENCE
The Pressure Is On!

Use math to learn about force and pressure.

FORMULA: $Pressure (Pa) = \frac{Force (N)}{Area (m^2)}$ $P_a = \frac{N}{m^2}$

Apply Some Pressure!

Pressure in the Atmosphere

34 MATH IN SCIENCE: INTEGRATED SCIENCE
Sound Reasoning

Use math skills to understand dolphin echolocation.

35 MATH IN SCIENCE: INTEGRATED SCIENCE
Using Temperature Scales

Convert between degrees Fahrenheit and degrees Celsius.

FORMULAS: Conversion from Fahrenheit to Celsius: $\frac{5}{9} \times (°F - 32) = °C$

Conversion from Celsius to Fahrenheit: $\frac{9}{5} \times °C + 32 = °F$

Turn Up the Temperature!

Challenge Yourself!

36 MATH IN SCIENCE: INTEGRATED SCIENCE
Radioactive Decay and the Half-life

Use half-lives of elements to learn about radioactive dating.

Table of Half-lives

Element	Half-life	Element	Half-life
Bismuth-212	60.5 minutes	Phosphorus-24	14.3 days
Carbon-14	5730 years	Polonium-215	0.0018 seconds
Chlorine-36	400,000 years	Radium-226	1600 years
Cobalt-60	5.26 years	Sodium-24	15 hours
Iodine-131	8.07 days	Uranium-238	4.5 billion years

1. Use the data in the table above to complete the following chart:

Table of Remaining Radium

Number of years after formation	0	1600	3200	6400	12,800
Percent of radium-226 remaining	100%	50%			

37 MATH IN SCIENCE: INTEGRATED SCIENCE
Rain-Forest Math

Calculate the damage to the world's rain forests.

The Damage Done

Math Skills for Science (continued)

MATH IN SCIENCE: LIFE SCIENCE

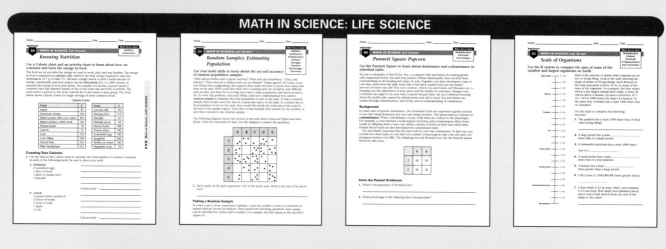

38 — Knowing Nutrition

39 — Random Samples: Estimating Population

40 — Punnett Square Popcorn

41 — Scale of Organisms

MATH IN SCIENCE: EARTH SCIENCE

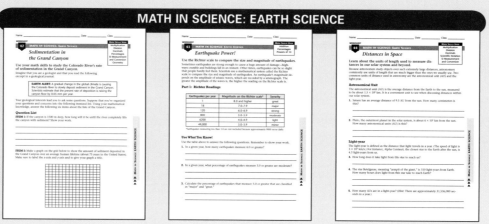

42 — Sedimentation in the Grand Canyon

43 — Earthquake Power!

44 — Distances in Space

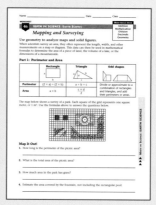

45 — Geologic Time Scale

46 — Mapping and Surveying

Math Skills for Science (continued)

MATH IN SCIENCE: PHYSICAL SCIENCE

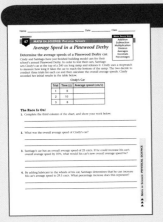

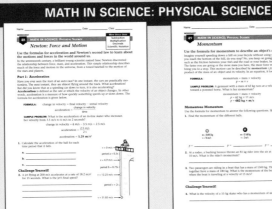

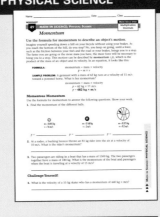

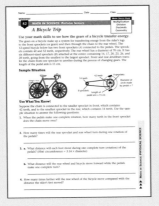

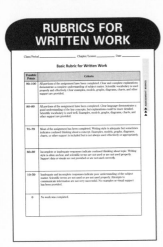

Assessment Checklist & Rubrics

The following is just a sample of over 50 checklists and rubrics contained in this booklet.

RUBRICS FOR WRITTEN WORK

RUBRIC FOR EXPERIMENTS

TEACHER EVALUATION OF COOPERATIVE LEARNING

TEACHER EVALUATION OF STUDENT PROGRESS

National Science Education Standards

The following lists show the chapter correlation of **Holt Science & Technology: Forces, Motion, and Energy** with the **National Science Education Standards** (grades 1–4).

Unifying Concepts and Processes

Standard	Chapter Correlation	
Systems, order, and organization Code: UCP 1	Chapter 5 Chapter 6	5.3 6.1, 6.4
Evidence, models, and explanation Code: UCP 2	Chapter 6	6.1, 6.2, 6.3
Change, constancy, and measurement Code: UCP 3	Chapter 1 Chapter 2 Chapter 4 Chapter 5 Chapter 6	1.1, 1.4 2.1, 2.2 4.1, 4.2, 4.3 5.2, 5.3 6.2, 6.3
Evolution and equilibrium Code: UCP 4	Chapter 1 Chapter 2	1.2 2.2
Form and function Code: UCP 5	Chapter 3 Chapter 4	3.3 4.3

Science as Inquiry

Standard	Chapter Correlation	
Abilities necessary to do scientific inquiry Code: SAI 1	Chapter 1 Chapter 2 Chapter 3 Chapter 4 Chapter 5 Chapter 6	1.1, 1.3, 1.4 2.1, 2.2 3.1, 3.2, 3.3 4.1, 4.2, 4.3 5.1 6.1, 6.2
Understandings about scientific inquiry Code: SAI 2	Chapter 1 Chapter 2 Chapter 4 Chapter 6	1.1, 1.3 2.1 4.1, 4.2 6.1

Science and Technology

Standard	Chapter Correlation	
Abilities of technological design Code: ST 1	Chapter 2	2.1
	Chapter 4	4.3
Understandings about science and technology Code: ST 2	Chapter 1	1.4
	Chapter 3	3.1, 3.2, 3.3
	Chapter 4	4.2, 4.3
	Chapter 5	5.3

Science in Personal and Social Perspectives

Standard	Chapter Correlation	
Populations, resources, and environments Code: SPSP 2	Chapter 5	5.4
	Chapter 6	6.4
Science and technology in society Code: SPSP 5	Chapter 1	1.2, 1.4

History and Nature of Science

Standard	Chapter Correlation	
Science as a human endeavor Code: HNS 1	Chapter 1	1.4
	Chapter 2	2.1
	Chapter 5	5.4
History of science Code: HNS 3	Chapter 1	1.4
	Chapter 3	3.2, 3.3

Physical Science Content Standards

Properties and changes of properties in matter

Standard	Chapter Correlation
A substance has characteristic properties, such as density, a boiling point, and solubility, all of which are independent of the amount of the sample. A mixture of substances often can be separated into the original substances using one or more of the characteristic properties. Code: PS 1a	**Chapter 3** 3.2, 3.3

Motion and forces

Standard	Chapter Correlation
The motion of an object can be described by its position, direction of motion, and speed. That motion can be measured and represented on a graph. Code: PS 2a	**Chapter 1** 1.1
An object that is not being subjected to a force will continue to move at a constant speed and in a straight line. Code: PS 2b	**Chapter 1** 1.2 **Chapter 2** 2.2
If more than one force acts on an object along a straight line, then the forces will reinforce or cancel one another, depending on their direction and magnitude. Unbalanced forces will cause changes in the speed or direction of an object's motion. Code: PS 2c	**Chapter 1** 1.2, 1.3, 1.4 **Chapter 2** 2.2 **Chapter 3** 3.2

Transfer of energy

Standard	Chapter Correlation
Energy is a property of many substances and is associated with heat, light, electricity, mechanical motion, sound, nuclei, and the nature of a chemical. Energy is transferred in many ways. Code: PS 3a	**Chapter 4** 4.1 **Chapter 5** 5.1, 5.2, 5.3, 5.4 **Chapter 6** 6.1, 6.2, 6.3, 6.4
Heat moves in predictable ways, flowing from warmer objects to cooler ones, until both reach the same temperature. Code: PS 3b	**Chapter 6** 6.1, 6.2, 6.3, 6.4
Electrical circuits provide a means of transferring electrical energy when heat, light, sound, and chemical changes are produced. Code: PS 3d	**Chapter 5** 5.1
In most chemical and nuclear reactions, energy is transferred into or out of a system. Heat, light, mechanical motion, or electricity might all be involved in such transfers. Code: PS 3e	**Chapter 5** 5.1, 5.4
The sun is a major source of energy for changes on the earth's surface. The sun loses energy by emitting light. A tiny fraction of that light reaches the earth, transferring energy from the sun to the earth. The sun's energy arrives as light with a range of wavelengths, consisting of visible light, infrared, and ultraviolet radiation. Code: PS 3f	**Chapter 5** 5.1, 5.2, 5.4

HOLT
SCIENCE &
TECHNOLOGY

Forces, Motion, and Energy

HOLT, RINEHART AND WINSTON

A Harcourt Education Company

Orlando • **Austin** • New York • San Diego • Toronto • London

Acknowledgments

Contributing Authors

Leila Dumas, MA
Former Physics Teacher
Lago Vista, Texas

William G. Lamb, Ph.D.
Winningstad Chair in the Physical Sciences
Oregon Episcopal School
Portland, Oregon

Inclusion and Special Needs Consultant

Ellen McPeek Glisan
Special Needs Consultant
San Antonio, Texas

Safety Reviewer

Jack Gerlovich, Ph.D.
Associate Professor
School of Education
Drake University
Des Moines, Iowa

Academic Reviewers

Howard L. Brooks, Ph.D.
Professor of Physics & Astronomy
Department of Physics & Astronomy
DePauw University
Greencastle, Indiana

Simonetta Frittelli, Ph.D.
Associate Professor
Department of Physics
Duquesne University
Pittsburgh, Pennsylvania

David S. Hall, Ph.D.
Assistant Professor of Physics
Department of Physics
Amherst College
Amherst, Massachusetts

William H. Ingham, Ph.D.
Professor of Physics
James Madison University
Harrisonburg, Virginia

David Lamp, Ph.D.
Associate Professor of Physics
Physics Department
Texas Tech University
Lubbock, Texas

Mark Mattson, Ph.D.
Director, College of Science and Mathematics Learning Center
James Madison University
Harrisonburg, Virginia

H. Michael Sommermann, Ph.D.
Professor of Physics
Physics Department
Westmont College
Santa Barbara, California

Lab Testing

Barry L. Bishop
Science Teacher and Department Chair
San Rafael Junior High School
Ferron, Utah

Vicky Farland
Science Teacher
Crane Junior High School
Yuma, Arizona

Rebecca Ferguson
Science Teacher
North Ridge Middle School
North Richland Hills, Texas

Jennifer Ford
Science Teacher and Dept. Chair
North Ridge Middle School
North Richland Hills, Texas

C. John Graves
Science Teacher
Monforton Middle School
Bozeman, Montana

Dennis Hanson
Science Teacher and Dept. Chair
Big Bear Middle School
Big Bear Lake, California

Norman E. Holcomb
Science Teacher
Marion Elementary School
Marion, Ohio

Edith C. McAlanis
Science Teacher and Department Chair
Socorro Middle School
El Paso, Texas

Terry J. Rakes
Science Teacher
Elmwood Junior High School
Rogers, Arkansas

David M. Sparks
Science Teacher
Redwater Junior High School
Redwater, Texas

Larry Tackett
Science Teacher and Department Chair
Andrew Jackson Middle School
Cross Lanes, West Virginia

Elsie N. Waynes
Science Teacher and Department Chair
R. H. Terrell Junior High School
Washington, D.C.

Sharon L. Woolf
Science Teacher
Langston Hughes Middle School
Reston, Virginia

John Zambo
Science Teacher
Elizabeth Ustach Middle School
Modesto, California

Printed in the United States of America

ISBN 0-03-035984-8

1 2 3 4 5 6 7 048 09 08 07 06 05

M Forces, Motion, and Energy

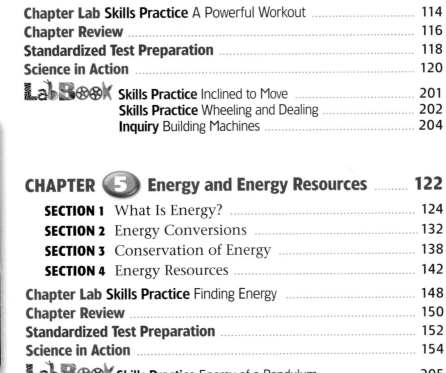

Labs and Activities

INTERNET ACTIVITY

Go to go.hrw.com and type in the red keyword.

SCHOOL to HOME

READING STRATEGY

How to Use Your Textbook

Your Roadmap for Success with Holt Science and Technology

What You Will Learn

At the beginning of every section you will find the section's objectives and vocabulary terms. The objectives tell you what you'll need to know after you finish reading the section.

Vocabulary terms are listed for each section. Learn the definitions of these terms because you will most likely be tested on them. Each term is highlighted in the text and is defined at point of use and in the margin. You can also use the glossary to locate definitions quickly.

STUDY TIP Reread the objectives and the definitions to the terms when studying for a test to be sure you know the material.

Get Organized

A Reading Strategy at the beginning of every section provides tips to help you organize and remember the information covered in the section. Keep a science notebook so that you are ready to take notes when your teacher reviews the material in class. Keep your assignments in this notebook so that you can review them when studying for the chapter test.

SECTION 4

Gravity: A Force of Attraction

Have you ever seen a video of astronauts on the moon? They bounce around like beach balls even though they wear big, bulky spacesuits. Why is leaping on the moon easier than leaping on Earth?

The answer is gravity. **Gravity** is a force of attraction between objects that is due to their masses. The force of gravity can change the motion of an object by changing its speed, direction, or both. In this section, you will learn about gravity and its effects on objects, such as the astronaut in **Figure 1.**

The Effects of Gravity on Matter

All matter has mass. Gravity is a result of mass. Therefore, all matter is affected by gravity. That is, all objects experience an attraction toward all other objects. This gravitational force pulls objects toward each other. Right now, because of gravity, you are being pulled toward this book, your pencil, and every other object around you.

These objects are also being pulled toward you and toward each other because of gravity. So why don't you see the effects of this attraction? In other words, why don't you notice objects moving toward each other? The reason is that the mass of most objects is too small to cause a force large enough to move objects toward each other. However, you are familiar with one object that is massive enough to cause a noticeable attraction—the Earth.

What You Will Learn

- Describe gravity and its effect on matter.
- Explain the law of universal gravitation.
- Describe the difference between mass and weight.

Vocabulary
gravity
weight
mass

READING STRATEGY

Paired Summarizing Read this section silently. In pairs, take turns summarizing the material. Stop to discuss ideas that seem confusing.

gravity a force of attraction between objects that is due to their masses

Figure 1 Because the moon has less gravity than the Earth does, walking on the moon's surface was a very bouncy experience for the Apollo astronauts.

134   Chapter 5   Matter in Motion

Be Resourceful—Use the Web

SciLinks boxes in your textbook take you to resources that you can use for science projects, reports, and research papers. Go to **scilinks.org** and type in the **SciLinks code** to find information on a topic.

Visit go.hrw.com
Check out the **Current Science®** magazine articles and other materials that go with your textbook at **go.hrw.com.** Click on the textbook icon and the table of contents to see all of the resources for each chapter.

The Size of Earth's Gravitational Force

Compared with all objects around you, Earth has a huge mass. Therefore, Earth's gravitational force is very large. You must apply forces to overcome Earth's gravitational force any time you lift objects or even parts of your body.

Earth's gravitational force pulls everything toward the center of Earth. Because of this force, the books, tables, and chairs in the room stay in place, and dropped objects fall to Earth rather than moving together or toward you.

Reading Check Why must you exert a force to pick up an object? *(See the Appendix for answers to Reading Checks.)*

Newton and the Study of Gravity

For thousands of years, people asked two very puzzling questions: Why do objects fall toward Earth, and what keeps the planets moving in the sky? The two questions were treated separately until 1665 when a British scientist named Sir Isaac Newton realized that they were two parts of the same question.

The Core of an Idea

The legend is that Newton made the connection between the two questions when he watched a falling apple, as shown in **Figure 2.** He knew that unbalanced forces are needed to move or change the motion of objects. He concluded that an unbalanced force on the apple made the apple fall. And he reasoned that an unbalanced force on the moon kept the moon moving circularly around Earth. He proposed that these two forces are actually the same force—a force of attraction called *gravity*.

The Birth of a Law

Newton summarized his ideas about gravity in a law now known as th[...] *gravitation.* 1[...] the relation[...] gravitational [...] distance. Th[...] *versal* becau[...] objects in th[...]

CONNECTION TO Biology

Seeds and Gravity Seeds respond to gravity. The ability to respond to gravity causes seeds to send roots down and the green shoot up. But scientists do not understand how seeds can sense gravity. Plan an experiment to study how seedlings respond to gravity. After getting your teacher's approval, do your experiment and report your observations in a poster.

ACTIVITY

Figure 2 *Sir Isaac Newton realized that the same unbalanced force affected the motions of the apple and the moon.*

Units of Weight and Mass

You have learned that the SI unit of force is a newton (N). Gravity is a force, and weight is a measure of gravity. So, weight is also measured in newtons. The SI unit of mass is the kilogram (kg). Mass is often measured in grams (g) and milligrams (mg) as well. On Earth, a 100 g object, such as the apple shown in **Figure 7**, weighs about 1 N.

When you use a bathroom scale, you are measuring the gravitational force between your body and Earth. So, you are measuring your weight, which should be given in newtons. However, many bathroom scales have units of pounds and kilograms instead of newtons. Thus, people sometimes mistakenly think that the kilogram (like the pound) is a unit of weight.

Figure 7 *A small apple weighs approximately 1 N.*

SECTION Review

Summary

- Gravity is a force of attraction between objects that is due to their masses.
- The law of universal gravitation states that all objects in the universe attract each other through gravitational force.
- Gravitational force increases as mass increases.
- Gravitational force decreases as distance increases.
- Weight and mass are not the same. Mass is the amount of matter in an object. Weight is a measure of the gravitational force on an object.

Using Key Terms

1. In your own words, write a definition for the term *gravity*.

2. Use each of the following terms in a separate sentence: *mass* and *weight*.

Understanding Key Ideas

3. If Earth's mass doubled without changing its size, your weight would
   a. increase because gravitational force increases.
   b. decrease because gravitational force increases.
   c. increase because gravitational force decreases.
   d. not change because you are still on Earth.

4. What is the law of universal gravitation?

5. How does the mass of an object relate to the gravitational force that the object exerts on other objects?

6. How does the distance between objects affect the gravitational force between them?

7. Why are mass and weight often confused?

Math Skills

8. The gravitational force on Jupiter is approximately 2.3 times the gravitational force on Earth. If an object has a mass of 70 kg and a weight of 686 N on Earth, what would the object's mass and weight be on Jupiter?

Critical Thinking

9. **Applying Concepts** Your friend thinks that there is no gravity in space. How could you explain to your friend that there must be gravity in space?

10. **Making Comparisons** Explain why it is your weight and not your mass that would change *if you landed on Mars*.

SCILINKS. **NSTA**

Developed and maintained by the National Science Teachers Association

For a variety of links related to this chapter, go to **www.scilinks.org**

Topic: Matter and Gravity
SciLinks code: HSM0922

139

Use the Illustrations and Photos

Art shows complex ideas and processes. Learn to analyze the art so that you better understand the material you read in the text.

Tables and graphs display important information in an organized way to help you see relationships.

A picture is worth a thousand words. Look at the photographs to see relevant examples of science concepts that you are reading about.

Answer the Section Reviews

Section Reviews test your knowledge of the main points of the section. Critical Thinking items challenge you to think about the material in greater depth and to find connections that you infer from the text.

STUDY TIP When you can't answer a question, reread the section. The answer is usually there.

Do Your Homework

Your teacher may assign worksheets to help you understand and remember the material in the chapter.

STUDY TIP Don't try to answer the questions without reading the text and reviewing your class notes. A little preparation up front will make your homework assignments a lot easier. Answering the items in the Chapter Review will help prepare you for the chapter test.

Visit Holt Online Learning

If your teacher gives you a special password to log onto the **Holt Online Learning** site, you'll find your complete textbook on the Web. In addition, you'll find some great learning tools and practice quizzes. You'll be able to see how well you know the material from your textbook.

SAFETY FIRST!

Exploring, inventing, and investigating are essential to the study of science. However, these activities can also be dangerous. To make sure that your experiments and explorations are safe, you must be aware of a variety of safety guidelines. You have probably heard of the saying, "It is better to be safe than sorry." This is particularly true in a science classroom where experiments and explorations are being performed. Being uninformed and careless can result in serious injuries. Don't take chances with your own safety or with anyone else's.

The following pages describe important guidelines for staying safe in the science classroom. Your teacher may also have safety guidelines and tips that are specific to your classroom and laboratory. Take the time to be safe.

Safety Rules!

Start Out Right

Always get your teacher's permission before attempting any laboratory exploration. Read the procedures carefully, and pay particular attention to safety information and caution statements. If you are unsure about what a safety symbol means, look it up or ask your teacher. You cannot be too careful when it comes to safety. If an accident does occur, inform your teacher immediately regardless of how minor you think the accident is.

If you are instructed to note the odor of a substance, wave the fumes toward your nose with your hand. Never put your nose close to the source.

Safety Symbols

All of the experiments and investigations in this book and their related worksheets include important safety symbols to alert you to particular safety concerns. Become familiar with these symbols so that when you see them, you will know what they mean and what to do. It is important that you read this entire safety section to learn about specific dangers in the laboratory.

Eye protection	Clothing protection	Hand safety

Heating safety	Electric safety	Chemical safety

Animal safety	Sharp object	Plant safety

Eye Safety

Wear safety goggles when working around chemicals, acids, bases, or any type of flame or heating device. Wear safety goggles any time there is even the slightest chance that harm could come to your eyes. If any substance gets into your eyes, notify your teacher immediately and flush your eyes with running water for at least 15 minutes. Treat any unknown chemical as if it were a dangerous chemical. Never look directly into the sun. Doing so could cause permanent blindness.

Avoid wearing contact lenses in a laboratory situation. Even if you are wearing safety goggles, chemicals can get between the contact lenses and your eyes. If your doctor requires that you wear contact lenses instead of glasses, wear eye-cup safety goggles in the lab.

Safety Equipment

Know the locations of the nearest fire alarms and any other safety equipment, such as fire blankets and eyewash fountains, as identified by your teacher, and know the procedures for using the equipment.

Neatness

Keep your work area free of all unnecessary books and papers. Tie back long hair, and secure loose sleeves or other loose articles of clothing, such as ties and bows. Remove dangling jewelry. Don't wear open-toed shoes or sandals in the laboratory. Never eat, drink, or apply cosmetics in a laboratory setting. Food, drink, and cosmetics can easily become contaminated with dangerous materials.

Certain hair products (such as aerosol hair spray) are flammable and should not be worn while working near an open flame. Avoid wearing hair spray or hair gel on lab days.

Sharp/Pointed Objects

Use knives and other sharp instruments with extreme care. Never cut objects while holding them in your hands. Place objects on a suitable work surface for cutting.

Be extra careful when using any glassware. When adding a heavy object to a graduated cylinder, tilt the cylinder so that the object slides slowly to the bottom.

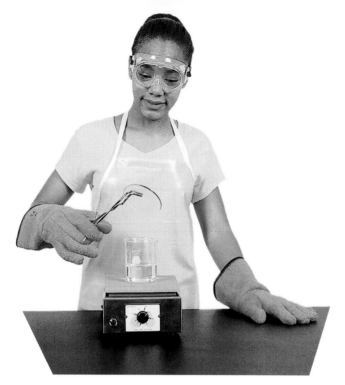

Chemicals

Wear safety goggles when handling any potentially dangerous chemicals, acids, or bases. If a chemical is unknown, handle it as you would a dangerous chemical. Wear an apron and protective gloves when you work with acids or bases or whenever you are told to do so. If a spill gets on your skin or clothing, rinse it off immediately with water for at least 5 minutes while calling to your teacher.

Never mix chemicals unless your teacher tells you to do so. Never taste, touch, or smell chemicals unless you are specifically directed to do so. Before working with a flammable liquid or gas, check for the presence of any source of flame, spark, or heat.

Heat

Wear safety goggles when using a heating device or a flame. Whenever possible, use an electric hot plate as a heat source instead of using an open flame. When heating materials in a test tube, always angle the test tube away from yourself and others. To avoid burns, wear heat-resistant gloves whenever instructed to do so.

Electricity

Be careful with electrical cords. When using a microscope with a lamp, do not place the cord where it could trip someone. Do not let cords hang over a table edge in a way that could cause equipment to fall if the cord is accidentally pulled. Do not use equipment with damaged cords. Be sure that your hands are dry and that the electrical equipment is in the "off" position before plugging it in. Turn off and unplug electrical equipment when you are finished.

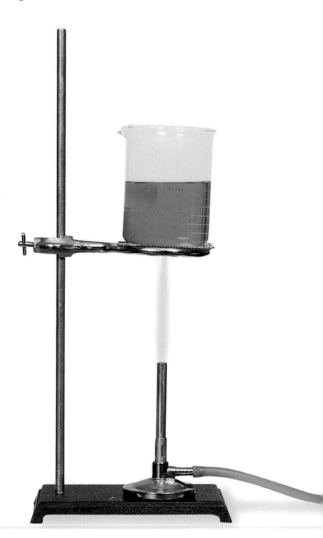

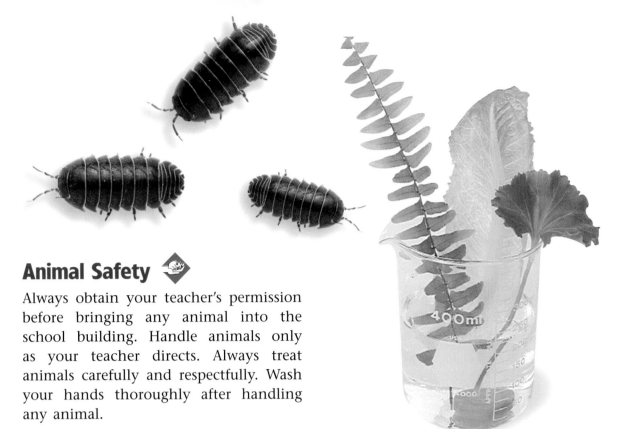

Animal Safety

Always obtain your teacher's permission before bringing any animal into the school building. Handle animals only as your teacher directs. Always treat animals carefully and respectfully. Wash your hands thoroughly after handling any animal.

Plant Safety

Do not eat any part of a plant or plant seed used in the laboratory. Wash your hands thoroughly after handling any part of a plant. When in nature, do not pick any wild plants unless your teacher instructs you to do so.

Glassware

Examine all glassware before use. Be sure that glassware is clean and free of chips and cracks. Report damaged glassware to your teacher. Glass containers used for heating should be made of heat-resistant glass.

Matter in Motion
Chapter Planning Guide

Compression guide:
To shorten instruction because of time limitations, omit Section 4.

OBJECTIVES	LABS, DEMONSTRATIONS, AND ACTIVITIES	TECHNOLOGY RESOURCES
PACING • 135 min pp. 2–9 **Chapter Opener**	**SE** Start-up Activity, p. 3 GENERAL	**OSP** Parent Letter ■ **CD** Student Edition on CD-ROM **CD** Guided Reading Audio CD ■ **TR** Chapter Starter Transparency* **VID** Brain Food Video Quiz
Section 1 Measuring Motion • Describe the motion of an object by the position of the object in relation to a reference point. • Identify the two factors that determine speed. • Explain the difference between speed and velocity. • Analyze the relationship between velocity and acceleration. • Demonstrate that changes in motion can be measured and represented on a graph.	**TE** Demonstration Models, p. 4 GENERAL **SE** School-to-Home Activity What's Your Speed?, p. 5 GENERAL **TE** Connection Activity Math, p. 5 GENERAL **TE** Activity The Speed of Light, p. 6 ADVANCED **TE** Activity Diagramming Acceleration, p. 7 BASIC **SE** Skills Practice Lab Detecting Acceleration, p. 26 GENERAL **SE** Skills Practice Lab Built for Speed, p. 192 GENERAL **LB** Calculator-Based Labs, The Fast Track ADVANCED **LB** Calculator-Based Labs, Graphing Your Motion ADVANCED	**OSP** Lesson Plans (also in print) **TR** Bellringer Transparency* **TR** P11 A Graph Showing Speed* **TR** P12 Finding Resultant Velocity* **TR** P13 Calculating Average Acceleration* **TR** P14 A Graph Showing Acceleration* **CRF** SciLinks Activity* GENERAL **CD** Interactive Explorations CD-ROM Force in the Forest GENERAL **CD** Science Tutor
PACING • 45 min pp. 10–13 **Section 2 What Is a Force?** • Describe forces, and explain how forces act on objects. • Determine the net force when more than one force is acting on an object. • Compare balanced and unbalanced forces. • Describe ways that unbalanced forces cause changes in motion.	**TE** Activity Bridge Building, p. 10 GENERAL **SE** Science in Action Math, Social Studies, and Language Arts Activities, pp. 32–33 GENERAL	**OSP** Lesson Plans (also in print) **TR** Bellringer Transparency* **TR** P15 Forces in the Same Direction; Forces in Opposite Directions* **CD** Science Tutor
PACING • 45 min pp. 14–19 **Section 3 Friction: A Force That Opposes Motion** • Explain why friction occurs. • List the two types of friction, and give examples of each type. • Explain how friction can be both harmful and helpful.	**TE** Activity Fingerprints, p. 14 GENERAL **SE** Quick Lab The Friction 500, p. 15 GENERAL **SE** School-to-Home Activity Comparing Friction, p. 16 GENERAL **TE** Connection Activity Real World, p. 16 ADVANCED **SE** Quick Lab Reducing Friction, p. 18 GENERAL **SE** Skills Practice Lab Science Friction, p. 194 GENERAL	**OSP** Lesson Plans (also in print) **TR** Bellringer Transparency* **TR** P16 Force and Friction* **TR** P17 Static Friction* **SE** Internet Activity, p. 17 GENERAL **CD** Interactive Explorations CD-ROM Stranger Than Friction GENERAL **CD** Science Tutor
PACING • 45 min pp. 20–25 **Section 4 Gravity: A Force of Attraction** • Describe gravity and its effect on matter. • Explain the law of universal gravitation. • Describe the difference between mass and weight.	**TE** Group Activity Gravity Poster, p. 20 GENERAL **SE** Connection to Biology Seeds and Gravity, p. 21 GENERAL **TE** Demonstration Modeling Gravity, p. 21 ◆ GENERAL **TE** Connection Activity Math, p. 22 ADVANCED **TE** Activity Story Analysis, p. 23 GENERAL **SE** Skills Practice Lab Relating Mass and Weight, p. 193 GENERAL **LB** Long-Term Projects & Research Ideas ADVANCED	**OSP** Lesson Plans (also in print) **TR** Bellringer Transparency* **TR** LINK TO EARTH SCIENCE E57 Tidal Variations: Spring Tides; Neap Tides* **TR** P18 Gravitational Force Depends on Mass; Gravitational Force Depends on Distance* **TR** P19 Weight and Mass* **CD** Science Tutor

PACING • 90 min

CHAPTER REVIEW, ASSESSMENT, AND STANDARDIZED TEST PREPARATION

CRF Vocabulary Activity* GENERAL
SE Chapter Review, pp. 28–29 GENERAL
CRF Chapter Review* ■ GENERAL
CRF Chapter Tests A* ■ GENERAL, B* ADVANCED, C* SPECIAL NEEDS
SE Standardized Test Preparation, pp. 30–31 GENERAL
CRF Standardized Test Preparation* GENERAL
CRF Performance-Based Assessment* GENERAL
OSP Test Generator, Test Item Listing

Online and Technology Resources

 Holt Online Learning

Visit go.hrw.com for access to Holt Online Learning, or enter the keyword **HP7 Home** for a variety of free online resources.

 One-Stop Planner® CD-ROM

This CD-ROM package includes:
• Lab Materials QuickList Software
• Holt Calendar Planner
• Customizable Lesson Plans
• Printable Worksheets
• ExamView® Test Generator
• Interactive Teacher's Edition
• Holt PuzzlePro®
• Holt PowerPoint® Resources

SKILLS DEVELOPMENT RESOURCES	SECTION REVIEW AND ASSESSMENT	CORRELATIONS
SE Pre-Reading Activity, p. 2 GENERAL **OSP** Science Puzzlers, Twisters & Teasers GENERAL		National Science Education Standards UCP 3; SAI 1; PS 2a
CRF Directed Reading A* ■ BASIC, B* SPECIAL NEEDS **IT** Interactive Textbook* Struggling Readers **CRF** Vocabulary and Section Summary* ■ GENERAL **TE** Inclusion Strategies, p. 5 **SE** Math Focus Calculating Average Speed, p. 6 GENERAL **TE** Support for English Language Learners, p. 7 **SE** Math Practice Calculating Acceleration, p. 8 GENERAL **MS** Math Skills for Science The Unit Factor and Dimensional Analysis,* Average Speed in a Pinewood Derby* GENERAL **SS** Science Skills Organizing Your Research* GENERAL **CRF** Reinforcement Worksheet Bug Race* BASIC	**SE** Reading Checks, pp. 4, 6, 8 GENERAL **TE** Homework, p. 5 ADVANCED **TE** Homework, p. 7 GENERAL **TE** Reteaching, p. 8 BASIC **TE** Quiz, p. 8 GENERAL **TE** Alternative Assessment, p. 8 GENERAL **SE** Section Review,* p. 9 ■ GENERAL **CRF** Section Quiz* ■ GENERAL	UCP 1, 3; SAI 1; PS 2a; *Chapter Lab:* SAI 1; *LabBook:* UCP 3; SAI 1, 2; ST 1; PS 2a
CRF Directed Reading A* ■ BASIC, B* SPECIAL NEEDS **IT** Interactive Textbook* Struggling Readers **CRF** Vocabulary and Section Summary* ■ GENERAL **SE** Reading Strategy Reading Organizer, p. 10 GENERAL **TE** Reading Strategy Prediction Guide, p. 11 GENERAL **TE** Support for English Language Learners, p. 11	**SE** Reading Checks, pp. 11, 12 GENERAL **TE** Reteaching, p. 12 BASIC **TE** Quiz, p. 12 GENERAL **TE** Alternative Assessment, p. 12 GENERAL **SE** Section Review,* p. 13 ■ GENERAL **CRF** Section Quiz* ■ GENERAL	UCP 1; PS 2b, 2c
CRF Directed Reading A* ■ BASIC, B* SPECIAL NEEDS **IT** Interactive Textbook* Struggling Readers **CRF** Vocabulary and Section Summary* ■ GENERAL **SE** Reading Strategy Brainstorming, p. 14 GENERAL **TE** Inclusion Strategies, p. 16 **SE** Connection to Social Studies Invention of the Wheel, p. 17 GENERAL **TE** Support for English Language Learners, p. 17 **CRF** Reinforcement Worksheet Friction Action* BASIC	**SE** Reading Checks, pp. 15, 17, 18 GENERAL **TE** Reteaching, p. 18 BASIC **TE** Quiz, p. 18 GENERAL **TE** Alternative Assessment, p. 18 GENERAL **SE** Section Review,* p. 19 ■ GENERAL **CRF** Section Quiz* ■ GENERAL	SAI 1; PS 2c; *LabBook:* SAI 1; PS 2c
CRF Directed Reading A* ■ BASIC, B* SPECIAL NEEDS **IT** Interactive Textbook* Struggling Readers **CRF** Vocabulary and Section Summary* ■ GENERAL **SE** Reading Strategy Paired Summarizing, p. 20 GENERAL **TE** Reading Strategy Prediction Guide, p. 21 GENERAL **TE** Support for English Language Learners, p. 22 **SE** Connection to Language Arts Gravity Story, p. 24 GENERAL **CRF** Reinforcement Worksheet A Weighty Problem* BASIC **CRF** Critical Thinking A Mission in Motion* ADVANCED	**SE** Reading Checks, pp. 21, 22, 24 GENERAL **TE** Reteaching, p. 24 BASIC **TE** Quiz, p. 24 GENERAL **TE** Alternative Assessment, p. 24 GENERAL **SE** Section Review,* p. 25 ■ GENERAL **CRF** Section Quiz* ■ GENERAL	UCP 1, 3; SAI 1; ST 2; SPSP 5; HNS 1, 3; PS 2c; *LabBook:* UCP 3; SAI 1

SCI LINKS.
NSTA
www.scilinks.org
Maintained by the **National Science Teachers Association.** See Chapter Enrichment pages that follow for a complete list of topics.

Current Science®

Check out *Current Science* articles and activities by visiting the HRW Web site at go.hrw.com. Just type in the keyword **HP5CS05T.**

Classroom Videos

• **Lab Videos** demonstrate the chapter lab.
• **Brain Food Video Quizzes** help students review the chapter material.

Classroom CD-ROMs

• **Guided Reading Audio CD** (Also in Spanish)
• **Interactive Explorations**
• **Virtual Investigations**
• **Visual Concepts**
• **Science Tutor**

Holt Lab Generator CD-ROM

Search for any lab by topic, standard, difficulty level, or time. Edit any lab to fit your needs, or create your own labs. Use the Lab Materials QuickList software to customize your lab materials list.

Visual Resources

CHAPTER STARTER TRANSPARENCY

Would You Believe . . . ?

There was once a game that could be played by as few as 5 or as many as 1,000 players. The game could be played on a small field for a few hours or on a huge tract of land for several days. The game was not just for fun—in fact, it was often used as a substitute for war. One of the few rules was that the players couldn't touch the ball with their hands—they had to use a special

BELLRINGER TRANSPARENCIES

Section: Measuring Motion

Write a formal description in your **science journal** of your position in the classroom using a reference point and a set of reference directions. For example, you might say, "I sit three desks behind Ahmed's desk," or "I sit 2 m east of the vent hood and 10 m north of the emergency shower." Then, write a similar description for your home, and for an object in your room.

TEACHING TRANSPARENCIES

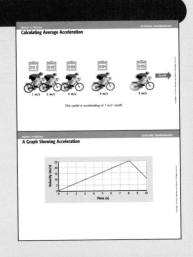

Weight and Mass

Weight is measured using a spring scale.

Mass is measured by using a balance.

A Graph Showing Speed

Finding Resultant Velocity

Person's resultant velocity
15 m/s east + 1 m/s west = 16 m/s east

When you combine two velocities that are in the same direction, add them together to find the resultant velocity.

Person's resultant velocity
15 m/s east − 1 m/s west = 14 m/s east

When you combine two velocities that are in opposite directions, subtract the smaller velocity from the larger velocity to find the resultant velocity. The resultant velocity is in the direction of the larger velocity.

Calculating Average Acceleration

This cyclist is accelerating at 1 m/s² south.

A Graph Showing Acceleration

TEACHING TRANSPARENCIES

Forces in the Same Direction

Forces in Opposite Directions

Force and Friction

① There is more friction between the book with more weight and the table than there is between the book with less weight and the table. A harder push is needed to move the heavier book.

Force acting on the book | Force of friction
Force acting on the book | Force of friction
Force acting on the book | Force of Motion

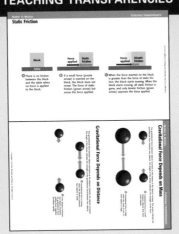

Static Friction

① There is no friction between the block and the table when no force is applied to the block.

② If a small force (purple arrow) is exerted on the block, the block does not move. The force of static friction (green arrow) balances the force applied.

③ When the force exerted on the block is greater than the force of static friction, the block starts moving. When the block starts moving, static friction is gone, and only kinetic friction (green arrow) opposes the force applied.

Gravitational Force Depends on Distance

Gravitational Force Depends on Mass

Tidal Variations: Spring Tides; Neap Tides

Spring Tides During spring tides, the gravitational forces of the sun and moon pull on the Earth either from the same direction (left) or from opposite directions (right).

Neap Tides During neap tides, the sun and moon are at right angles with respect to the Earth. This arrangement lessens their gravitational effect on the Earth.

LINK TO EARTH SCIENCE

Chapter: The Movement of Ocean Water

CONCEPT MAPPING TRANSPARENCY

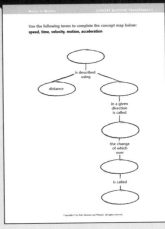

Use the following terms to complete the concept map below:
speed, time, velocity, motion, acceleration

is described using

distance

in a given direction is called

the change of which over

is called

Planning Resources

LESSON PLANS

Lesson Plan   SAMPLE

Section: Waves

Pacing
Regular Schedule: with lab(s):2 days   without lab(s):if days
Block Schedule: with lab(s):1 1/2 days without lab(s): day

Objectives
1. Relate the seven properties of life to a living organism.
2. Describe seven themes that can help you to organize what you learn about biology.
3. Identify the tiny structures that make up all living organisms.
4. Differentiate between reproduction and heredity and between metabolism and homeostasis.

National Science Education Standards Covered
LSInter6:Cells have particular structures that underlie their functions.
LSMat1:Most cell functions involve chemical reactions.
LSMat1:Cells store and use information to guide their functions.
UCP1:Cell functions are regulated.
SI1: Cells can differentiate and form complete multicellular organisms.
PS1: Species evolve over time.
ESS1: The great diversity of organisms is the result of more than 3.5 billion years of evolution.
ESS2: Natural selection and its evolutionary consequences provide a scientific explanation for the fossil record of ancient life forms as well as for the striking molecular similarities observed among the diverse species of living organisms.
ST1: The millions of different species of plants, animals, and microorganisms that live on Earth today are related by descent from common ancestors.
ST2: The energy for life primarily comes from the sun.
SPSP1: The complexity and organization of organisms accommodates the partial explanation for the fossil record of ancient life forms as well as for obtaining, transforming, transporting, releasing, and eliminating the matter and energy used to sustain the organism.
SPSP6: As matter and energy flows through different levels of organization of living systems—cells, organs, communities—and between living systems and the physical environment, chemical elements are recombined in different ways.
HNS1: Organisms have behavioral responses to internal changes and to external stimuli.

PARENT LETTER

SAMPLE

Dear Parent,

Your son's or daughter's science class will soon begin exploring the chapter entitled "The World of Physical Science." In this chapter, students will learn about how the scientific method applies to the world of physical science and the role of physical science in the world. By the end of the chapter, students should demonstrate a clear understanding of the chapter's main ideas and be able to discuss the following topics:

1. physical science is the study of energy and matter (Section 1)
2. the role of physical science in the world around them (Section 1)
3. careers that rely on physical science (Section 1)
4. the steps used in the scientific method (Section 2)
5. examples of technology (Section 2)
6. how the scientific method is used to answer questions and solve problems (Section 2)
7. how our knowledge of science changes over time (Section 2)
8. how models represent real objects or systems (Section 3)
9. examples of different ways models are used in science (Section 3)
10. the importance of the International System of Units (Section 4)
11. the appropriate units to use for particular measurements (Section 4)
12. how area and density are derived quantities (Section 4)

Questions to Ask Along the Way

You can help your son or daughter learn about these topics by asking interesting questions such as the following:

• What are some surprising careers that use physical science?
• What is a characteristic of a good hypothesis?
• When is it a good idea to use a model?
• Why do Americans measure things in terms of inches and yards, and meters?

ALSO IN SPANISH

TEST ITEM LISTING

TEST ITEM LISTING
The World of Science   SAMPLE

MULTIPLE CHOICE

1. A limitation of models is that
   a. they are large enough to see.
   b. they do not act exactly like the things that they model.
   c. they are smaller than the things that they model.
   d. they model unfamiliar things.
   Answer: B   Difficulty: 1   Section: 3   Objective: 2

2. The length 10 m is equal to
   a. 100 cm.   c. 10,000 mm.
   b. 1,000 cm.   d. Both (b) and (c)
   Answer: B   Difficulty: 1   Section: 2   Objective: 2

3. To be valid, a hypothesis must be
   a. testable.   c. made into a law.
   b. supported by evidence. d. Both (a) and (b)
   Answer: B   Difficulty: 1   Section: 3   Objective: 2

4. The statement "Sheila has a stain on her shirt" is an example of a(n)
   a. law.   c. observation.
   b. hypothesis   d. prediction.
   Answer: B   Difficulty: 1   Section: 3   Objective: 2

5. A hypothesis is often developed out of
   a. observations.   c. laws.
   b. experiments.   d. Both (a) and (b)
   Answer: B   Difficulty: 1   Section: 3   Objective: 2

6. How many milliliters are in 3.5 kL?
   a. 3,500 mL   c. 3,500,000 mL
   b. 0.0035 mL   d. 35,000 mL
   Answer: B   Difficulty: 1   Section: 2   Objective: 2

7. A map of Seattle is an example of a
   a. law.   c. model.
   b. theory   d. unit.
   Answer: B   Difficulty: 1   Section: 3   Objective: 2

8. A lab has the safety icons shown below. These icons mean that you should wear
   a. only safety goggles. c. safety goggles and a lab apron.
   b. only a lab apron.   d. safety goggles, a lab apron, and gloves.
   Answer: B   Difficulty: 1   Section: 3   Objective: 2

9. The law of conservation of mass says that the lot al mass before a chemical change is
   a. only safety goggles. c. safety goggles and a lab apron.
   b. less than the total mass after the change.
   c. the same as the total mass after the change.
   d. not the same as the total mass after the change.
   Answer: B   Difficulty: 1   Section: 3   Objective: 2

10. In which of the following areas might you find a geochemist at work?
    a. studying the chemistry of rocks   c. studying fishes
    b. studying forestry   d. studying the atmosphere
    Answer: B   Difficulty: 1   Section: 3   Objective: 2

One-Stop Planner® CD-ROM

This CD-ROM includes all of the resources shown here and the following time-saving tools:

• Lab Materials QuickList Software
• Customizable lesson plans
• Holt Calendar Planner
• The powerful ExamView® Test Generator

Meeting Individual Needs

DIRECTED READING A
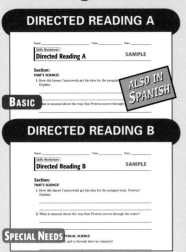

Skills Worksheet
Directed Reading A SAMPLE

Section:
THAT'S SCIENCE!
1. How did James Czarnowski get his idea for the penguin boat? Explain.

ALSO IN SPANISH

_____ that is unusual about the way that Proteus moves through

BASIC

DIRECTED READING B

Skills Worksheet
Directed Reading B SAMPLE

Section:
THAT'S SCIENCE!
1. How did James Czarnowski get his idea for the penguin boat, Proteus? Explain.

2. What is unusual about the way that Proteus moves through the water?

____ PHYSICAL SCIENCE
_____ and, and a cheetah have in common?

SPECIAL NEEDS

VOCABULARY ACTIVITY
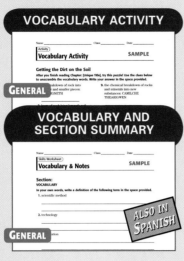

Activity
Vocabulary Activity SAMPLE

Getting the Dirt on the Soil
After you finish reading Chapter [Unique Title], try this puzzle! Use the clues below to unscramble the vocabulary words. Write your answer in the space provided.

_____ breakdown of rock into ____ and smaller pieces:
____IGNETH

9. the chemical breakdown of rocks and minerals into new substances: CAMILCHE THEARIGWEN

GENERAL

VOCABULARY AND SECTION SUMMARY

Skills Worksheet
Vocabulary & Notes SAMPLE

Section:
VOCABULARY
In your own words, write a definition of the following term in the space provided.
1. scientific method

2. technology

ALSO IN SPANISH

GENERAL _____ion

REINFORCEMENT
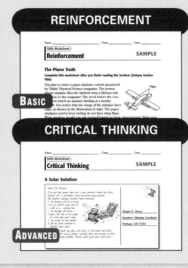

Skills Worksheet
Reinforcement SAMPLE

The Plane Truth
Complete this worksheet after you finish reading the Section: [Unique Section Title]

You plan to enter a paper airplane content sponsored by Talkin' Physical Science magazine. The person whose airplane flies the farthest wins a lifetime subscription to the magazine! The week before the contest you watch an airplane landing at a nearby _____. You notice that the wings of the airplane have flaps, as shown in the illustration at right. The paper airplanes you've been testing do not have wing flaps. _____ question would you ask yourself based on these observations? Write your

Flaps

BASIC

CRITICAL THINKING

Skills Worksheet
Critical Thinking SAMPLE

A Solar Solution

Dear Mr. Burns,
_____
_____

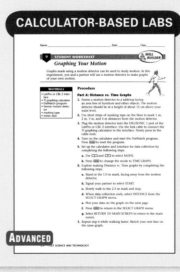

Joseph D. Burns
Inventors' Advisory Consultants
Portland, OR 97201

_____ Next my idea will work, I will make the Eldis _____ solar without wasting time and money in test-_____ my models. Please write back now with your

ADVANCED

SCILINKS ACTIVITY

Activity
SciLinks Activity SAMPLE

MARINE ECOSYSTEMS
Go to www.scilinks.org. To find links related to marine ecosystems, type in the keyword HL5000. Then, use the links to answer the ___ questions about marine ecosys-
_____ percentage of the Earth's surface is covered by water?

SC_LINKS
National Science Teachers Association

Go to: www.scilinks.org
Topic: Reproductive System
Irregularities
SciLinks Code: HL5000

GENERAL

SCIENCE PUZZLERS, TWISTERS & TEASERS

CHAPTER
5 SCIENCE PUZZLERS, TWISTERS & TEASERS
Matter in Motion

Daffy Definitions
1. Below are some really silly definitions for words found in the chapter. The number after each word shows the number of letters in the answer. See how many you can solve!
   a. A very weighty subject (7)
   b. Opposite of a lubricant (9)
   c. Web propulsion (8)
   d. Roman "five," low metropolis (8)
   e. Presently falling forward, also _____ (10)
   _____ of 2,000 frics (8)
   g. Playground pastime; type of friction (7)

GENERAL

Labs and Activities

LONG-TERM PROJECTS & RESEARCH IDEAS
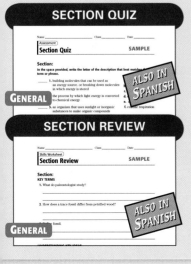

PROJECT
55 STUDENT WORKSHEET
DESIGN YOUR OWN
Tiny Troubles

The evil Dr. Minnie Mizer has shrunk you to the size of a small mouse with her incredible shrink ray! She's left you on her desk, which is too high for you to climb down. The nearest piece of furniture is a bookshelf 25 cm away. On the shelf is a lamp with a cord that you are pretty certain you can climb down. You could easily escape if you could just reach that lamp. But you are unable to make such a long jump. The only things on the desktop are a small bottle of glue and several boxes of toothpicks. Suddenly, you have an idea. If you can use the glue and the toothpicks to build a bridge across the gaping chasm, you could flee to safety. You better hurry, because Dr. Mizer's cat, Snacker, may show up any minute now!

Toothpick Task Force
Balanced forces are very important when it comes to bridge designs. Research how different kinds of bridges are made. What forces do engineers consider when designing a bridge? Build a bridge with toothpicks and glue. You may use craft sticks instead of toothpicks. The bridge should span 25 cm and should be strong enough to hold your textbook. For a challenge, hold a contest to see whose bridge can support the most weight.

SUGGESTED MATERIALS
• aluminum foil
• bamboo skewers
• drinking straws
• glue
• rubber bands
• masking tape
• plastic film canister lids
• jar lids
• sand paper
• tongue depressors

Another Long-Term Project Idea
2. Design and construct a model of a motorless car that will move in a straight line. The car should accelerate to top speed by traveling down a ramp, and must continue traveling a distance of 3 m on a smooth surface. Build your car from scrap materials, like the materials listed at left. Calculate the speed of your car over a fixed distance and average it over three trials. Where should friction be minimized on the car? What materials can be used to reduce friction? Where does the force of friction help the car move faster? What materials can be used to increase friction? How does mass affect the car? Demonstrate for the class what your car can do. Be sure to explain which features of the car allow it to reach top speed.

Research Idea
3. You know that you use a scale to measure weight and a balance to measure mass. But, how are scales and balances constructed? What measurements are used in association with them? How do various types of scales and balances differ? Why are some types of scales considered more reliable than others? Make a poster displaying what you have learned.

ADVANCED

CALCULATOR-BASED LABS

LAB
3 STUDENT WORKSHEET
DISCOVERY LAB
The Fast Track

Speed and velocity are rates. They tell us how much distance is covered in a unit of time. What factors affect velocity? In this experiment, you will study the velocity of a car after it is released from different points on a ramp. You will use a motion detector to measure velocity.

MATERIALS
• LabPro or CBL 2 interface
• TI graphing calculator
• DataMate program
• Vernier motion detector
• board 1.8 m long
• several books
• meterstick
• small toy car
• small index card

Procedure
1. Place a ramp on the floor, set up a ramp on books as shown in the illustration below. The high end of the ramp should be 45 cm above the floor.
2. Place a meterstick down the center of the ramp. The 0 cm mark on the meterstick should be at the very bottom of the ramp. Tape the meterstick to the ramp in two places. The meterstick will serve as a guide rail for your car.
3. Fasten the Vernier motion detector at the top and center of the ramp as shown in the illustration below.
4. Plug the motion detector into the DIG/SONIC 1 port of the LabPro or CBL 2 interface. Use the link cable to connect the TI graphing calculator to the interface. Firmly press in the cable ends.
5. Turn on the calculator, and start the DataMate program. Press ____ to reset the program.
6. Set up the calculator and interface for data collection by completing the following steps.
   a. Select SETUP from the main screen. Use ____ and ____ to select MODE and press ____.
   b. Select TIME GRAPH from the SELECT MODE menu.
   c. Select CHANGE TIME SETTINGS from the TIME GRAPH SETTINGS menu.
   d. Enter "0.2" as the time between samples in seconds.

e. Enter "15" as the number of samples. Data collection will last three seconds.
6. Select OK to return to the setup screen. Select OK again to return to the main screen.

dynamic cart

meterstick

motion detector

ramp

books

ADVANCED

CALCULATOR-BASED LABS
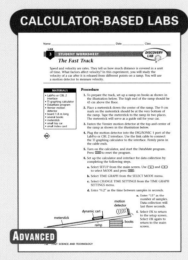

LAB
9 STUDENT WORKSHEET
SKILL BUILDER
Graphing Your Motion

Graphs made using a motion detector can be used to study motion. In this experiment, you and a partner will use a motion detector to make graphs of your own motion.

MATERIALS
• LabPro or CBL 2 interface
• TI graphing calculator
• Vernier motion detector
• masking tape
• meter stick

Procedure

Part A: Distance vs. Time Graphs
1. Fasten a motion detector to a tabletop facing an area free of furniture and other objects. The motion detector should be at a height of about 15 cm above your waist level.
2. Use short strips of masking tape on the floor to mark 1 m, 2 m, 3 m, and 4 m distances from the motion detector.
3. Plug the motion detector into the DIG/SONIC 1 port of the LabPro or CBL 2 interface. Use the link cable to connect the TI graphing calculator to the interface. Firmly press in the cable ends.
4. Turn on the calculator and start the DataMate program.
5. Set up the calculator and interface for data collection by completing the following steps.
   a. Use ____ and ____ to select MODE.
   b. Press ____ to change the mode to TIME GRAPH.
   c. Select Distance vs. Time graph by completing the following steps.
6. Stand at the 1.0 m mark, facing away from the motion detector.
7. Signal your partner to select START.
8. Slowly walk to the 2.5 m mark and stop.
9. When data collection ends, select DISTANCE from the SELECT GRAPH screen.
   a. Plot your data on the graph on the next page.
   b. Select RETURN TO MAIN SCREEN to return to the main screen.
   c. Select RETURN TO MAIN MENU to return to the select graph menu.
7. Repeat step 6 while walking faster. Sketch your new line on the same graph.

ADVANCED

DATASHEETS FOR QUICK LABS

TEACHER RESOURCE PAGE

Quick Lab DATASHEET FOR QUICK LAB
Reaction to Stress SAMPLE

Background
The graph below illustrates changes that occur in the membrane potential of a neuron during an action potential. Use the graph to answer the following questions. Refer to Figure 3 as needed.

DATASHEETS FOR CHAPTER LABS

TEACHER RESOURCE PAGE

Skills Practice Lab DATASHEET FOR CHAPTER LAB
Using Scientific Methods SAMPLE

Teacher's Notes
TIME REQUIRED
One 45-minute class period.

DATASHEETS FOR LABBOOK
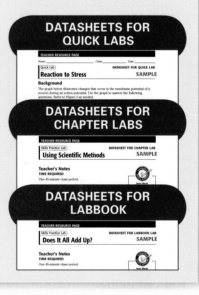

TEACHER RESOURCE PAGE

Skills Practice Lab DATASHEET FOR LABBOOK LAB
Does It All Add Up? SAMPLE

Teacher's Notes
TIME REQUIRED
One 45-minute class period.

Review and Assessments

SECTION QUIZ

Assessment
Section Quiz SAMPLE

Section:
In the space provided, write the letter of the description that best matches the term or phrase.
____ 1. building molecules that can be used as an energy source, or breaking down molecules in which energy is stored
____ 2. the process by which light energy is converted to chemical energy
____ 3. an organism that uses sunlight or inorganic substances to make organic compounds

ALSO IN SPANISH

GENERAL

SECTION REVIEW

Skills Worksheet
Section Review SAMPLE

Section:
KEY TERMS
1. What do paleontologist study?

2. How does a trace fossil differ from petrified wood?

_____ fossil.

ALSO IN SPANISH

GENERAL

CHAPTER REVIEW

Skills Worksheet
Chapter Review SAMPLE

USING VOCABULARY
1. Define biome in your own words.

2. Describe the characteristics of a savanna and a desert.

ALSO IN SPANISH

GENERAL

CHAPTER TEST A

Assessment
Chapter Test A SAMPLE

MULTIPLE CHOICE
In the space provided, write the letter of the term or phrase that best completes each statement or best answers each question.
____ 1. Surface currents are formed by
   a. the moon's gravity.   c. wind.
   b. the sun's gravity.   d. increased water density.
____ 2. When waves come near the shore,
   a. they speed up.   c. their wavelength increases.
   b. they maintain their speed. d. their wave height increases.
____ 3. Longshore currents transport sediment
   a. out to the open ocean.   c. only during low tide.
   b. along the shore.   d. only during high tide.
____ 4. Which of the following does NOT control surface currents?

ALSO IN SPANISH

GENERAL

CHAPTER TEST B
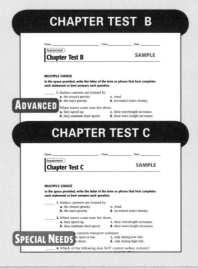

Assessment
Chapter Test B SAMPLE

MULTIPLE CHOICE
In the space provided, write the letter of the term or phrase that best completes each statement or best answers each question.
____ 1. Surface currents are formed by
   a. the moon's gravity.   c. wind.
   b. the sun's gravity.   d. increased water density.
____ 2. When waves come near the shore,
   a. they speed up.   c. their wavelength increases.
   b. they maintain their speed. d. their wave height increases.

ADVANCED

CHAPTER TEST C

Assessment
Chapter Test C SAMPLE

MULTIPLE CHOICE
In the space provided, write the letter of the term or phrase that best completes each statement or best answers each question.
____ 1. Surface currents are formed by
   a. the moon's gravity.   c. wind.
   b. the sun's gravity.   d. increased water density.
____ 2. When waves come near the shore,
   a. they speed up.   c. their wavelength increases.
   b. they maintain their speed. d. their wave height increases.
____ 3. _____ currents transport sediment
   a. out to the open ocean.   c. only during low tide.
   b.   d. only during high tide.
____ 4. Which of the following does NOT control surface currents?

SPECIAL NEEDS

STANDARDIZED TEST PREPARATION

Assessment
Standardized Test Preparation SAMPLE

READING
Read the passages below. Then, read each question that follows the passage. Decide which is the best answer to each question.

Passage 1 adventurous summer camp in the world. Billy can't _____ to head for the outdoors. Billy checked the recommended _____ supply list: light, summer clothes; sunscreen; rain gear; heavy, _____ flannel-lined jacket; ski mask; and thick gloves. Wait a minute! Billy _____ thought he was traveling to only one destination, so he didn't _____ need to bring such a wide variety of clothes?! On further investiga-

GENERAL

PERFORMANCE-BASED ASSESSMENT
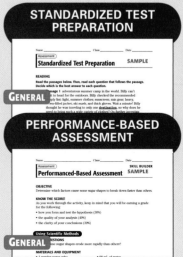

Assessment
Performanced-Based Assessment SKILL BUILDER SAMPLE

OBJECTIVE
Determine which factors cause some sugar shapes to break down faster than others.

KNOW THE SCORE!
As you work through the activity, keep in mind that you will be earning a grade for the following:
• how you form and test the hypothesis (30%)
• the quality of your analysis (40%)
• the clarity of your conclusions (30%)

Using Scientific Methods
_____ QUESTIONS
_____ some sugar shapes erode more rapidly than others?
MATERIALS AND EQUIPMENT
• 1 regular sugar cube   • 90 mL of water

GENERAL

This Chapter Enrichment provides relevant and interesting information to expand and enhance your presentation of the chapter material.

Section 1

Measuring Motion
The Scientific Revolution

- The movement now called the Scientific Revolution took place between the 16th and 18th centuries. Mainstream science of the time still taught the Aristotelian view of the universe. With the translation of Greek, Roman, and Arabic texts and the improvement of the printing press, ideas that are now the basis of modern science first became available to a large number of people.

- In astronomy, the theory that the sun is the center of the solar system was proposed by Copernicus. Galileo laid the foundations of the principles of mechanics (the study of motion) and first turned a telescope toward the sky. Philosophers such as Descartes began to develop the idea of nature as a complicated system of particles in motion.

- Sir Isaac Newton (1642–1727) was a central figure in the Scientific Revolution during the 17th century. He was born in 1642, the year Galileo died.

Acceleration

- Remember that acceleration, like velocity, always includes direction. However, the relationship between acceleration and motion differs from the relationship between veloc-ity and motion. An object's motion is always in the same direction as its velocity. But an object's motion is not always in the same direction as its acceleration. For example, when an object is in circular motion, its acceleration is toward the center of the circle, but its motion is not.

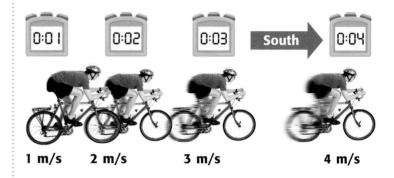

0:01   0:02   0:03   South   0:04

1 m/s   2 m/s   3 m/s   4 m/s

Is That a Fact!

- ◆ A fast runner can reach a speed of 32 km/h (about 20 mi/h). But the highest speed a person can attain when swimming is only about 8 km/h (about 5 mi/h).

Section 2

What Is a Force?
Basic Forces of Nature

- Scientists have found evidence that the interactions of only four basic forces can describe all physical properties and relationships in nature. These forces are
  - the gravitational force, which acts on all matter (which has mass) and on light (which has no mass)
  - the electromagnetic force, which is responsible for the attraction and repulsion of all kinds of matter that have electric or magnetic properties

  - the strong nuclear force, which binds the protons and neutrons of atoms together in the nucleus
  - the weak nuclear force, which describes some interactions between subatomic particles

Is That a Fact!

◆ Gravitational force and electromagnetic force were discovered long before nuclear forces because people can observe their effects on ordinary matter. The strong and weak nuclear forces were not discovered until the 20th century, when scientists were able to probe the structure of nuclei.

Tug-of-War and Force

● In a tug-of-war contest, both teams and the rope move in the direction of the net force.

Section 3

Friction: A Force That Opposes Motion

Sports and Friction

● Many sports partici-pants want to reduce friction as much as possible. Downhill skiers wax their skis to reduce friction between the skis and the snow. Surfers wax their boards to reduce friction between the boards and the water. However, in some sports, increased fric-

tion is what the athlete wants. A runner in the 100 m dash wants maximum friction between his or her shoes and the running track.

Is That a Fact!

◆ Athletic shoes come in so many varieties because they are designed to provide the proper amount of friction for maximum performance in each sport.

Wheels

● A wheel makes movement easier by reducing friction. Yet without friction between the wheel and the ground, the wheel would just spin around and the object to which the wheel is attached would go nowhere.

Section 4

Gravity: A Force of Attraction

Gravity

● Every object in the universe is constantly subject to the pull of gravity from other objects. The net gravitational force acting on the object may be extremely small, but it is always present.

Newton's Universal Law of Gravitation

● The gravitational force exists between two objects anywhere in the universe. The gravitational force is purely attractive—each object is pulled by the other one. These two forces are equal and opposite.

● The magnitude of the gravitational force is related to the masses of the objects and the distance between them. The equation for Newton's universal law of gravitation is as follows:

$$F_g = G\frac{m_1 m_2}{d^2}$$

where F_g is the gravitational force, G is the constant of universal gravitation, m_1 is the mass of object 1, m_2 is the mass of object 2, and d is the distance between the centers of mass of objects 1 and 2. The value for G is 6.67×10^{-11} N•m²/kg².

SCI LINKS

NSTA
Developed and maintained by the National Science Teachers Association

SciLinks is maintained by the National Science Teachers Association to provide you and your students with interesting, up-to-date links that will enrich your classroom presentation of the chapter.

Visit www.scilinks.org and enter the SciLinks code for more information about the topic listed.

Topic: Measuring Motion
SciLinks code: HSM0927

Topic: Matter and Gravity
SciLinks code: HSM0922

Topic: Forces
SciLinks code: HSM0604

Topic: Force of Gravity
SciLinks code: HSM0602

Topic: Force and Friction
SciLinks code: HSM0601

Overview

Tell students that this chapter is about measuring motion and about how forces affect motion. Students will learn how to calculate average speed and average acceleration. The chapter also explains balanced and unbalanced forces, friction, and gravity.

Assessing Prior Knowledge

Students should be familiar with the following topics:

• SI units

• mass

Identifying Misconceptions

As students learn the material in this chapter, some of them may be confused about the difference between mass and weight. Explain to students that the weight of an object depends on gravity but that the mass of the object does not. Also explain that the weight of an object will change if the object is moved to the moon or to other planets but that the mass of the object will remain the same. However, because mass and weight are proportional and constant on Earth, people tend to confuse the two concepts and often use the terms *mass* and *weight* interchangeably in everyday usage.

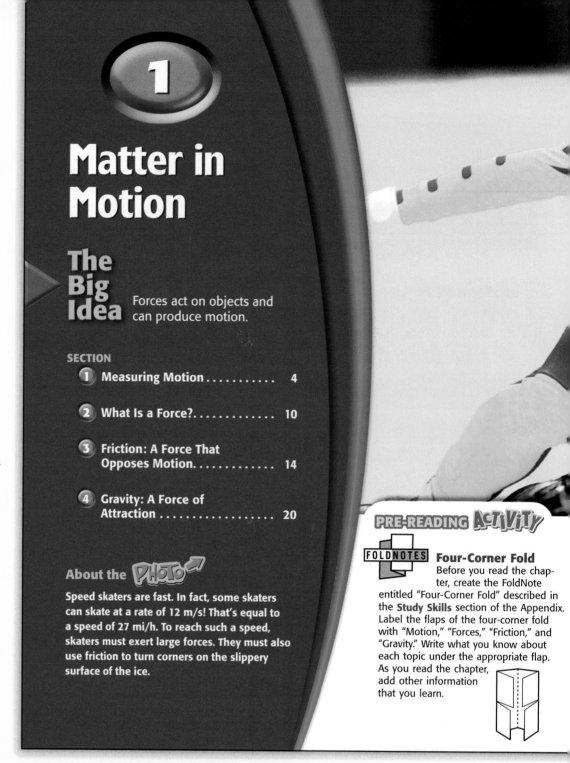

Matter in Motion

The Big Idea

Forces act on objects and can produce motion.

About the PHOTO

Speed skaters are fast. In fact, some skaters can skate at a rate of 12 m/s! That's equal to a speed of 27 mi/h. To reach such a speed, skaters must exert large forces. They must also use friction to turn corners on the slippery surface of the ice.

PRE-READING ACTIVITY

FOLDNOTES **Four-Corner Fold**
Before you read the chapter, create the FoldNote entitled "Four-Corner Fold" described in the **Study Skills** section of the Appendix. Label the flaps of the four-corner fold with "Motion," "Forces," "Friction," and "Gravity." Write what you know about each topic under the appropriate flap. As you read the chapter, add other information that you learn.

Standards Correlations

National Science Education Standards

The following codes indicate the National Science Education Standards that correlate to this chapter. The full text of the standards is at the front of the book.

Chapter Opener
UCP 3; SAI 1; PS 2a

Section 1 Measuring Motion
UCP 1, 3; SAI 1; PS 2a; *LabBook*: UCP 3; SAI 1, 2; ST 1; PS 2a

Section 2 What Is a Force?
UCP 1; PS 2b, 2c

Section 3 Friction: A Force that Opposes Motion
SAI 1; PS 2c; *LabBook*: SAI 1; PS 2c

Section 4 Gravity: A Force of Attraction
UCP 1, 3; SAI 1; ST 2; SPSP 5; HNS 1, 3; PS 2c; *LabBook*: UCP 3; SAI 1

Chapter Lab
SAI 1

Chapter Review
PS 2a, 2c

Science in Action
ST 2, SPSP 5; HNS 1

START-UP ACTIVITY
MATERIALS
FOR EACH GROUP
- dominoes, 25
- meterstick
- stopwatch

Teacher's Notes: You might want to allow students to line up their dominoes along the side edge of a meterstick to ensure that the dominoes are in a straight line.

You may also wish to demonstrate how to line up the dominoes in case your students do not fully understand the instructions given.

Answers
1. Answers may vary.
2. Students should determine that putting dominoes very close together and putting them very far apart both lead to slower average speed. The average speed is fastest when the distance between the dominoes is about half the length of a domino. Accept all reasonable predictions. Students will likely find that the results do not confirm their predictions. They will probably predict that setting the dominoes very close together will reduce the time taken for all the dominoes to fall and thus will increase the average speed.

START-UP ACTIVITY

The Domino Derby
Speed is the distance traveled by an object in a certain amount of time. In this activity, you will observe one factor that affects the speed of falling dominoes.

Procedure
1. Set up **25 dominoes** in a straight line. Try to keep equal spacing between the dominoes.
2. Use a **meterstick** to measure the total length of your row of dominoes, and record the length.
3. Use a **stopwatch** to time how long it takes for the dominoes to fall. Record this measurement.
4. Predict what would happen to that amount of time if you changed the distance between the dominoes. Write your predictions.

5. Repeat steps 2 and 3 several times using distances between the dominoes that are smaller and larger than the distance used in your first setup. Use the same number of dominoes in each trial.

Analysis
1. Calculate the average speed for each trial by dividing the total distance (the length of the domino row) by the time the dominoes take to fall.
2. How did the spacing between dominoes affect the average speed? Is this result what you expected? If not, explain.

Chapter Starter Transparency
Use this transparency to help students begin thinking about motion, speed, and force.

Chapter 1 • Matter in Motion 3

SECTION 1

Focus

Overview

This section introduces students to the concept of motion. It introduces the idea of a *reference point* as a necessary starting point to observe motion. Students learn about average speed, velocity, and acceleration.

 Bellringer

Have students describe their position in the classroom using a reference point and a set of reference directions. For example, a student might say, "I sit three desks behind Ahmed's desk," or "I sit 2 m east of the vent hood and 10 m north of the emergency shower."

Motivate

Demonstration — GENERAL

Models Place two identical wind-up toys on a table, one wound, the other not wound, so that one toy moves across the table while the other one remains motionless. Ask students to explain the difference between the toys. Help students understand that the difference is movement. Ask students to define motion in their own terms. Explain that in this section, they will learn how to identify and measure different quantities related to motion.
LS Visual

What You Will Learn

● Describe the motion of an object by the position of the object in relation to a reference point.
● Identify the two factors that determine speed.
● Explain the difference between speed and velocity.
● Analyze the relationship between velocity and acceleration.
● Demonstrate that changes in motion can be measured and represented on a graph.

Vocabulary

motion   velocity
speed   acceleration

READING STRATEGY

Discussion Read this section silently. Write down questions that you have about this section. Discuss your questions in a small group.

Measuring Motion

Look around you—you are likely to see something in motion. Your teacher may be walking across the room, or perhaps your friend is writing with a pencil.

Even if you don't see anything moving, motion is still occurring all around you. Air particles are moving, the Earth is circling the sun, and blood is traveling through your blood vessels!

Observing Motion by Using a Reference Point

You might think that the motion of an object is easy to detect—you just watch the object. But you are actually watching the object in relation to another object that appears to stay in place. The object that appears to stay in place is a *reference point*. When an object changes position over time relative to a reference point, the object is in **motion**. You can describe the direction of the object's motion with a reference direction, such as north, south, east, west, up, or down.

✓ *Reading Check* **What is a reference point?** (*See the Appendix for answers to Reading Checks.*)

Common Reference Points

The Earth's surface is a common reference point for determining motion, as shown in **Figure 1**. Nonmoving objects, such as trees and buildings, are also useful reference points.

A moving object can also be used as a reference point. For example, if you were on the hot-air balloon shown in **Figure 1**, you could watch a bird fly by and see that the bird was changing position in relation to your moving balloon.

Figure 1 *During the interval between the times that these pictures were taken, the hot-air balloon changed position relative to a reference point—the mountain.*

CHAPTER RESOURCES

Chapter Resource File

 • Lesson Plan
  • Directed Reading A BASIC
  • Directed Reading B SPECIAL NEEDS

Technology

 Transparencies
  • Bellringer
  • P11 A Graph Showing Speed

Workbooks

 Interactive Textbook Struggling Readers

MISCONCEPTION ///ALERT\\\

Describing Position The text defines *motion* as an object's change in position over time when compared with a reference point. Remind students that an object's *position* can be described in terms of a reference point and a set of reference directions. Common reference directions are compass directions (such as south and west) and relative directions (such as left of, just beyond, and in front of).

Speed Depends on Distance and Time

Speed is the distance traveled by an object divided by the time taken to travel that distance. Look again at **Figure 1.** Suppose the time interval between the pictures was 10 s and that the balloon traveled 50 m in that time. The speed of the balloon is (50 m)/(10 s), or 5 m/s.

The SI unit for speed is meters per second (m/s). Kilometers per hour (km/h), feet per second (ft/s), and miles per hour (mi/h) are other units commonly used to express speed.

Determining Average Speed

Most of the time, objects do not travel at a constant speed. For example, you probably do not walk at a constant speed from one class to the next. So, it is very useful to calculate *average speed* using the following equation:

$$\text{average speed} = \frac{\text{total distance}}{\text{total time}}$$

Recognizing Speed on a Graph

Suppose a person drives from one city to another. The blue line in the graph in **Figure 2** shows the total distance traveled during a 4 h period. Notice that the distance traveled during each hour is different. The distance varies because the speed is not constant. The driver may change speed because of weather, traffic, or varying speed limits. The average speed for the entire trip can be calculated as follows:

$$\text{average speed} = \frac{360 \text{ km}}{4 \text{ h}} = 90 \text{ km/h}$$

The red line on the graph shows how far the driver must travel each hour to reach the same city if he or she moved at a constant speed. The slope of this line is the average speed.

A Graph Showing Speed

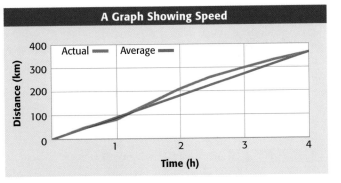

motion an object's change in position relative to a reference point

speed the distance traveled divided by the time interval during which the motion occurred

SCHOOL to HOME

What's Your Speed?

Measure a distance of 5 m or a distance of 25 ft inside or outside. Ask a family member to use a stopwatch or a watch with a second hand to time you as you travel the distance you measured. Then, find your average speed. Find the average speed of other members of your family in the same way. **ACTIVITY**

Figure 2 *Speed can be shown on a graph of distance versus time.*

READING STRATEGY — GENERAL

Writing Activity After students have read about velocity, have them write a paragraph in their **science journal** that gives examples of when it is sufficient to know only the speed of something and when it is important to know the velocity. **LS** Verbal

Answers to Math Focus

1. 2 m/s
2. 5 km/h
3. 360 km/h

ACTIVITY — ADVANCED

The Speed of Light Have students research the history of the measurement of the speed of light. Have them focus on the measurements involving distance and time. Ask students to write a short report that lists the difficulties in making these measurements and the factors that improved their accuracy. **LS** Verbal

Research — GENERAL

Navigational Terms Have students research navigational terms referring to speed and velocity. Ask students to list the terms that are used in sailing, aviation, and rocketry and to compare the usages. Tell students to focus on the importance placed on direction in the terms. **LS** Logical

MATH FOCUS

Calculating Average Speed An athlete swims a distance from one end of a 50 m pool to the other end in a time of 25 s. What is the athlete's average speed?

Step 1: Write the equation for average speed.

$$average\ speed = \frac{total\ distance}{total\ time}$$

Step 2: Replace the total distance and total time with the values given, and solve.

$$average\ speed = \frac{50\ m}{25\ s} = 2\ m/s$$

Now It's Your Turn

1. Kira jogs to a store 72 m away in a time of 36 s. What is Kira's average speed?
2. If you travel 7.5 km and walk for 1.5 h, what is your average speed?
3. An airplane traveling from San Francisco to Chicago travels 1,260 km in 3.5 h. What is the airplane's average speed?

Figure 3 *The speeds of these cars may be similar, but the velocities of the cars differ because the cars are going in different directions.*

Velocity: Direction Matters

Imagine that two birds leave the same tree at the same time. They both fly at 10 km/h for 5 min, 12 km/h for 8 min, and 5 km/h for 10 min. Why don't they end up at the same place?

Have you figured out the answer? The birds went in different directions. Their speeds were the same, but they had different velocities. **Velocity** (vuh LAHS uh tee) is the speed of an object in a particular direction.

Be careful not to confuse the terms *speed* and *velocity*. They do not have the same meaning. Velocity must include a reference direction. If you say that an airplane's velocity is 600 km/h, you would not be correct. But you could say the plane's velocity is 600 km/h south. **Figure 3** shows an example of the difference between speed and velocity.

Changing Velocity

You can think of velocity as the rate of change of an object's position. An object's velocity is constant only if its speed and direction don't change. Therefore, constant velocity is always motion along a straight line. An object's velocity changes if either its speed or direction changes. For example, as a bus traveling at 15 m/s south speeds up to 20 m/s south, its velocity changes. If the bus continues to travel at the same speed but changes direction to travel east, its velocity changes again. And if the bus slows down at the same time that it swerves north to avoid a cat, the velocity of the bus changes, too.

Reading Check What are the two ways that velocity can change?

Answer to Reading Check
Velocity can change by changing speed or changing direction.

CHAPTER RESOURCES

Technology

 Transparencies
• P12 Finding Resultant Velocity

Workbooks

Science Skills
• Organizing Your Research **GENERAL**

Figure 4 Finding Resultant Velocity

When you combine two velocities that are **in the same direction,** add them together to find the resultant velocity.

Person's resultant velocity
15 m/s east + 1 m/s east = 16 m/s east

When you combine two velocities that are **in opposite directions,** subtract the smaller velocity from the larger velocity to find the resultant velocity. The resultant velocity is in the direction of the larger velocity.

Person's resultant velocity
15 m/s east − 1 m/s west = 14 m/s east

Combining Velocities

Imagine that you are riding in a bus that is traveling east at 15 m/s. You and the other passengers are also traveling at a velocity of 15 m/s east. But suppose you stand up and walk down the bus's aisle while the bus is moving. Are you still moving at the same velocity as the bus? No! **Figure 4** shows how you can combine velocities to find the *resultant velocity.*

Acceleration

Although the word *accelerate* is commonly used to mean "speed up," the word means something else in science. **Acceleration** (ak SEL uhr AY shuhn) is the rate at which velocity changes. Velocity changes if speed changes, if direction changes, or if both change. So, an object accelerates if its speed, its direction, or both change.

An increase in velocity is commonly called *positive acceleration.* A decrease in velocity is commonly called *negative acceleration,* or *deceleration.* Keep in mind that acceleration is not only how much velocity changes but also how fast velocity changes. The faster the velocity changes, the greater the acceleration is.

velocity the speed of an object in a particular direction

acceleration the rate at which velocity changes over time; an object accelerates if its speed, direction, or both change

ACTIVITY ———— BASIC

Diagramming Acceleration Read aloud each of the following situations. Diagram them on the board or overhead projector. Then, discuss with students whether or not acceleration occurred and why.

- You are riding your bike at 9 km/h. Ten minutes later, your speed is 6 km/h. (Acceleration occurred because speed decreased.)

- You ride your bike around the block at a constant speed of 11 km/h. (Acceleration occurred because direction changed.)

- You ride your bike in a straight line at a constant speed of 10 km/h. (No acceleration occurred because neither speed nor direction changed.) **English Language Learners**
 LS Visual

SUPPORT FOR

English Language Learners
Combining Velocities
A visual aid will help students understand velocity. Have students draw a number line on a sheet of graph paper to practice adding and subtracting velocities. Using the situations shown in the diagram on finding resultant velocity, have students draw arrows representing the velocity of the bus and the walker. Demonstrate that by putting the arrows in sequence head to tail, they can add the velocities. By superimposing the shorter arrow over the longer one and finding the difference, they can subtract the velocities. **LS** Visual/Logical

READING STRATEGY ——— GENERAL

Prediction Guide Before reading about acceleration, ask students to predict whether the following sentences are true or false:

- If you slow down on your bicycle, you accelerate. (true)

- If you ride your bicycle at a constant speed, you cannot accelerate. (false)

- Changing the speed and changing the direction of your bicycle are both examples of acceleration. (true)
LS Verbal

Homework ——— GENERAL

Problem Writing Have students develop three of their own problems involving the addition and subtraction of velocities. The problems should come from events in their own experience. For example, they might develop a problem based on kicking a soccer ball down the field or from watching actors running along the top of a train in an adventure movie. Students should provide answers to their problems. **LS** Verbal

Section 1 • Measuring Motion 7

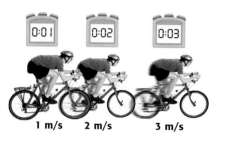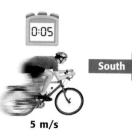

1 m/s   2 m/s   3 m/s   4 m/s   5 m/s

South

Figure 5 *This cyclist is accelerating at 1 m/s² south.*

MATH PRACTICE

Calculating Acceleration

Use the equation for average acceleration to do the following problem.

A plane passes over point A at a velocity of 240 m/s north. Forty seconds later, it passes over point B at a velocity of 260 m/s north. What is the plane's average acceleration?

Calculating Average Acceleration

You can find average acceleration by using the equation:

$$average\ acceleration = \frac{final\ velocity - starting\ velocity}{time\ it\ takes\ to\ change\ velocity}$$

Velocity is expressed in meters per second (m/s), and time is expressed in seconds (s). So acceleration is expressed in meters per second per second, or (m/s)/s, which equals m/s². For example, look at **Figure 5.** Every second, the cyclist's southward velocity increases by 1 m/s. His average acceleration can be calculated as follows:

$$average\ acceleration = \frac{5\ m/s - 1\ m/s}{4\ s} = 1\ m/s^2\ south$$

Reading Check What are the units of acceleration?

Recognizing Acceleration on a Graph

Suppose that you are riding a roller coaster. The roller-coaster car moves up a hill until it stops at the top. Then, you are off! The graph in **Figure 6** shows your acceleration for the next 10 s. During the first 8 s, you move down the hill. You can tell from the graph that your acceleration is positive for the first 8 s because your velocity increases as time passes. During the last 2 s, your car starts climbing the next hill. Your acceleration is negative because your velocity decreases as time passes.

Figure 6 *Acceleration can be shown on a graph of velocity versus time.*

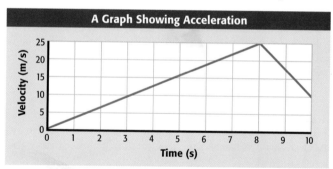

A Graph Showing Acceleration

Velocity (m/s) vs. Time (s)

Circular Motion: Continuous Acceleration

You may be surprised to know that even when you are completely still, you are experiencing acceleration. You may not seem to be changing speed or direction, but you are! You are traveling in a circle as the Earth rotates. An object traveling in a circular motion is always changing its direction. Therefore, its velocity is always changing, so it is accelerating. The acceleration that occurs in circular motion is known as *centripetal acceleration* (sen TRIP uht uhl ak SEL uhr AY shuhn). Centripetal acceleration occurs on a Ferris wheel at an amusement park or as the moon orbits Earth. Another example of centripetal acceleration is shown in **Figure 7**.

Figure 7 *The blades of these windmills are constantly changing direction. Thus, centripetal acceleration is occurring.*

SECTION Review

Summary

- An object is in motion if it changes position over time in relation to a reference point.
- Speed is the distance traveled by an object divided by the time the object takes to travel that distance.
- Velocity is speed in a given direction.
- Acceleration is the rate at which velocity changes.
- An object can accelerate by changing speed, direction, or both.
- Speed can be represented on a graph of distance versus time.
- Acceleration can be represented by graphing velocity versus time.

Using Key Terms

1. In your own words, write definitions for each of the following terms: *motion* and *acceleration*.

2. Use each of the following terms in a separate sentence: *speed* and *velocity*.

Understanding Key Ideas

3. Which of the following is NOT an example of acceleration?
   a. a person jogging at 3 m/s along a winding path
   b. a car stopping at a stop sign
   c. a cheetah running 27 m/s east
   d. a plane taking off

4. Which of the following would be a good reference point to describe the motion of a dog?
   a. the ground
   b. another dog running
   c. a tree
   d. All of the above

5. Explain the difference between speed and velocity.

6. What two things must you know to determine speed?

7. How are velocity and acceleration related?

Math Skills

8. Find the average speed of a person who swims 105 m in 70 s.

9. What is the average acceleration of a subway train that speeds up from 9.6 m/s to 12 m/s in 0.8 s on a straight section of track?

Critical Thinking

10. **Applying Concepts** Why is it more helpful to know a tornado's velocity rather than its speed?

11. **Evaluating Data** A wolf is chasing a rabbit. Graph the wolf's motion using the following data: 15 m/s at 0 s, 10 m/s at 1 s, 5 m/s at 2 s, 2.5 m/s at 3 s, 1 m/s at 4 s, and 0 m/s at 5 s. What does the graph tell you?

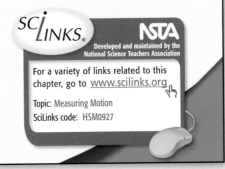

For a variety of links related to this chapter, go to www.scilinks.org

Topic: Measuring Motion
SciLinks code: HSM0927

Answers to Section Review

1. Sample answer: Motion is the change in position of an object relative to a reference point. Acceleration is the change in velocity over time.

2. Sample answer: The cat is moving with a speed of 1 m/s. The cat is moving with a velocity of 1 m/s to the east.

3. c

4. d

5. Speed does not include direction; velocity does.

6. the distance traveled and the time taken to travel that distance

7. Acceleration is the rate at which velocity changes.

8. 1.5 m/s

9. 3 m/s^2

10. It would be important to know the velocity because velocity includes direction. Knowing only the speed of a tornado would not tell the direction that the tornado is traveling. Knowing a tornado's direction of travel would allow people to avoid or escape its path.

11. The graph shows that the wolf has negative acceleration (slows down) until it comes to a stop.

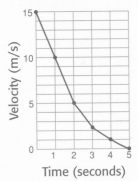

CHAPTER RESOURCES

Chapter Resource File

- Section Quiz **GENERAL**
- Section Review **GENERAL**
- Vocabulary and Section Summary **GENERAL**
- Reinforcement Worksheet **BASIC**
- SciLinks Activity **GENERAL**

Focus

Overview

This section defines *force* and describes how all forces act on objects. Students learn to determine the net force on an object and compare balanced and unbalanced forces.

Bellringer

Have students look around the room and think about the objects they see in terms of force. Tell them that a force is always exerted by one object on another object. Ask them the following question:

> Where do you see a force happening in the room right now? Which object is exerting the force, and which is receiving it?

Motivate

 ——————— GENERAL

Bridge Building Have students work in groups to build a bridge using toothpicks and glue. The bridge should span a 15 cm gap and be wide enough to hold a toy car. Students should identify the forces acting on their bridge. (An alternate and less time consuming activity would be to have students build a house of cards that can support a 500 g mass.) **LS** Kinesthetic

What You Will Learn

- Describe forces, and explain how forces act on objects.
- Determine the net force when more than one force is acting on an object.
- Compare balanced and unbalanced forces.
- Describe ways that unbalanced forces cause changes in motion.

Vocabulary
force
newton
net force

READING STRATEGY

Reading Organizer As you read this section, make a table comparing balanced forces and unbalanced forces.

What Is a Force?

You have probably heard the word **force** in everyday conversation. People say things such as "That storm had a lot of force" or "Our football team is a force to be reckoned with." But what, exactly, is a force?

In science, a **force** is simply a push or a pull. All forces have both size and direction. A force can change the acceleration of an object. This acceleration can be a change in the speed or direction of the object. In fact, any time you see a change in an object's motion, you can be sure that the change in motion was created by a force. Scientists express force using a unit called the **newton** (N).

Forces Acting on Objects

All forces act on objects. For any push to occur, something has to receive the push. You can't push nothing! The same is true for any pull. When doing schoolwork, you use your fingers to pull open books or to push the buttons on a computer keyboard. In these examples, your fingers are exerting forces on the books and the keys. So, the forces act on the books and keys. Another example of a force acting on an object is shown in **Figure 1**.

However, just because a force acts on an object doesn't mean that motion will occur. For example, you are probably sitting on a chair. But the force you are exerting on the chair does not cause the chair to move. The chair doesn't move because the floor is also exerting a force on the chair.

Figure 1 *The bulldozer is exerting a force on the pile of soil. But the pile of soil also exerts a force by just sitting on the ground!*

CHAPTER RESOURCES

Chapter Resource File

- **Lesson Plan**
- **Directed Reading A** BASIC
- **Directed Reading B** SPECIAL NEEDS

Technology

Transparencies
- Bellringer
- P15 Forces in the Same Direction; Forces in Opposite Directions

Workbooks

Interactive Textbook Struggling Readers

Is That a Fact!

Some trains are too massive to be moved by one locomotive. To compensate for the larger mass, extra locomotives are added until the net force provided by all the locomotives is large enough to move the train.

Unseen Sources and Receivers of Forces

It is not always easy to tell what is exerting a force or what is receiving a force, as shown in **Figure 2.** You cannot see what exerts the force that pulls magnets to refrigerators. And you cannot see that the air around you is held near Earth's surface by a force called *gravity*.

Determining Net Force

Usually, more than one force is acting on an object. The **net force** is the combination all of the forces acting on an object. So, how do you determine the net force? The answer depends on the directions of the forces.

Forces in the Same Direction

Suppose the music teacher asks you and a friend to move a piano. You pull on one end and your friend pushes on the other end, as shown in **Figure 3.** The forces you and your friend exert on the piano act in the same direction. The two forces are added to determine the net force because the forces act in the same direction. In this case, the net force is 45 N. This net force is large enough to move the piano—if it is on wheels, that is!

✔️ *Reading Check* How do you determine the net force on an object if all forces act in the same direction? (*See the Appendix for answers to Reading Checks.*)

Figure 2 *Something that you cannot see exerts a force that makes this cat's fur stand up.*

force a push or a pull exerted on an object in order to change the motion of the object; force has size and direction

newton the SI unit for force (symbol, N)

net force the combination of all of the forces acting on an object

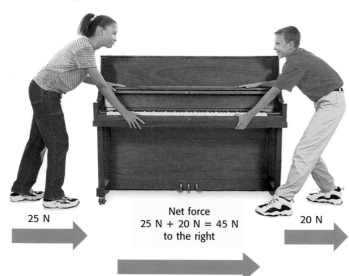

25 N

Net force
25 N + 20 N = 45 N
to the right

20 N

Figure 3 *When forces act in the same direction, you add the forces to determine the net force. The net force will be in the same direction as the individual forces.*

Answer to Reading Check
If all of the forces act in the same direction, you must add the forces to determine the net force.

📖 **READING STRATEGY** ——— GENERAL

Prediction Guide Before students read about determining net force, have them look at **Figures 3** and **4** in this section. While they are looking at these pictures, ask students to predict what happens when forces act in the same direction and when forces act in opposite directions. LS **Visual**

Force and Pressure Force and pressure are different from each other. Magicians depend on this difference when they lie down on a bed of nails. The **force**—the magician's weight—is fairly large, but because there are hundreds or even thousands of nails, the **pressure** (the amount of force exerted on a given area) from each nail is not enough to break the magician's skin.

Discussion ——— GENERAL

Everyday Forces Using objects in the room or situations with which students are familiar (like riding a bicycle), discuss with students the forces that are operating on them. Ask students in each case to identify which object is exerting the force and which is receiving it. (Sample answers for riding a bicycle: feet exert force on the pedals, the tires exert force on the ground, fingers exert force on the hand brakes, the brake pads exert force on the wheel rims) Continue the discussion by asking them to identify other types of daily activities that involve forces. LS **Verbal**

Reteaching ———— BASIC

Finding the Net Force Have students look at **Figure 3** in this section. Ask them to find the net force if the girl continued to exert the same force on the piano while the boy pushes the piano with a force of 20 N to the left. Ask students to predict which direction the piano will move. (The net force would be 5 N to the right. The piano would move to the right.) **LS** Logical

Quiz ———— GENERAL

1. What is a net force? (the combination of all the forces acting on an object)

2. Are the forces on a kicked soccer ball balanced or unbalanced? How do you know? (unbalanced; because the ball changes speed and/or direction)

Alternative Assessment ———— GENERAL

Poster Project Have students make a poster that shows an example of balanced forces (such as an elevator at rest or a gymnast motionless on a balance beam). The poster should show the forces acting on the object and should show what happens to the object if the forces become unbalanced. **LS** Visual

Figure 4 When two forces act in opposite directions, you subtract the smaller force from the larger force to determine the net force. The net force will be in the same direction as the larger force.

10 N

Net force
12 N − 10 N = 2 N
to the right

12 N

Forces in Different Directions

Look at the two dogs playing tug of war in **Figure 4.** Each dog is exerting a force on the rope. But the forces are in opposite directions. Which dog will win the tug of war?

Because the forces are in opposite directions, the net force on the rope is found by subtracting the smaller force from the larger one. In this case, the net force is 2 N in the direction of the dog on the right. Give that dog a dog biscuit!

✔ Reading Check What is the net force on an object when you combine a force of 7 N north with a force of 5 N south?

Balanced and Unbalanced Forces

If you know the net force on an object, you can determine the effect of the net force on the object's motion. Why? The net force tells you whether the forces on the object are balanced or unbalanced.

Balanced Forces

When the forces on an object produce a net force of 0 N, the forces are *balanced*. Balanced forces will not cause a change in the motion of a moving object. And balanced forces do not cause a nonmoving object to start moving.

Many objects around you have only balanced forces acting on them. For example, a light hanging from the ceiling does not move because the force of gravity pulling down on the light is balanced by the force of the cord pulling upward. A bird's nest in a tree and a hat resting on your head are also examples of objects that have only balanced forces acting on them. **Figure 5** shows another example of balanced forces.

Figure 5 Because all the forces on this house of cards are balanced, none of the cards move.

Answer to Reading Check
2 N north

Unbalanced Forces

When the net force on an object is not 0 N, the forces on the object are *unbalanced*. Unbalanced forces produce a change in motion, such as a change in speed or a change in direction. Unbalanced forces are necessary to cause a nonmoving object to start moving.

Unbalanced forces are also necessary to change the motion of moving objects. For example, consider the soccer game shown in **Figure 6.** The soccer ball is already moving when it is passed from one player to another. When the ball reaches another player, that player exerts an unbalanced force—a kick—on the ball. After the kick, the ball moves in a new direction and has a new speed.

An object can continue to move when the unbalanced forces are removed. For example, when it is kicked, a soccer ball receives an unbalanced force. The ball continues to roll on the ground long after the force of the kick has ended.

Figure 6 *The soccer ball moves because the players exert an unbalanced force on the ball each time they kick it.*

SECTION Review

Summary

- A force is a push or a pull. Forces have size and direction and are expressed in newtons.
- Force is always exerted by one object on another object.
- Net force is determined by combining forces. Forces in the same direction are added. Forces in opposite directions are subtracted.
- Balanced forces produce no change in motion. Unbalanced forces produce a change in motion.

Using Key Terms

1. In your own words, write a definition for each of the following terms: *force* and *net force.*

Understanding Key Ideas

2. Which of the following may happen when an object receives unbalanced forces?
   a. The object changes direction.
   b. The object changes speed.
   c. The object starts to move.
   d. All of the above

3. Explain the difference between balanced and unbalanced forces.

4. Give an example of an unbalanced force causing a change in motion.

5. Give an example of an object that has balanced forces acting on it.

6. Explain the meaning of the phrase "Forces act on objects."

Math Skills

7. A boy pulls a wagon with a force of 6 N east as another boy pushes it with a force of 4 N east. What is the net force?

Critical Thinking

8. **Making Inferences** When finding net force, why must you know the directions of the forces acting on an object?

9. **Applying Concepts** List three forces that you exert when riding a bicycle.

Developed and maintained by the National Science Teachers Association

For a variety of links related to this chapter, go to www.scilinks.org

Topic: Forces
SciLinks code: HSM0604

CHAPTER RESOURCES

Chapter Resource File

- Section Quiz GENERAL
- Section Review GENERAL
- Vocabulary and Section Summary GENERAL

Focus

Overview

This section introduces and describes friction. Students learn about the kinds of friction and about the role of friction in everyday life.

🔊 Bellringer

Have students answer the following question:

> Suppose you and a younger sister or brother are at a neighborhood pool. Your sister or brother asks why there are signs that say "NO RUNNING." What would be your answer?

Motivate

 ──────── GENERAL

Fingerprints Humans have ridges in the skin of their hands. These ridges increase friction between the skin and objects the hands touch. Have students make a fingerprint to better see the ridges on one finger. Give students dark-colored, washable markers. Tell students to use the marker to color the pad of one finger, and to immediately press the finger to a sheet of paper 3 or 4 times. Show students pictures of different types of fingerprints and have them classify their fingerprints as arches, loops, or whorls. **LS** Kinesthetic

What You Will Learn

● Explain why friction occurs.
● List the two types of friction, and give examples of each type.
● Explain how friction can be both harmful and helpful.

Vocabulary
friction

READING STRATEGY

Brainstorming The key idea of this section is friction. Brainstorm words and phrases related to friction.

friction a force that opposes motion between two surfaces that are in contact

Friction: A Force That Opposes Motion

While playing ball, your friend throws the ball out of your reach. Rather than running for the ball, you walk after it. You know that the ball will stop. But do you know why?

You know that the ball is slowing down. An unbalanced force is needed to change the speed of a moving object. So, what force is stopping the ball? The force is called friction. **Friction** is a force that opposes motion between two surfaces that are in contact. Friction can cause a moving object, such as a ball, to slow down and eventually stop.

The Source of Friction

Friction occurs because the surface of any object is rough. Even surfaces that feel smooth are covered with microscopic hills and valleys. When two surfaces are in contact, the hills and valleys of one surface stick to the hills and valleys of the other surface, as shown in **Figure 1.** This contact causes friction.

The amount of friction between two surfaces depends on many factors. Two factors include the force pushing the surfaces together and the roughness of the surfaces.

The Effect of Force on Friction

The amount of friction depends on the force pushing the surfaces together. If this force increases, the hills and valleys of the surfaces can come into closer contact. The close contact increases the friction between the surfaces. Objects that weigh less exert less downward force than objects that weigh more do, as shown in **Figure 2.** But changing how much of the surfaces come in contact does not change the amount of friction.

Figure 1 *When the hills and valleys of one surface stick to the hills and valleys of another surface, friction is created.*

CHAPTER RESOURCES

Chapter Resource File

• **Lesson Plan**
• **Directed Reading A** BASIC
• **Directed Reading B** SPECIAL NEEDS

Technology

Transparencies
• Bellringer
• P16 Force and Friction

Workbooks

Interactive Textbook Struggling Readers

MISCONCEPTION ALERT

The Cause of Friction Many people believe that friction is caused when the hills and valleys of one surface "climb" over the hills and valleys of another surface. In fact, friction is caused by chemical bonds that are formed and broken between the hills and valleys of two surfaces. Scientists call this phenomenon the "stick and slip" cause of friction.

Figure 2 Force and Friction

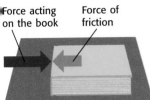 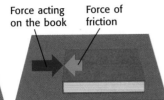 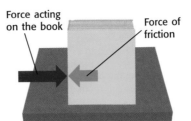

(a) There is more friction between the book with more weight and the table than there is between the book with less weight and the table. A harder push is needed to move the heavier book.

(b) Turning a book on its edge does not change the amount of friction between the table and the book.

Force acting on the book — Force of friction

Force acting on the book — Force of friction

Force acting on the book — Force of friction

The Effect of Rougher Surfaces on Friction

Rough surfaces have more microscopic hills and valleys than smooth surfaces do. So, the rougher the surface is, the greater the friction is. For example, a ball rolling on the ground slows down because of the friction between the ball and the ground. A large amount of friction is produced because the ground has a rough surface. But imagine that you were playing ice hockey. If the puck passed out of your reach, it would slide across the ice for a long while before stopping. The reason the puck would continue to slide is that the ice is a smooth surface that has very little friction.

Reading Check Why is friction greater between surfaces that are rough? (*See the Appendix for answers to Reading Checks.*)

The Friction 500

1. Make a short ramp out of **a piece of cardboard** and **one or two books** on a table.

2. Put a **toy car** at the top of the ramp, and let go of the car. If necessary, adjust the ramp height so that your car does not roll off the table.

3. Put the car at the top of the ramp again, and let go of the car. Record the distance the car travels after leaving the ramp.

4. Repeat step 3 two more times, and calculate the average for your results.

5. Change the surface of the table by covering the table with **sandpaper**. Repeat steps 3 and 4.

6. Change the surface of the table one more time by covering the table with **cloth**. Repeat steps 3 and 4 again.

7. Which surface had the most friction? Why? What do you predict would happen if the car were heavier?

Tom: **This match won't light.**

Jerry: **What's the matter with it?**

Tom: **I don't know; it worked a minute ago.**

WEIRD SCIENCE

Air hockey is challenging because the puck floats on a very thin layer of air. Tiny holes in the table surface allow pressurized air to escape from underneath. The puck moves with very little friction.

Teach

Quick Lab

MATERIALS

FOR EACH GROUP
- books (2)
- cardboard, corrugated
- cloth, fuzzy or nappy
- meterstick
- sandpaper, very coarse
- toy car

Teacher's Notes: You can substitute pieces of plywood or several metersticks for the corrugated cardboard.

To keep the cars from rolling off the table, have students use one or two thin books. Students may also do the lab on the floor if they are having trouble keeping the car on the table.

If your classroom is carpeted, you can move the ramp to the floor for one of the trials.

To reduce cost, have students lay narrow strips of sandpaper and cloth in front of the ramp rather than covering the table top.

Answer

7. Answers may vary. Sample answer: The sandpaper surface had the most friction because it is the roughest. A heavier car would result in even more friction between the car and the surface because the force pushing the surfaces together would be increased. (**Note:** If students start the car from the same spot, the mass of the car will not affect the distance it travels on a given surface.)

Answer to Reading Check

Friction is greater between rough surfaces because rough surfaces have more microscopic hills and valleys.

Tires and Friction
Vehicle tires are designed to use friction to increase grip. Have students find information on as many different kinds of tires, tire compounds, and tread designs as they can. Have them do a poster or other project showing some of the types of tires and treads they have learned about. **English Language Learners**
LS Visual

INCLUSION Strategies

• *Learning Disabled*
• *Attention Deficit Disorder*
• *Developmentally Delayed*

Let students experience the two kinds of friction. Choose several students to participate in the activity. Ask each student to try both options. Use the following situations to create each of the types of friction:

Static Friction—Gently push a school desk and feel the resistance before it starts moving.

Kinetic Friction—Push a school desk across the floor and feel the resistance to the movement. **English Language Learners**
LS Kinesthetic

SCHOOL to HOME

Comparing Friction
Ask an adult at home to sit on the floor. Try to push the adult across the room. Next, ask the adult to sit on a chair that has wheels and to keep his or her feet off the floor. Try pushing the adult and the chair across the room. If you do not have a chair that has wheels, try pushing the adult on different kinds of flooring. Explain why there was a difference between the two trials in your **science journal.**

ACTIVITY

Types of Friction

There are two types of friction. The friction you observe when sliding books across a tabletop is called *kinetic friction.* The other type of friction is *static friction.* You observe static friction when you push on a piece of furniture and it does not move.

Kinetic Friction

The word *kinetic* means "moving." So, kinetic friction is friction between moving surfaces. The amount of kinetic friction between two surfaces depends in part on how the surfaces move. Surfaces can slide past each other. Or a surface can roll over another surface. Usually, the force of sliding kinetic friction is greater than the force of rolling kinetic friction. Thus, it is usually easier to move objects on wheels than to slide the objects along the floor, as shown in **Figure 3.**

Kinetic friction is very useful in everyday life. You use sliding kinetic friction when you apply the brakes on a bicycle and when you write with a pencil or a piece of chalk. You also use sliding kinetic friction when you scratch a part of your body that is itchy!

Rolling kinetic friction is an important part of almost all means of transportation. Anything that has wheels—bicycles, in-line skates, cars, trains, and planes—uses rolling kinetic friction.

Figure 3   Comparing Kinetic Friction

ⓐ Moving a heavy piece of furniture in your room can be hard work because **the force of sliding kinetic friction is large.**

ⓑ Moving a heavy piece of furniture is easier if you put it on wheels. **The force of rolling kinetic friction is smaller** and easier to overcome.

MISCONCEPTION
///ALERT

Rolling Versus Sliding Rolling kinetic friction is usually smaller than sliding kinetic friction, but it depends on the situation. If both surfaces are hard, rolling friction is smaller. But if one of the surfaces is soft, such as deep snow, the sliding friction of skis or a sled might be a lot smaller than the rolling friction of a loaded wagon. Friction depends on several characteristics of both surfaces.

Answer to School-to-Home
It is easier to push a person in a chair with wheels because rolling kinetic friction is less than sliding kinetic friction. Alternate answer: It is easier to push a person on a smooth floor because there is less friction between the person and the floor. (**Teacher's Notes:** Tell students that they can have their parents put on roller skates or roller blades or stand on skateboard instead of sitting in a chair with wheels.)

Figure 4 Static Friction

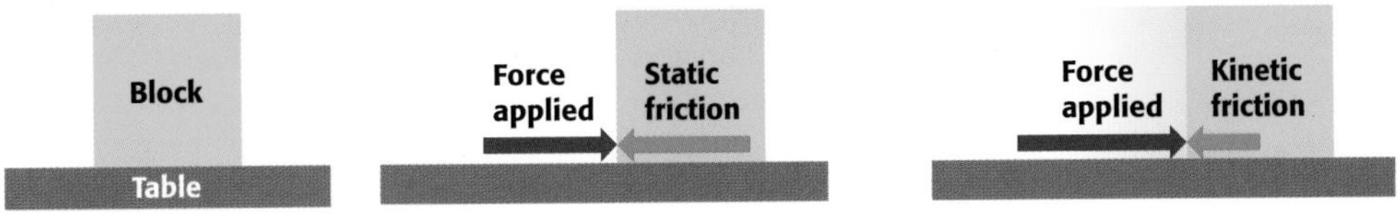

a There is no friction between the block and the table when no force is applied to the block.

b If a small force (purple arrow) is exerted on the block, the block does not move. The force of static friction (green arrow) balances the force applied.

c When the force exerted on the block is greater than the force of static friction, the block starts moving. When the block starts moving, all static friction is gone, and only kinetic friction (green arrow) opposes the force applied.

Static Friction

When a force is applied to an object but does not cause the object to move, *static friction* occurs. The word *static* means "not moving." The object does not move because the force of static friction balances the force applied. Static friction can be overcome by applying a large enough force. Static friction disappears as soon as an object starts moving, and then kinetic friction immediately occurs. Look at **Figure 4** to understand under what conditions static friction affects an object.

Reading Check What does the word *static* mean?

Friction: Harmful and Helpful

Think about how friction affects a car. Without friction, the tires could not push against the ground to move the car forward, and the brakes could not stop the car. Without friction, a car is useless. However, friction can also cause problems in a car. Friction between moving engine parts increases their temperature and causes the parts to wear down. A liquid coolant is added to the engine to keep the engine from overheating. And engine parts need to be changed as they wear out.

Friction is both harmful and helpful to you and the world around you. Friction can cause holes in your socks and in the knees of your jeans. Friction by wind and water can cause erosion of the topsoil that nourishes plants. On the other hand, friction between your pencil and your paper is necessary to allow the pencil to leave a mark. Without friction, you would just slip and fall when you tried to walk. Because friction can be both harmful and helpful, it is sometimes necessary to decrease or increase friction.

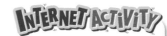

INTERNET ACTIVITY

For another activity related to this chapter, go to **go.hrw.com** and type in the keyword **HP5MOTW.**

CONNECTION TO Social Studies

WRITING SKILL **Invention of the Wheel** Archeologists have found evidence that the first vehicles with wheels were used in ancient Mesopotamia sometime between 3500 and 3000 BCE. Before wheels were invented, people used planks or sleds to carry loads. In your **science journal,** write a paragraph about how your life would be different if wheels did not exist.

SUPPORT FOR

English Language Learners

Friction Experiment To provide students with hands-on experience with the concepts in this section, have them experiment with friction. Show pairs of students how to make a ramp using a piece of cardboard that has been covered tightly with plastic wrap. Have students select three or four common objects in the classroom that they think might have different amounts of friction. Pairs of students can experiment by placing objects on the ramp while it is flat, and, then, lifting one end until each object slides down. Have them use a ruler to measure how high the ramp must be lifted before each object slides down. Ask them to record their observations in a table and to write a short explanation for their findings. Evaluate the explanation for clarity of expression and understanding of the concepts as well as grammar and spelling. **LS Verbal/Logical/Interpersonal**

Answer to Reading Check

Static means "not moving."

Research — GENERAL

PORTFOLIO **Uses for Teflon** Polytetrafluoroethylene (PTFE), also known as Teflon®, is one of the slipperiest substances known to humans. It was discovered by accident in 1938. Most students know Teflon as a nonstick coating for frying pans. Have them research the many uses of Teflon and make posters to present to the class. **LS Visual**

SCIENCE HUMOR

An impatient young girl named Lenore
Tried to run on a freshly waxed floor.
Since the friction was less,
She made quite a mess
As she slid right under the door.

CHAPTER RESOURCES

Technology

Transparencies
- P17 Static Friction

Close

Reteaching — **BASIC**

Helpful and Harmful Friction

Have half the class draw a comic strip showing a situation in which friction is helpful. Have the other half draw a comic strip showing a situation in which friction is harmful. Ask student volunteers to share their comic strips with the class. **LS** Visual

Quiz — **GENERAL**

1. Which of the following would NOT help you move a heavy object across a concrete floor? water, ball bearings, oil, liquid soap, steel rods, foam rubber (foam rubber)

2. Name three common items you might use to increase friction. (Sample answers: sticky tape, sand, work gloves)

Alternative Assessment — **GENERAL**

Designing a Bowling Alley

Ask students to imagine that they have been asked to design a bowling alley. Have them describe the areas where they would try to reduce friction and the areas where they would try to increase friction. Have them describe what materials they would use and why. **LS** Logical

Answer to Reading Check

Three common lubricants are oil, grease, and wax.

Reducing Friction

1. Stack **two or three heavy books** on a table. Use one finger to push the books across the table.

2. Place **five round pens or pencils** under the books, and push the books again.

3. Compare the force used in step 1 with the force used in step 2. Explain.

4. Open a **jar** with your hands, and close it again.

5. Spread a small amount of **liquid soap** on your hands.

6. Try to open the jar again. Was the jar easier or harder to open with the soap? Explain your observations.

7. In which situation was friction helpful? In which situation was friction harmful?

Figure 5 *When you work on a bicycle, watch out for the chain! You might get dirty from the grease or oil that keeps the chain moving freely. Without this lubricant, friction between the sections of the chain would quickly wear the chain out.*

Some Ways to Reduce Friction

One way to reduce friction is to use lubricants (LOO bri kuhnts). *Lubricants* are substances that are applied to surfaces to reduce the friction between the surfaces. Some examples of common lubricants are motor oil, wax, and grease. Lubricants are usually liquids, but they can be solids or gases. An example of a gas lubricant is the air that comes out of the tiny holes of an air-hockey table. **Figure 5** shows one use of a lubricant.

Friction can also be reduced by switching from sliding kinetic friction to rolling kinetic friction. Ball bearings placed between the wheels and axles of in-line skates and bicycles make it easier for the wheels to turn by reducing friction.

Another way to reduce friction is to make surfaces that rub against each other smoother. For example, rough wood on a park bench is painful to slide across because there is a large amount of friction between your leg and the bench. Rubbing the bench with sandpaper makes the bench smoother and more comfortable to sit on. The reason the bench is more comfortable is that the friction between your leg and the bench is reduced.

Reading Check List three common lubricants.

MATERIALS

FOR EACH GROUP
- books, heavy (2–3)
- jar, with lid
- liquid soap
- pens or pencils, round (5)

Teacher's Note: To control the amount of soap used, you may wish to assign a single student to dispense the soap.

Answers

3. Less force was needed in step 2 because the friction was reduced by changing sliding kinetic friction to rolling kinetic friction.

6. The jar was harder to open with the soap. The soap was a lubricant that reduced the friction between my hands and the jar.

7. Friction is helpful when trying to open a jar. Friction is harmful when trying to push books across the table.

Some Ways to Increase Friction

One way to increase friction is to make surfaces rougher. For example, sand scattered on icy roads keeps cars from skidding. Baseball players sometimes wear textured batting gloves to increase the friction between their hands and the bat so that the bat does not fly out of their hands.

Another way to increase friction is to increase the force pushing the surfaces together. For example, if you are sanding a piece of wood, you can sand the wood faster by pressing harder on the sandpaper. Pressing harder increases the force pushing the sandpaper and wood together. So, the friction between the sandpaper and wood increases. **Figure 6** shows another example of friction increased by pushing on an object.

Figure 6 *No one likes cleaning dirty pans. To get this chore done quickly, press down with the scrubber to increase friction.*

SECTION Review

Summary

- Friction is a force that opposes motion.
- Friction is caused by hills and valleys on the surfaces of two objects touching each other.
- The amount of friction depends on factors such as the roughness of the surfaces and the force pushing the surfaces together.
- Two kinds of friction are kinetic friction and static friction.
- Friction can be helpful or harmful.

Using Key Terms

1. In your own words, write a definition for the term *friction*.

Understanding Key Ideas

2. Why is it easy to slip when there is water on the floor?
   a. The water is a lubricant and reduces the friction between your feet and the floor.
   b. The friction between your feet and the floor changes from kinetic to static friction.
   c. The water increases the friction between your feet and the floor.
   d. The friction between your feet and the floor changes from sliding kinetic friction to rolling kinetic friction.

3. Explain why friction occurs.

4. How does the roughness of surfaces that are touching affect the friction between the surfaces?

5. Describe how the amount of force pushing two surfaces together affects friction.

6. Name two ways in which friction can be increased.

7. List the two types of friction, and give an example of each.

Interpreting Graphics

8. Why do you think the sponge shown below has a layer of plastic bristles attached to it?

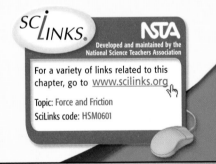

Critical Thinking

9. **Applying Concepts** Name two ways that friction is harmful and two ways that friction is helpful to you when riding a bicycle.

10. **Making Inferences** Describe a situation in which static friction is useful.

For a variety of links related to this chapter, go to www.scilinks.org

Topic: Force and Friction
SciLinks code: HSM0601

Answers to Section Review

1. Sample answer: Friction is a force that works against the motion of an object.

2. a

3. Friction occurs because the microscopic hills and valleys of two touching surfaces stick to each other.

4. As the roughness of the surfaces increases, the friction between the surfaces increases.

5. As the force pushing two surfaces together increases, the friction between the surfaces increases.

6. Friction can be increased by making surfaces rougher and by increasing the force pushing the surfaces together.

7. The two kinds of friction are kinetic friction and static friction. Sample answer: An example of kinetic friction is the friction that happens when you slide a chair across the floor. An example of static friction is the friction that keeps an eraser sitting on a tilted book from sliding down.

8. The sponge has a layer of plastic bristles on it to make it rougher. The rough bristles increase the friction between the sponge and the surface being cleaned. The increased friction helps clean pots and pans.

9. Answers may vary. Sample answer: Friction is harmful because it causes tire tread to wear down and causes the brakes to wear down. Friction is helpful because it helps the wheels grip the road and helps your feet and hands stay on the pedals and handlebars.

10. Answers may vary. Sample answer: Static friction is useful when you lean against a table for support. The table doesn't move because of static friction between the feet of the table and the floor.

Focus

Overview

This section describes gravity and the relationship between gravitational force, mass, and distance. It also distinguishes between weight and mass.

 Bellringer

Significantly decreased gravity gives astronauts the sensation of being weightless and forces astronauts to make many adjustments in their activities. Ask students to write a paragraph explaining what they would like and dislike about living with reduced gravity.

Motivate

Group Activity — GENERAL

Gravity Poster Before beginning this activity, lead a brief discussion about gravity. During this discussion, be sure your students understand that gravity pulls objects toward Earth. Then, have students work in small groups. Each group should pick a sport or an activity that is affected by gravity. Each group should identify examples from the sport or activity in which gravity is beneficial and examples of when gravity is harmful. Ask each group to make a poster illustrating their examples.
LS Visual Co-op Learning

Gravity: A Force of Attraction

Have you ever seen a video of astronauts on the moon? They bounce around like beach balls even though they wear big, bulky spacesuits. Why is leaping on the moon easier than leaping on Earth?

The answer is gravity. **Gravity** is a force of attraction between objects that is due to their masses. The force of gravity can change the motion of an object by changing its speed, direction, or both. In this section, you will learn about gravity and its effects on objects, such as the astronaut in **Figure 1.**

The Effects of Gravity on Matter

All matter has mass. Gravity is a result of mass. Therefore, all matter is affected by gravity. That is, all objects experience an attraction toward all other objects. This gravitational force pulls objects toward each other. Right now, because of gravity, you are being pulled toward this book, your pencil, and every other object around you.

These objects are also being pulled toward you and toward each other because of gravity. So why don't you see the effects of this attraction? In other words, why don't you notice objects moving toward each other? The reason is that the mass of most objects is too small to cause a force large enough to move objects toward each other. However, you are familiar with one object that is massive enough to cause a noticeable attraction—the Earth.

What You Will Learn

- Describe gravity and its effect on matter.
- Explain the law of universal gravitation.
- Describe the difference between mass and weight.

Vocabulary
gravity
weight
mass

READING STRATEGY

Paired Summarizing Read this section silently. In pairs, take turns summarizing the material. Stop to discuss ideas that seem confusing.

gravity a force of attraction between objects that is due to their masses

Figure 1 *Because the moon has less gravity than the Earth does, walking on the moon's surface was a very bouncy experience for the Apollo astronauts.*

CHAPTER RESOURCES

Chapter Resource File

- • Lesson Plan
- • Directed Reading A **BASIC**
- • Directed Reading B **SPECIAL NEEDS**

Technology

Transparencies
- • Bellringer
- • **LINK TO EARTH SCIENCE** E57 Tidal Variations: Spring Tides; Neap Tides

Workbooks

Interactive Textbook Struggling Readers

The Size of Earth's Gravitational Force

Compared with all objects around you, Earth has a huge mass. Therefore, Earth's gravitational force is very large. You must apply forces to overcome Earth's gravitational force any time you lift objects or even parts of your body.

Earth's gravitational force pulls everything toward the center of Earth. Because of this force, the books, tables, and chairs in the room stay in place, and dropped objects fall to Earth rather than moving together or toward you.

Reading Check Why must you exert a force to pick up an object? *(See the Appendix for answers to Reading Checks.)*

Newton and the Study of Gravity

For thousands of years, people asked two very puzzling questions: Why do objects fall toward Earth, and what keeps the planets moving in the sky? The two questions were treated separately until 1665 when a British scientist named Sir Isaac Newton realized that they were two parts of the same question.

The Core of an Idea

The legend is that Newton made the connection between the two questions when he watched a falling apple, as shown in **Figure 2.** He knew that unbalanced forces are needed to change the motion of objects. He concluded that an unbalanced force on the apple made the apple fall. And he reasoned that an unbalanced force on the moon kept the moon moving circularly around Earth. He proposed that these two forces are actually the same force—a force of attraction called *gravity*.

The Birth of a Law

Newton summarized his ideas about gravity in a law now known as the *law of universal gravitation*. This law describes the relationships between gravitational force, mass, and distance. The law is called *universal* because it applies to all objects in the universe.

CONNECTION TO Biology

Seeds and Gravity Seeds respond to gravity. The ability to respond to gravity causes seeds to send roots down and the green shoot up. But scientists do not understand how seeds can sense gravity. Plan an experiment to study how seedlings respond to gravity. After getting your teacher's approval, do your experiment and report your observations in a poster. **ACTIVITY**

Figure 2 *Sir Isaac Newton realized that the same unbalanced force affected the motions of the apple and the moon.*

Is That a Fact!

In the reduced gravity of space, astronauts lose bone and muscle mass. Sleep patterns may be affected and so may cardiovascular strength and the immune response. These same effects happen more gradually as people age on Earth. Scientists are interested in studying the effects of microgravity so they can find ways to counteract them in space and here on Earth.

Answer to Reading Check
You must exert a force to overcome the gravitational force between the object and Earth.

Teach

READING STRATEGY — GENERAL

Prediction Guide Before students read this section, ask them to predict whether the following statements are true or false:

• Objects of any size exert a gravitational force. (true)

• The moon is held in its orbit by unbalanced forces. (true)

• If you traveled to Jupiter and you neither gained nor lost mass, your weight on Jupiter would be much greater than your weight on Earth. (true)

LS Verbal

Demonstration — GENERAL

MATERIALS
• beanbag
• sock
• string
• toilet-paper tube

Safety Caution: Everyone should wear safety goggles during this demonstration.

Modeling Gravity Cut a length of string about 2 m long. Ball up the sock, and tie one end of the string around it. Pull the free end of the string through the tube, then tie it around the beanbag. Hold the tube, and twirl the beanbag in a circle. The sock represents the sun, and the beanbag represents Earth. Explain that the string represents the gravitational attraction between Earth and the sun. **LS** Visual

CONNECTION to Earth Science — GENERAL

Gravity and the Tides Use the teaching transparency titled "Tidal Variations" to help students understand the effects the moon's gravitational force has on Earth's tides. **LS** Visual

Jupiter's Moons Have students research the unusual characteristics of Io and Europa, two of the moons of Jupiter studied by the *Voyager* and *Galileo* spacecraft. Have students write a report that describes the effects of Jupiter's gravitational force on the moons and explains why scientists think Europa may have life forms. **LS** Verbal

CONNECTION ACTIVITY
Math —————— ADVANCED

The Law of Universal Gravitation Have students find the mathematical formula for the law of universal gravitation. Ask students to write the equation and write what each symbol means. Then, have students write a brief paragraph explaining the mathematical relationships between the variables in the equation. (The equation and an explanation of the variables can be found in the Chapter Enrichment pages of the Teacher's Edition. The relationships between the variables are as follows: Gravitational force and the masses of the objects are directly proportional (gravitational force will increase if either mass increases). Gravitational force is inversely proportional to the square of the distance between the objects (gravitational force will decrease if the distance between the masses increases). **LS** Logical

CONNECTION TO
Astronomy

WRITING SKILL **Black Holes** Black holes are 4 times to 1 billion times as massive as our sun. So, the gravitational effects around a black hole are very large. The gravitational force of a black hole is so large that objects that enter a black hole can never get out. Even light cannot escape from a black hole. Because black holes do not emit light, they cannot be seen. Research how astronomers can detect black holes without seeing them. Write a one-page paper that details the results of your research.

The Law of Universal Gravitation

The law of universal gravitation is the following: All objects in the universe attract each other through gravitational force. The size of the force depends on the masses of the objects and the distance between the objects. Understanding the law is easier if you consider it in two parts.

Part 1: Gravitational Force Increases as Mass Increases

Imagine an elephant and a cat. Because an elephant has a larger mass than a cat does, the amount of gravity between an elephant and Earth is greater than the amount of gravity between a cat and Earth. So, a cat is much easier to pick up than an elephant! There is also gravity between the cat and the elephant, but that force is very small because the cat's mass and the elephant's mass are so much smaller than Earth's mass. **Figure 3** shows the relationship between mass and gravitational force.

This part of the law of universal gravitation also explains why the astronauts on the moon bounce when they walk. The moon has less mass than Earth does. Therefore, the moon's gravitational force is less than Earth's. The astronauts bounced around on the moon because they were not being pulled down with as much force as they would have been on Earth.

✓ **Reading Check** How does mass affect gravitational force?

Figure 3 **How Mass Affects Gravitational Force**

The gravitational force between objects increases as the masses of the objects increase. The arrows indicate the gravitational force between two objects. The length of the arrows indicates the strength of the force.

ⓐ Gravitational force is small between objects that have small masses.

ⓑ Gravitational force is large when the mass of one or both objects is large.

SUPPORT FOR

English Language Learners

Law of Universal Gravitation Experimenting for themselves will help students better understand the concepts of the law of universal gravitation. Tell students that they are going to experiment with part 1 of the law of universal gravitation: gravitational force increases as mass increases. Give groups of 3 students three common objects of contrasting masses: a pencil, a pad of paper, and their science textbook, for example. Then, have them pick up each object in succession using one hand. According to part 1 of the law of universal gravitation, the lightest object should be the easiest to pick up. Ask the class which object was easiest for them. Which was the most difficult? (The answers should be pencil and textbook.) If necessary, help them see the relationship between mass and gravity by directing them to explanations in the book and through class discussion. **LS** Visual/Kinesthetic

Part 2: Gravitational Force Decreases as Distance Increases

The gravitational force between you and Earth is large. Whenever you jump up, you are pulled back down by Earth's gravitational force. On the other hand, the sun is more than 300,000 times more massive than Earth. So why doesn't the sun's gravitational force affect you more than Earth's does? The reason is that the sun is so far away.

You are about 150 million kilometers (93 million miles) away from the sun. At this distance, the gravitational force between you and the sun is very small. If there were some way you could stand on the sun, you would find it impossible to move. The gravitational force acting on you would be so great that you could not move any part of your body!

Although the sun's gravitational force on your body is very small, the force is very large on Earth and the other planets, as shown in **Figure 4**. The gravity between the sun and the planets is large because the objects have large masses. If the sun's gravitational force did not have such an effect on the planets, the planets would not stay in orbit around the sun. **Figure 5** will help you understand the relationship between gravitational force and distance.

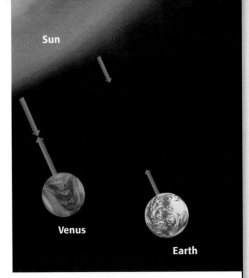

Figure 4 *Venus and Earth have approximately the same mass. But because Venus is closer to the sun, the gravitational force between Venus and the sun is greater than the gravitational force between Earth and the sun.*

Figure 5 | How Distance Affects Gravitational Force

The gravitational force between objects decreases as the distance between the objects increases. The length of the arrows indicates the strength of the gravitational force between two objects.

ⓐ Gravitational force is strong when the distance between two objects is small.

ⓑ If the distance between two objects increases, the gravitational force pulling them together decreases rapidly.

Science Bloopers

It's Not the Moon's Fault The moon used to be blamed for some strange behaviors in humans and animals (the word *lunatic* comes from the Latin word *luna*, meaning "moon"). Scientists once thought the moon affected the human body's fluids the same way it affects ocean tides. Women's menstrual cycles reinforced this belief. Today, scientists know that there is little evidence to support these beliefs.

CHAPTER RESOURCES

Technology

- **Transparencies**
  - P18 Gravitational Force Depends on Mass; Gravitational Force Depends on Distance

ACTiViTY ———— GENERAL

Story Analysis Have students read H. G. Wells's 1901 story "The First Men in the Moon." Take one class to discuss the story and Wells's use of "Cavorite." Discuss how well the story fits with current scientific knowledge of the moon and gravity. How might the story be different if it were written today?
LS Verbal

Research ———— ADVANCED

Gravitational Force on Other Planets Have students research and compare the gravitational force on other planets with the gravitational force on Earth. Then, have students write a short story or make a poster about what life would be like with different gravitational forces acting on their bodies.
LS Visual English Language Learners

Answer to Reading Check

Gravitational force increases as mass increases. (**Teacher's note:** Gravitational force increases as one or both of the masses increase.)

MISCONCEPTION ALERT

Gravitational Force and Altitude Although the gravitational attraction of an object toward Earth does decrease with altitude, this difference is very small. For all practical purposes, Earth's gravitational force on any object remains essentially the same anywhere in the atmosphere.

Illustrating Mass and Weight
To reinforce the difference between mass and weight, have students make a poster similar to **Figure 6**. In the posters students should compare the mass and weight of an object on Earth and on another planet.
LS Visual

Quiz ——— GENERAL

1. What is the difference between mass and weight?
(Mass is the amount of matter in an object. Weight is a measure of the gravitational force on an object.)

2. What must you know in order to calculate the gravitational force between two objects?
(their masses and the distance between them)

3. Where would you weigh the most, on a boat, on the space shuttle, or on the moon?
(on a boat)

Alternative Assessment ——— GENERAL

Gravity Improvisation Have small groups of students use objects they find in the classroom to explain the relationship between mass, distance, and gravitational force. Tell students that they may move around the classroom and move objects if needed. **LS** Kinesthetic

---

CONNECTION TO
Language Arts

WRITING SKILL **Gravity Story**
Suppose you had a device that could increase or decrease the gravitational force of Earth. In your **science journal,** write a short story describing what you might do with the device, what you would expect to see, and what effect the device would have on the weight of objects.

weight a measure of the gravitational force exerted on an object; its value can change with the location of the object in the universe

mass a measure of the amount of matter in an object

Weight as a Measure of Gravitational Force

Gravity is a force of attraction between objects. **Weight** is a measure of the gravitational force on an object. When you see or hear the word *weight,* it usually refers to Earth's gravitational force on an object. But weight can also be a measure of the gravitational force exerted on objects by the moon or other planets.

The Differences Between Weight and Mass

Weight is related to mass, but they are not the same. Weight changes when gravitational force changes. **Mass** is the amount of matter in an object. An object's mass does not change. Imagine that an object is moved to a place that has a greater gravitational force—such as the planet Jupiter. The object's weight will increase, but its mass will remain the same. **Figure 6** shows the weight and mass of an astronaut on Earth and on the moon. The moon's gravitational force is about one-sixth of Earth's gravitational force.

Gravitational force is about the same everywhere on Earth. So, the weight of any object is about the same everywhere. Because mass and weight are constant on Earth, the terms *weight* and *mass* are often used to mean the same thing. This can be confusing. Be sure you understand the difference!

✓ Reading Check How is gravitational force related to the weight of an object?

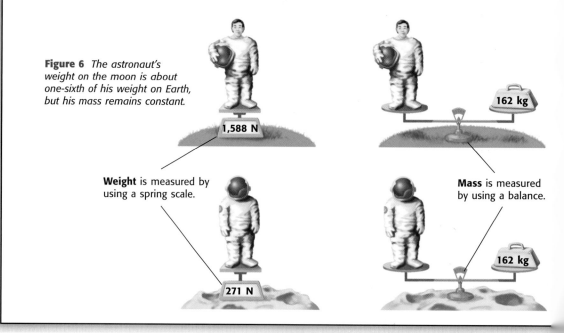

Figure 6 *The astronaut's weight on the moon is about one-sixth of his weight on Earth, but his mass remains constant.*

1,588 N

162 kg

Weight is measured by using a spring scale.

271 N

Mass is measured by using a balance.

162 kg

Answer to Reading Check
The weight of an object is a measure of the gravitational force on the object.

CHAPTER RESOURCES
Technology
📁 **Transparencies**   • P19 Weight and Mass

Units of Weight and Mass

You have learned that the SI unit of force is a newton (N). Gravity is a force, and weight is a measure of gravity. So, weight is also measured in newtons. The SI unit of mass is the kilogram (kg). Mass is often measured in grams (g) and milligrams (mg) as well. On Earth, a 100 g object, such as the apple shown in **Figure 7,** weighs about 1 N.

When you use a bathroom scale, you are measuring the gravitational force between your body and Earth. So, you are measuring your weight, which should be given in newtons. However, many bathroom scales have units of pounds and kilograms instead of newtons. Thus, people sometimes mistakenly think that the kilogram (like the pound) is a unit of weight.

Figure 7 *A small apple weighs approximately 1 N.*

SECTION Review

Summary

- Gravity is a force of attraction between objects that is due to their masses.
- The law of universal gravitation states that all objects in the universe attract each other through gravitational force.
- Gravitational force increases as mass increases.
- Gravitational force decreases as distance increases.
- Weight and mass are not the same. Mass is the amount of matter in an object. Weight is a measure of the gravitational force on an object.

Using Key Terms

1. In your own words, write a definition for the term *gravity*.

2. Use each of the following terms in a separate sentence: *mass* and *weight*.

Understanding Key Ideas

3. If Earth's mass doubled without changing its size, your weight would
   a. increase because gravitational force increases.
   b. decrease because gravitational force increases.
   c. increase because gravitational force decreases.
   d. not change because you are still on Earth.

4. What is the law of universal gravitation?

5. How does the mass of an object relate to the gravitational force that the object exerts on other objects?

6. How does the distance between objects affect the gravitational force between them?

7. Why are mass and weight often confused?

Math Skills

8. The gravitational force on Jupiter is approximately 2.3 times the gravitational force on Earth. If an object has a mass of 70 kg and a weight of 686 N on Earth, what would the object's mass and weight on Jupiter be?

Critical Thinking

9. **Applying Concepts** Your friend thinks that there is no gravity in space. How could you explain to your friend that there must be gravity in space?

10. **Making Comparisons** Explain why it is your weight and not your mass that would change if you landed on Mars.

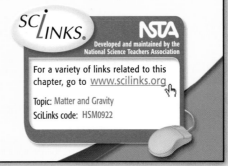

SCI LINKS.

NSTA
Developed and maintained by the
National Science Teachers Association

For a variety of links related to this chapter, go to www.scilinks.org

Topic: Matter and Gravity
SciLinks code: HSM0922

Answers to Section Review

1. Sample answer: Gravity is a force of attraction between objects that is due to their masses.

2. Sample answer: The mass of the astronaut is the same whether he is on Earth or in space. The weight of a small apple is about 1 N.

3. a

4. The law of universal gravitation states that all objects attract each other through gravitational force and that the size of the gravitational force between objects depends on their masses and the distance between them.

5. The greater an object's mass, the larger the gravitational force it exerts on other objects.

6. As the distance between objects increases, the gravitational force between them decreases. As the distance between objects decreases, the gravitational force between them increases.

7. Mass and weight are often confused because they both are constant on Earth and because the terms *mass* and *weight* are sometimes used to mean the same thing.

8. On Jupiter, the object's mass would be 70 kg and its weight would be 1577.8 N.

9. Sample answer: You can tell your friend that there must be gravity in space because gravity holds the planets in orbit around the sun.

10. Your weight would change if you landed on Mars because the gravitational force on Mars is different from the gravitational force on Earth. But your mass would not change because the amount of matter in your body would not change.

Detecting Acceleration

Teacher's Notes

Time Required

One or two 45-minute class periods

Lab Ratings

EASY ————————————→ HARD

Teacher Prep 🧪
Student Set-Up 🧪🧪
Concept Level 🧪🧪🧪
Clean Up 🧪🧪

MATERIALS

The materials listed are for each student or each small group of 2–3 students. Instead of using modeling clay to secure the thread to the bottle cap, students can cut the thread long enough so that it hangs out while the lid is screwed on tightly.

Safety Caution

Remind students to review all safety cautions and icons before beginning this lab activity.

Preparation Notes

You may wish to build an accelerometer before class to show students. You may wish to have students make a chart to collect their data.

Skills Practice Lab

Skills Practice Lab

OBJECTIVES

Build an accelerometer.

Explain how an accelerometer works.

MATERIALS

- container, 1 L, with watertight lid
- cork or plastic-foam ball, small
- modeling clay
- pushpin
- scissors
- string
- water

SAFETY

Detecting Acceleration

Have you ever noticed that you can "feel" acceleration? In a car or in an elevator, you may notice changes in speed or direction—even with your eyes closed! You are able to sense these changes because of tiny hair cells in your ears. These cells detect the movement of fluid in your inner ear. The fluid accelerates when you do, and the hair cells send a message about the acceleration to your brain. This message allows you to sense the acceleration. In this activity, you will build a device that detects acceleration. This device is called an *accelerometer* (ak SEL uhr AHM uht uhr).

Procedure

1. Cut a piece of string that reaches three-quarters of the way into the container.

2. Use a pushpin to attach one end of the string to the cork or plastic-foam ball.

3. Use modeling clay to attach the other end of the string to the center of the inside of the container lid. The cork or ball should hang no farther than three-quarters of the way into the container.

4. Fill the container with water.

5. Put the lid tightly on the container. The string and cork or ball should be inside the container.

6. Turn the container upside down. The cork should float about three-quarters of the way up inside the container, as shown at left. You are now ready to detect acceleration by using your accelerometer and completing the following steps.

7. Put the accelerometer on a tabletop. The container lid should touch the tabletop. Notice that the cork floats straight up in the water.

8. Now, gently push the accelerometer across the table at a constant speed. Notice that the cork quickly moves in the direction you are pushing and then swings backward. If you did not see this motion, repeat this step until you are sure you can see the first movement of the cork.

 Holt Lab Generator CD-ROM

Search for any lab by topic, standard, difficulty level, or time. Edit any lab to fit your needs, or create your own labs. Use the Lab Materials QuickList software to customize your lab materials list.

Elsie Waynes
Terrell Junior High
Washington, D.C.

CHAPTER RESOURCES

Chapter Resource File

- • Datasheet for Chapter Lab
- • Lab Notes and Answers

Technology

 Classroom Videos
• Lab Video

LabBook

- • Built for Speed
- • Relating Mass and Weight
- • Science Friction

9 After you are familiar with how to use your accelerometer, try the following changes in motion. For each change, record your observations of the cork's first motion.

a. As you move the accelerometer across the table, gradually increase its speed.

b. As you move the accelerometer across the table, gradually decrease its speed.

c. While moving the accelerometer across the table, change the direction in which you are pushing.

d. Make any other changes in motion you can think of. You should make only one change to the motion for each trial.

Analyze the Results

1 **Analyzing Results** When you move the bottle at a constant speed, why does the cork quickly swing backward after it moves in the direction of acceleration?

2 **Explaining Events** The cork moves forward (in the direction you were moving the bottle) when you speed up but moves backward when you slow down. Explain why the cork moves this way. (Hint: Think about the direction of acceleration.)

Draw Conclusions

3 **Making Predictions** Imagine you are standing on a corner and watching a car that is waiting at a stoplight. A passenger inside the car is holding some helium balloons. Based on what you observed with your accelerometer, what do you think will happen to the balloons when the car begins moving?

Applying Your Data

If you move the bottle in a circle at a constant speed, what do you predict the cork will do? Try it, and check your answer.

Analyze the Results

1. The bottle stops accelerating (it is moving with a constant speed), so the cork shows zero acceleration.

2. The cork will move opposite to the motion of the water. As the bottle accelerates forward, the water sloshes backward, which makes the cork move forward. The cork will always move in the direction of acceleration.

Draw Conclusions

3. As the car begins accelerating forward, the balloons will move forward because the air in the car moves backward. When the car reaches a steady speed, the balloons will move back to stand straight up.

Applying Your Data

The cork will also travel in a circle, staying closest to the side of the bottle nearest the center of the circle.

CHAPTER RESOURCES

Workbooks

 **Long-Term Projects & Research Ideas**
• Tiny Troubles ADVANCED

 **Calculator-Based Labs**
• The Fast Track ADVANCED
• Graphing Your Motion ADVANCED

Chapter Review

Assignment Guide

SECTION	QUESTIONS
1	4, 6, 10–12, 14–15, 17–19
2	2–3, 7, 20
3	1, 16
4	5, 8–9, 13

ANSWERS

Using Key Terms

1. Friction
2. newton
3. net force
4. velocity
5. weight

Understanding Key Ideas

6. b
7. d
8. c
9. c
10. c
11. Motion occurs when an object changes position over time when compared with a reference point (an object that appears to stay in place).
12. Acceleration can occur simply by a change in direction. Thus, no change in speed is necessary for acceleration.

USING KEY TERMS

Complete each of the following sentences by choosing the correct term from the word bank.

mass	gravity
friction	weight
speed	velocity
net force	newton

1. ___ opposes motion between surfaces that are touching.

2. The ___ is the unit of force.

3. ___ is determined by combining forces.

4. Acceleration is the rate at which ___ changes.

5. ___ is a measure of the gravitational force on an object.

UNDERSTANDING KEY IDEAS

Multiple Choice

6. If a student rides her bicycle on a straight road and does not speed up or slow down, she is traveling with a
   a. constant acceleration.
   b. constant velocity.
   c. positive acceleration.
   d. negative acceleration.

7. A force
   a. is expressed in newtons.
   b. can cause an object to speed up, slow down, or change direction.
   c. is a push or a pull.
   d. All of the above

8. If you are in a spacecraft that has been launched into space, your weight would
   a. increase because gravitational force is increasing.
   b. increase because gravitational force is decreasing.
   c. decrease because gravitational force is decreasing.
   d. decrease because gravitational force is increasing.

9. The gravitational force between 1 kg of lead and Earth is ___ the gravitational force between 1 kg of marshmallows and Earth.
   a. greater than   c. the same as
   b. less than   d. None of the above

10. Which of the following is a measurement of velocity?
    a. 16 m east   c. 55 m/h south
    b. 25 m/s^2 d. 60 km/h

Short Answer

11. Describe the relationship between motion and a reference point.

12. How is it possible to be accelerating and traveling at a constant speed?

13. Explain the difference between mass and weight.

13. Mass is the amount of matter in an object, and its value does not change with the object's location. Weight measures the gravitational force on an object, so it can change as the amount of gravitational force changes.

Math Skills

14. A kangaroo hops 60 m to the east in 5 s. Use this information to answer the following questions.

a. What is the kangaroo's average speed?

b. What is the kangaroo's average velocity?

c. The kangaroo stops at a lake for a drink of water and then starts hopping again to the south. Each second, the kangaroo's velocity increases 2.5 m/s. What is the kangaroo's acceleration after 5 s?

CRITICAL THINKING

15. Concept Mapping Use the following terms to create a concept map: *speed, velocity, acceleration, force, direction,* and *motion.*

16. Applying Concepts Your family is moving, and you are asked to help move some boxes. One box is so heavy that you must push it across the room rather than lift it. What are some ways you could reduce friction to make moving the box easier?

17. Analyzing Ideas Considering the scientific meaning of the word *acceleration,* how could using the term *accelerator* when talking about a car's gas pedal lead to confusion?

18. Identifying Relationships Explain why it is important for airplane pilots to know wind velocity and not just wind speed during a flight.

INTERPRETING GRAPHICS

Use the figures below to answer the questions that follow.

19. Is the graph below showing positive acceleration or negative acceleration? How can you tell?

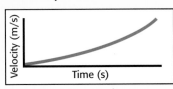

20. You know how to combine two forces that act in one or two directions. The same method can be used to combine several forces acting in several directions. Look at the diagrams, and calculate the net force in each diagram. Predict the direction each object will move.

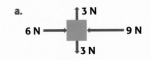

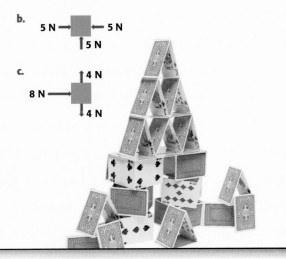

Critical Thinking

14. a. 12 m/s

b. 12 m/s east

c. 2.5 m/s² south

15. An answer to this exercise can be found at the end of this book.

16. Accept all reasonable answers. Sample answers: Use a handcart or dolly to take advantage of rolling kinetic friction. Polish the floor to reduce sliding kinetic friction.

17. The car's gas pedal is pressed by the driver to increase the car's speed. Since the scientific meaning of the term *acceleration* can include slowing down and even changing direction, *accelerator* is not an accurate term for this device.

18. It is helpful for pilots to know wind velocity because velocity includes direction. Pilots need to know the wind's speed and direction so that they will know whether the wind is blowing in the same direction as the plane (which could increase the plane's resultant velocity and lead to an earlier arrival time) or in a different direction than the plane (which might lead to a later arrival).

Interpreting Graphics

19. The graph shows positive acceleration. Velocity increases as time passes.

20. a. 3 N to the left

b. 5 N up

c. 8 N to the right

CHAPTER RESOURCES

Chapter Resource File

- Chapter Review **GENERAL**
- Chapter Test A **GENERAL**
- Chapter Test B **ADVANCED**
- Chapter Test C **SPECIAL NEEDS**
- Vocabulary Activity **GENERAL**

Workbooks

Study Guide
- Study Guide is also available in Spanish.

 **Standardized Test Preparation**

Teacher's Note

To provide practice under more realistic testing conditions, give students 20 minutes to answer all of the questions in this Standardized Test Preparation.

MISCONCEPTION ALERT

Answers to the standardized test preparation can help you identify student misconceptions and misunderstandings.

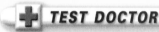 **READING**

Passage 1

1. C
2. I
3. B

TEST DOCTOR

Question 3: A definition for *wind tunnel* is not given in the reading passage. However, students can infer from the passage that a wind tunnel is a place that can be used to test the speed of objects in the air. The passage states that DiTullio tested the dimpled bat in a wind tunnel and states that DiTullio learned from the results in the wind tunnel that the dimpled bat could be swung faster.

READING

Read each of the passages below. Then, answer the questions that follow each passage.

Passage 1 If you look closely at the surface of a golf ball, you'll see dozens of tiny dimples. When air flows past these dimples, the air is stirred up and stays near the surface of the ball. By keeping air moving near the surface of the ball, the dimples help the golf ball move faster and farther through the air. Jeff DiTullio, a teacher at MIT in Cambridge, Massachusetts, decided to apply this principle to a baseball bat. When DiTullio tested his dimpled bat in a <u>wind tunnel</u>, he found that the bat could be swung 3% to 5% faster than a bat without dimples. That increase may not seem like much, but the dimpled bat could add about 5 m of distance to a fly ball!

1. Who is Jeff DiTullio?
   - **A** the inventor of the dimpled golf ball
   - **B** a teacher at Cambridge University
   - **C** the inventor of the dimpled bat
   - **D** a professional baseball player

2. Which of the following ideas is NOT stated in the passage?
   - **F** Dimples make DiTullio's bat move faster.
   - **G** MIT is in Cambridge, Massachusetts.
   - **H** Air that is stirred up near the surface of DiTullio's bat makes it easier to swing the bat faster.
   - **I** DiTullio will make a lot of money from his invention.

3. In the passage, what does *wind tunnel* mean?
   - **A** a place to practice batting
   - **B** a place to test the speed of objects in the air
   - **C** a baseball stadium
   - **D** a passageway that is shielded from the wind

Passage 2 The Golden Gate Bridge in San Francisco, California, is one of the most famous <u>landmarks</u> in the world. Approximately 9 million people from around the world visit the bridge each year.

The Golden Gate Bridge is a suspension bridge. A suspension bridge is one in which the roadway is hung, or suspended, from huge cables that extend from one end of the bridge to the other. The main cables on the Golden Gate Bridge are 2.33 km long. Many forces act on the main cables. For example, smaller cables pull down on the main cables to connect the roadway to the main cables. And two towers that are 227 m tall push up on the main cables. The forces on the main cable must be balanced, or the bridge will collapse.

1. In this passage, what does *landmarks* mean?
   - **A** large areas of land
   - **B** well-known places
   - **C** street signs
   - **D** places where people meet

2. Which of the following statements is a fact from the passage?
   - **F** The roadway of the Golden Gate Bridge is suspended from huge cables.
   - **G** The towers of the Golden Gate Bridge are 2.33 km tall.
   - **H** The main cables connect the roadway to the towers.
   - **I** The forces on the cables are not balanced.

3. According to the passage, why do people from around the world visit the Golden Gate Bridge?
   - **A** It is the longest bridge in the world.
   - **B** It is a suspension bridge.
   - **C** It is the only bridge that is painted orange.
   - **D** It is a famous landmark.

Passage 2

1. B
2. F
3. D

 **TEST DOCTOR**

Question 2: Students may chose answer G because they see the number 2.33 in the passage. However, the number 2.33 refers to the length of the main cables of the Golden Gate Bridge and not to the height of the bridge's towers. Some students should be able to eliminate this answer because it would be impossible to build towers that are 2.33 km tall.

The graph below shows the data collected by a student as she watched a squirrel running on the ground. Use the graph below to answer the questions that follow.

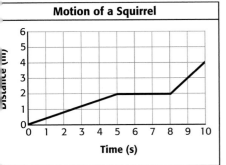

Motion of a Squirrel

Which of the following best describes the motion of the squirrel between 5 s and 8 s?

A The squirrel's speed increased.

B The squirrel's speed decreased.

C The squirrel's speed did not change.

D The squirrel moved backward.

Which of the following statements about the motion of the squirrel is true?

F The squirrel moved with the greatest speed between 0 s and 5 s.

G The squirrel moved with the greatest speed between 8 s and 10 s.

H The squirrel moved with a constant speed between 0 s and 8 s.

I The squirrel moved with a constant speed between 5 s and 10 s.

What is the average speed of the squirrel between 8 s and 10 s?

A 0.4 m/s

B 1 m/s

C 2 m/s

D 4 m/s

MATH

Read each question below, and choose the best answer.

1. The distance between Cedar Rapids, Iowa, and Sioux Falls, South Dakota, is about 660 km. How long will it take a car traveling with an average speed of 95 km/h to drive from Cedar Rapids to Sioux Falls?

   A less than 1 h

   B about 3 h

   C about 7 h

   D about 10 h

2. Martha counted the number of people in each group that walked into her school's cafeteria. In the first 10 groups, she counted the following numbers of people: 6, 4, 9, 6, 4, 10, 9, 5, 9, and 8. What is the mode of this set of data?

   F 6

   G 7

   H 9

   I 10

3. Which of the following terms describes the angle marked in the triangle below.

   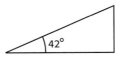

   A acute

   B obtuse

   C right

   D None of the above

4. Donnell collected money for a charity fundraiser. After one hour, he counted the money and found that he had raised $10.00 in bills and $3.74 in coins. Which of the following represents the number of coins he collected?

   F 4 pennies, 9 nickels, 18 dimes, and 6 quarters

   G 9 pennies, 7 nickels, 18 dimes, and 6 quarters

   H 6 pennies, 7 nickels, 15 dimes, and 8 quarters

   I 9 pennies, 8 nickels, 12 dimes, and 3 quarters

Standardized Test Preparation

INTERPRETING GRAPHICS

1. C

2. G

3. B

 **TEST DOCTOR**

Question 1: Students may be confused about the motion of the squirrel between 5 s and 8 s. According to the graph, the distance the squirrel traveled between 5 s and 8 s did not change. In other words, the squirrel did not move. Because the squirrel did not move between 5 s and 8 s, its speed did not change. During that time interval the speed of the squirrel remained constant at 0 m/s.

MATH

1. C

2. H

3. A

4. G

 **TEST DOCTOR**

Question 2: Some students may choose answer G because it is equal to the average of the numbers in the problem. Remind students that the *mode* of a set of numbers is the number that appears most frequently and that the *mean* of a set of numbers is the average.

CHAPTER RESOURCES

Chapter Resource File

 • Standardized Test Preparation GENERAL

State Resources

 For specific resources for your state, visit **go.hrw.com** and type in the keyword **HSMSTR**.

Science, Technology, and Society

Background

The Global Positioning System (GPS) is a network of 27 human-made satellites that orbit Earth. At any given time, 24 of the satellites are in operation. The other three satellites are in place as a backup system. Each satellite continually transmits a unique radio signal that can be picked up by GPS receivers on Earth. A GPS receiver normally receives signals from at least four satellites at one time. The receiver uses the signals and a process called *triangulation* to determine its location on Earth. Encourage interested students to learn how triangulation works. Students may present what they learn in a report to the class.

Weird Science

Discussion ——— GENERAL

Tell students that some cities are considering limiting or banning the use of Segways on sidewalks. Lead a discussion about why Segways might be considered dangerous to pedestrians. Also discuss possible rules that may be used to avoid the danger yet still allow people to use Segways.

Science in Action

Science, Technology, and Society

GPS Watch System

Some athletes are concerned about knowing their speed during training. To calculate speed, they need to know distance and time. Finding time by using a watch is easy to do. But determining distance is more difficult. However, a GPS watch system is now available to help with this problem. *GPS* stands for *global positioning system*. A GPS unit, which is worn on an athlete's upper arm, monitors the athlete's position by using signals from satellites. As the athlete moves, the GPS unit calculates the distance traveled. The GPS unit sends a signal to the watch, which keeps the athlete's time, and the watch displays the athlete's speed.

Math ACTIVITY

Suppose an athlete wishes to finish a 5 K race in under 25 min. The distance of a 5 K is 5 km. (Remember that 1 km = 1,000 m.) If the athlete runs the race at a constant speed of 3.4 m/s, will she meet her goal?

Weird Science

The Segway™ Human Transporter

In November 2002, a new people-moving machine was introduced, and people have been fascinated by the odd-looking device ever since. The device is called the *Segway Human Transporter*. The Segway is a two-wheeled device that is powered by a rechargeable battery. To move forward, the rider simply leans forward. Sensors detect this motion and send signals to the on-board computer. The computer, in turn, tells the motor to start going. To slow down, the rider leans backward, and to stop, the rider stands straight up. The Segway has a top speed of 20 km/h (about 12.5 mi/h) and can travel up to 28 km (about 17.4 mi) on a single battery charge.

Language Arts ACTIVITY

WRITING SKILL The inventor of the Segway thinks that the machine will make a good alternative to walking and bicycle riding. Write a one-page essay explaining whether you think using a Segway is better or worse than riding a bicycle.

Answer to Math Activity
Yes, the athlete will meet her goal. She will finish the race in about 24.5 min (1470 s).

Answer to Language Arts Activity
Accept all reasonable answers. All essays should discuss the benefits or drawbacks of using a Segway instead of riding a bicycle.

People in Science

Victor Petrenko

Snowboard and Ski Brakes Have you ever wished for emergency brakes on your snowboard or skis? Thanks to Victor Petrenko and the Ice Research Lab of Dartmouth College, snowboards and skis that have braking systems may soon be available.

Not many people know more about the properties of ice and ice-related technologies than Victor Petrenko does. He has spent most of his career researching the electrical and mechanical properties of ice. Through his research, Petrenko learned that ice can hold an electric charge. He used this property to design a braking system for snowboards. The system is a form of electric friction control.

The power source for the brakes is a battery. The battery is connected to a network of wires embedded on the bottom surface of a snowboard. When the battery is activated, the bottom of the snowboard gains a negative charge. This negative charge creates a positive charge on the surface of the snow. Because opposite charges attract, the snowboard and the snow are pulled together. The force that pulls the surfaces together increases friction, and the snowboard slows down.

Social Studies Activity

Research the history of skiing. Make a poster that includes a timeline of significant dates in the history of skiing. Illustrate your poster with photos or drawings.

go.hrw.com
To learn more about these Science in Action topics, visit go.hrw.com and type in the keyword HP5MOTF.

Current Science
Check out Current Science® articles related to this chapter by visiting go.hrw.com. Just type in the keyword HP5CS05.

Teaching Strategy – GENERAL

Explain and demonstrate the effects of static electricity to help students understand how the electric brakes designed by Victor Petrenko work. Start by telling students that objects can be charged by gaining or losing electrons. Objects that gain electrons become negatively charged and objects that lose electrons become positively charged. Objects that have opposite charges attract each other. To demonstrate this attraction, rub a balloon on your hair. Tell students that the friction between your hair and the balloon causes electrons to be transferred from your hair to the balloon. Then, hold the balloon away from your head. Your hair should be attracted to the balloon. Ask students why the hair is pulled to the balloon. (The hair is positively charged and the balloon is negatively charged. Oppositely charged object attract each other.) Tell students that a snowboard with an electric braking system is pulled toward the snow for the same reasons.

Note: This demonstration may not work if the air is too humid. If your hair is not long enough to do this demonstration, ask a student with long hair to volunteer.

Answer to Social Studies Activity
Accept all reasonable answers. All posters should include a timeline that marks significant dates in the history of skiing.

Forces and Motion
Chapter Planning Guide

Compression guide:
To shorten instruction because of time limitations, omit Section 3.

OBJECTIVES	LABS, DEMONSTRATIONS, AND ACTIVITIES	TECHNOLOGY RESOURCES
PACING • 90 min pp. 34–43 **Chapter Opener**	SE **Start-up Activity,** p. 35 GENERAL	OSP **Parent Letter** ■ CD **Student Edition on CD-ROM** CD **Guided Reading Audio CD** ■ TR **Chapter Starter Transparency*** VID **Brain Food Video Quiz**
Section 1 Gravity and Motion • Explain the effect of gravity and air resistance on falling objects. • Explain why objects in orbit are in free fall and appear to be weightless. • Describe how projectile motion is affected by gravity.	TE **Demonstration** Falling Objects, p. 36 GENERAL TE **Connection Activity** Social Studies, p. 37 ADVANCED TE **Connection Activity** Math, p. 37 GENERAL TE **Connection Activity** Earth Science, p. 38 GENERAL TE **Activity** The Meaning of a Vacuum, p. 39 BASIC TE **Connection Activity** Astronomy, p. 40 ADVANCED TE **Connection Activity** Math, p. 41 ADVANCED SE **Quick Lab** Penny Projectile Motion, p. 42 GENERAL SE **Skills Practice Lab** A Marshmallow Catapult, p. 196 GENERAL LB **Inquiry Lab** On the Fast Track ADVANCED LB **Calculator-Based Labs** Falling Objects ADVANCED LB **Calculator-Based Labs** Graphing Your Motion ADVANCED	OSP **Lesson Plans** (also in print) TR **Bellringer Transparency*** SE **Internet Activity,** p. 42 GENERAL TR **P20 Falling Objects Accelerate at a Constant Rate*** TR **P21 Effect of Air Resistance on a Falling Object*** TR **LINK TO EARTH SCIENCE** E58 Layers of the Atmosphere* TR **P22 How an Orbit Is Formed; Projectile Motion*** CD **Interactive Explorations** CD-ROM Extreme Skiing GENERAL CD **Science Tutor**
PACING • 90 min pp. 44–51 **Section 2 Newton's Laws of Motion** • Describe Newton's first law of motion, and explain how it relates to objects at rest and objects in motion. • State Newton's second law of motion, and explain the relationship between force, mass, and acceleration. • State Newton's third law of motion, and give examples of force pairs.	TE **Demonstration** Egg in a Buggy, p. 44 GENERAL SE **Quick Lab** First Law Skateboard, p. 45 ◆ GENERAL TE **Connection Activity** Real World, p. 45 GENERAL SE **Quick Lab** First-Law Magic, p. 46 GENERAL SE **Connection to Environmental Science** Car Sizes and Pollution, p. 47 GENERAL SE **School-to-Home Activity** Newton Ball, p. 49 GENERAL TE **Connection Activity** Life Science, p. 49 GENERAL SE **Skills Practice Lab** Inertia-Rama!, p. 56 GENERAL SE **Model-Making Lab** Blast Off!, p. 197 GENERAL LB **Whiz-Bang Demonstrations** Newton's Eggciting Experiment* BASIC LB **Whiz-Bang Demonstrations** Inertia Can Hurt Ya* GENERAL LB **Long-Term Projects & Research Ideas** "Any Color You Want, so Long as It's Black"* ADVANCED	OSP **Lesson Plans** (also in print) TR **Bellringer Transparency*** CRF **SciLinks Activity*** GENERAL TR **P23 Mass, Force, and Acceleration** VID **Lab Videos for Physical Science** CD **Science Tutor**
PACING • 45 min pp. 52–55 **Section 3 Momentum** • Calculate the momentum of moving objects. • Explain the law of conservation of momentum.	TE **Group Activity** Testing Momentum, p. 52 GENERAL SE **Science in Action** Math, Social Studies, and Language Arts Activities, pp. 62–63 GENERAL SE **Skills Practice Lab** Quite a Reaction, p. 198 GENERAL	OSP **Lesson Plans** (also in print) TR **Bellringer Transparency*** CD **Science Tutor**

PACING • 90 min

CHAPTER REVIEW, ASSESSMENT, AND STANDARDIZED TEST PREPARATION

CRF **Vocabulary Activity*** GENERAL
SE **Chapter Review,** pp. 58–59 GENERAL
CRF **Chapter Review*** ■ GENERAL
CRF **Chapter Tests A*** ■ GENERAL, **B*** ADVANCED, **C*** SPECIAL NEEDS
SE **Standardized Test Preparation,** pp. 60–61 GENERAL
CRF **Standardized Test Preparation*** GENERAL
CRF **Performance-Based Assessment*** GENERAL
OSP **Test Generator, Test Item Listing**

Online and Technology Resources

 Holt Online Learning

Visit go.hrw.com for access to Holt Online Learning, or enter the keyword **HP7 Home** for a variety of free online resources.

 One-Stop Planner® CD-ROM

This CD-ROM package includes:
- Lab Materials QuickList Software
- Holt Calendar Planner
- Customizable Lesson Plans
- Printable Worksheets
- ExamView® Test Generator
- Interactive Teacher's Edition
- Holt PuzzlePro®
- Holt PowerPoint® Resources

SKILLS DEVELOPMENT RESOURCES	SECTION REVIEW AND ASSESSMENT	CORRELATIONS
SE **Pre-Reading Activity**, p. 34 GENERAL OSP **Science Puzzlers, Twisters & Teasers** GENERAL		National Science Education Standards SAI 1; SPSP 5
CRF **Directed Reading A*** ■ BASIC **, B*** SPECIAL NEEDS IT **Interactive Textbook*** Struggling Readers CRF **Vocabulary and Section Summary*** ■ GENERAL SE **Reading Strategy** Reading Organizer, p. 36 GENERAL SE **Math Focus** Calculating the Velocity of Falling Objects, p. 37 GENERAL TE **Reading Strategy** Prediction Guide, p. 38 GENERAL TE **Inclusion Strategy,** p. 39 TE **Support for English Language Learners,** p. 41 MS **Math Skills for Science** Arithmetic with Decimals* GENERAL CRF **Reinforcement Worksheet** Falling Fast* BASIC	SE **Reading Checks**, pp. 37, 38, 40, 42 GENERAL TE **Reteaching,** p. 42 BASIC TE **Quiz,** p. 42 GENERAL TE **Alternative Assessment,** p. 42 GENERAL SE **Section Review,*** p. 43 ■ GENERAL CRF **Section Quiz*** ■ GENERAL	UCP 3; SAI 1, 2; ST 1; HNS 1, 2, 3; PS 2c; *LabBook:* SAI 1
CRF **Directed Reading A*** ■ BASIC **, B*** SPECIAL NEEDS IT **Interactive Textbook*** Struggling Readers CRF **Vocabulary and Section Summary*** ■ GENERAL SE **Reading Strategy** Paired Summarizing, p. 44 GENERAL TE **Inclusion Strategy,** p. 47 TE **Support for English Language Learners**, p. 47 SE **Math Focus** Second-Law Problems, p. 48 GENERAL MS **Math Skills for Science** Newton: Force and Motion* GENERAL	SE **Reading Checks**, pp. 45, 47, 49, 50 GENERAL TE **Homework,** p. 49 BASIC TE **Reteaching,** p. 50 BASIC TE **Quiz,** p. 50 GENERAL TE **Alternative Assessment,** p. 50 GENERAL SE **Section Review,*** p. 51 ■ GENERAL CRF **Section Quiz*** ■ GENERAL	UCP 3, 4; SAI 1; PS 2b, 2c; *Chapter Lab:* SAI 1; PS 2b *LabBook:* SAI 1; PS 2c
CRF **Directed Reading A*** ■ BASIC **, B*** SPECIAL NEEDS IT **Interactive Textbook*** Struggling Readers CRF **Vocabulary and Section Summary*** ■ GENERAL SE **Reading Strategy** Prediction Guide, p. 52 GENERAL SE **Math Focus** Momentum Calculations, p. 53 GENERAL TE **Support for English Language Learners,** p. 53 SE **Connection to Language Arts** p. 54 GENERAL MS **Math Skills for Science** Momentum* GENERAL CRF **Critical Thinking** Forces to Reckon With* ADVANCED	SE **Reading Checks**, pp. 53, 54 GENERAL TE **Reteaching,** p. 54 BASIC TE **Quiz,** p. 54 GENERAL TE **Alternative Assessment,** p. 54 ADVANCED SE **Section Review,*** p. 55 ■ GENERAL CRF **Section Quiz*** ■ GENERAL	SAI 1; *LabBook:* SAI 1

SCI LINKS.
NSTA

www.scilinks.org
Maintained by the **National Science Teachers Association.** See Chapter Enrichment pages that follow for a complete list of topics.

Current Science®

Check out *Current Science* articles and activities by visiting the HRW Web site at **go.hrw.com.** Just type in the keyword **HP5CS06T.**

 **Classroom Videos**

• **Lab Videos** demonstrate the chapter lab.
• **Brain Food Video Quizzes** help students review the chapter material.

 **Classroom CD-ROMs**

• **Guided Reading Audio CD** (Also in Spanish)
• **Interactive Explorations**
• **Virtual Investigations**
• **Visual Concepts**
• **Science Tutor**

 Holt Lab Generator CD-ROM

Search for any lab by topic, standard, difficulty level, or time. Edit any lab to fit your needs, or create your own labs. Use the Lab Materials QuickList software to customize your lab materials list.

Chapter Resources

Visual Resources

CHAPTER STARTER TRANSPARENCY

BELLRINGER TRANSPARENCIES

Section: Gravity and Motion
Answer the following questions in your **science journal:**

If Wile E. Coyote and a boulder fall off a cliff at the same time, which do you think will hit the ground first? Would it matter if the cliff were very high or particularly low? How could Mr. Coyote slow down his fall?

Section: Newton's Laws of Motion
Respond to the following question in your **science journal:**

If you are sitting still in your seat on a bus that is traveling 100 km/h on a highway, is your body at rest or in motion? Explain your answer. Use a diagram if it will help make your answer clear.

TEACHING TRANSPARENCIES

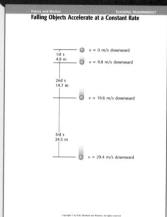

Falling Objects Accelerate at a Constant Rate

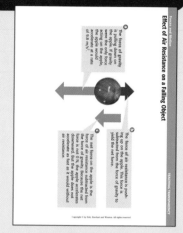

TEACHING TRANSPARENCIES

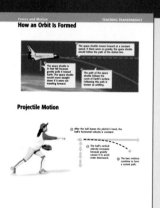

How an Orbit Is Formed

Projectile Motion

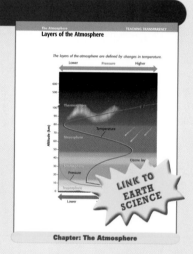

Layers of the Atmosphere

LINK TO EARTH SCIENCE

Chapter: The Atmosphere

CONCEPT MAPPING TRANSPARENCY

Planning Resources

LESSON PLANS

PARENT LETTER

ALSO IN SPANISH

TEST ITEM LISTING

One-Stop Planner® CD-ROM

This CD-ROM includes all of the resources shown here and the following time-saving tools:

- Lab Materials QuickList Software
- Customizable lesson plans
- Holt Calendar Planner
- The powerful ExamView® Test Generator

33C Chapter 2 • Forces and Motion

Meeting Individual Needs

DIRECTED READING A
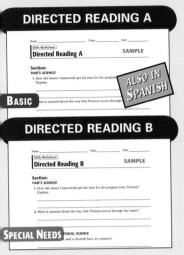
BASIC

DIRECTED READING B
SPECIAL NEEDS

VOCABULARY ACTIVITY
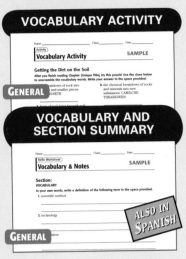
GENERAL

VOCABULARY AND SECTION SUMMARY
GENERAL

REINFORCEMENT
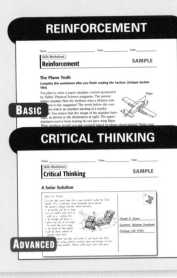
BASIC

CRITICAL THINKING
ADVANCED

SCILINKS ACTIVITY

GENERAL

SCIENCE PUZZLERS, TWISTERS & TEASERS
GENERAL

Labs and Activities

LONG-TERM PROJECTS & RESEARCH IDEAS

ADVANCED

INQUIRY LABS
ADVANCED

WHIZ-BANG DEMONSTRATIONS
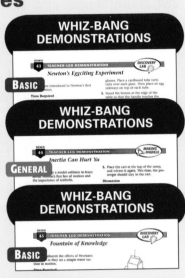
BASIC

WHIZ-BANG DEMONSTRATIONS
GENERAL

WHIZ-BANG DEMONSTRATIONS
BASIC

CALCULATOR-BASED LABS
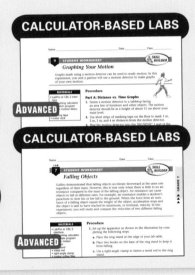
ADVANCED

CALCULATOR-BASED LABS
ADVANCED

DATASHEETS FOR QUICK LABS

DATASHEETS FOR CHAPTER LABS

DATASHEETS FOR LABBOOK

Review and Assessments

SECTION QUIZ
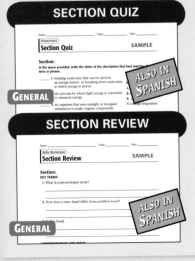
GENERAL

SECTION REVIEW
GENERAL

CHAPTER REVIEW
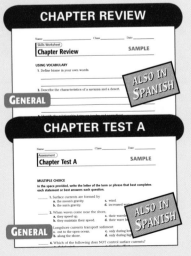
GENERAL

CHAPTER TEST A
GENERAL

CHAPTER TEST B
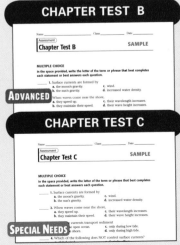
ADVANCED

CHAPTER TEST C
SPECIAL NEEDS

STANDARDIZED TEST PREPARATION
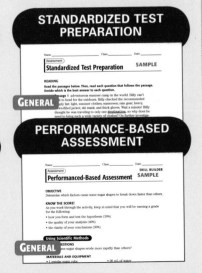
GENERAL

PERFORMANCE-BASED ASSESSMENT
GENERAL

This Chapter Enrichment provides relevant and interesting information to expand and enhance your presentation of the chapter material.

Section 1

Gravity and Motion

The Apple and the Moon

- Galileo's theory that all objects fall with the same acceleration has been verified on Earth many times. It wasn't the same old proof, though, on July 30, 1971, when astronaut David Randolph Scott stood on the surface of the moon and dropped a feather and a hammer simultaneously. Just as Galileo's theory had predicted, in the absence of air resistance, the feather hit the ground at the same time as the hammer.

- Sir Isaac Newton is said to have realized the importance of gravitational force in 1666, when he watched an apple fall from a tree in his garden. John Conduitt, one of Newton's contemporaries, said of Newton, ". . . [I]t came into his thought that the power of gravity (which brought an apple from the tree to the ground) was not limited to a certain distance from the earth, but that this power must extend much further than was usually thought. Why not as high as the Moon though he said to himself & that if so, that must influence her motion & perhaps retain her in her orbit. [W]hereupon he fell a-calculating what would be the effect of that supposition. . ."

- Newton calculated the acceleration of the moon in a circular orbit around Earth and compared this with an apple's downward acceleration. He discovered that the acceleration of the moon was approximately 3,600 times smaller than the acceleration of an object near the surface of Earth. Newton eventually accounted for this difference by assuming that the gravitational force was inversely proportional to the square of the distance from Earth.

Air Resistance and Terminal Velocity

- Air resistance, a type of friction, limits the velocity of an object as it falls. As long as a falling object is somewhat streamlined and has not accelerated to high velocity, its acceleration due to gravity near the surface of Earth is a constant 9.8 m/s².

- As the velocity of a falling object increases, more air must be pushed out of the way each second. Eventually, the force of the air resistance pushing upward on the falling object is equal to Earth's gravitational force pulling downward on the object.

- When the upward and downward forces are equal, the net force on the falling object is 0 N. Then, the object falls with a constant velocity, called the *terminal velocity.*

Parachutes

- How do parachutes work to increase air resistance? The parachute provides a larger surface area to pull through the air. The larger surface area requires a much larger amount of air be moved out of the way each second as the parachute falls toward Earth.

Is That a Fact!

◆ Galileo timed the motion of balls rolling down an inclined plane to prove that all objects fall with the same acceleration.

Section 2

Newton's Laws of Motion

Sir Isaac Newton (1642–1727)

● In 1661, Isaac Newton went to study at Cambridge University. But Newton made many of his most important discoveries while spending time at the family home, Woolsthorpe Manor, near Grantham, in Lincolnshire, England, in 1665 and 1666.

Principia

● Newton's *Principia,* published in 1687, explains the three basic laws that govern the way objects move and Newton's theory of gravity. Newton explained how the force of gravity keeps the planets moving around the sun. Interestingly, Newton used his laws to predict that Earth must be a slightly flattened sphere and that comets orbit the sun in elongated elliptical paths. These predictions were later shown to be true.

Frogs and Fastballs

● What does a jumping frog have in common with a 42 m/s fastball? What does the space shuttle have in common with a sky diver? They are all affected by gravity, and their flights are governed by certain laws of motion. Although some observers in ancient China theorized about objects in motion and objects at rest, Newton is usually given credit for stating and testing the three basic laws that describe and predict motion.

Section 3

Momentum

Momentum and Martial Arts

● Momentum is the product of an object's mass and its velocity. Like velocity, momentum always includes a direction. The direction of an object's momentum is always in the direction of its motion.

● When a person (the attacker) kicks or throws a punch during a martial arts match, the attacker has momentum in the forward direction. The attacker's opponent can take advantage of this momentum when blocking the hit. Instead of trying to stop the hit, the opponent sweeps the attacker's arm or leg away with his or her own arm. This motion redirects the hit away from the opponent's body. The attacker's momentum continues in a generally forward direction, which can cause the attacker to lose his or her balance.

SciLinks is maintained by the National Science Teachers Association to provide you and your students with interesting, up-to-date links that will enrich your classroom presentation of the chapter.

Visit www.scilinks.org and enter the SciLinks code for more information about the topic listed.

Topic: Force of Gravity
SciLinks code: HSM0602

Topic: Projectile Motion
SciLinks code: HSM1223

Topic: Gravity and Orbiting Objects
SciLinks code: HSM0692

Topic: Newton's Laws (of Motion)
SciLinks code: HSM1028

Topic: Momentum
SciLinks code: HSM0988

Overview

In this chapter, students will learn about gravity's role in the acceleration of falling objects, in orbiting, and in projectile motion. Students will also study Newton's laws of motion. Finally, students will learn how to calculate momentum and will study the law of conservation of momentum.

Assessing Prior Knowledge

Students should be familiar with the following topics:
- velocity and acceleration
- net force and balanced and unbalanced forces
- friction
- gravity

Identifying Misconceptions

Some students may think that an object will stay in motion only if a force continuously acts on the object. Explain to students that a force is needed to start the motion of an object but that the object will continue to move if no other forces (such as friction) act on the object. Discuss an air-hockey puck as an example of an object that moves with a (nearly) constant speed after the force causing its motion has ended.

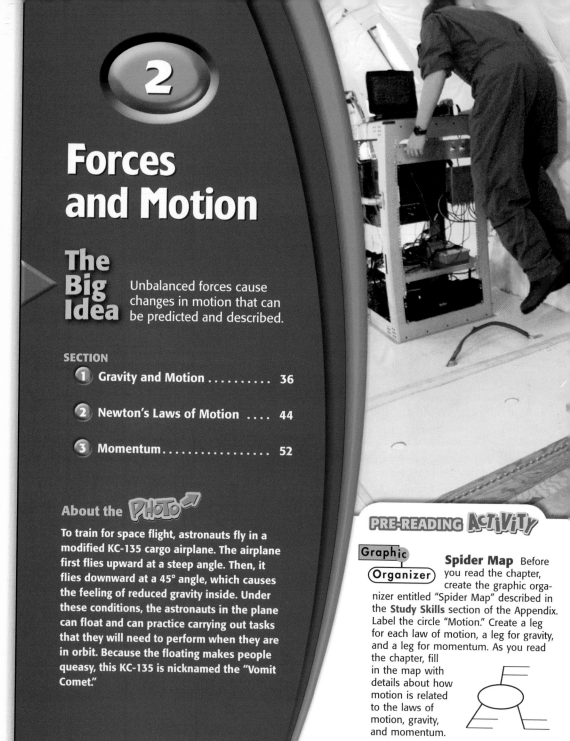

Forces and Motion

The Big Idea

Unbalanced forces cause changes in motion that can be predicted and described.

About the PHOTO

To train for space flight, astronauts fly in a modified KC-135 cargo airplane. The airplane first flies upward at a steep angle. Then, it flies downward at a 45° angle, which causes the feeling of reduced gravity inside. Under these conditions, the astronauts in the plane can float and can practice carrying out tasks that they will need to perform when they are in orbit. Because the floating makes people queasy, this KC-135 is nicknamed the "Vomit Comet."

PRE-READING ACTIVITY

Graphic Organizer

Spider Map Before you read the chapter, create the graphic organizer entitled "Spider Map" described in the **Study Skills** section of the Appendix. Label the circle "Motion." Create a leg for each law of motion, a leg for gravity, and a leg for momentum. As you read the chapter, fill in the map with details about how motion is related to the laws of motion, gravity, and momentum.

Standards Correlations

National Science Education Standards

The following codes indicate the National Science Education Standards that correlate to this chapter. The full text of the standards is at the front of the book.

Chapter Opener
SAI 1; SPSP 5

Section 1 Gravity and Motion
UCP 3; SAI 1, 2; HNS 1, 2, 3; PS 2c; *LabBook*: SAI 1

Section 2 Newton's Laws of Motion
UCP 3, 4; SAI 1; ST 1; PS 2b, 2c; *LabBook*: SAI 1; PS 2c

Section 3 Momentum
SAI 1; *LabBook*: SAI 1

Chapter Lab
SAI 1; PS 2b

Chapter Review
PS 2b

Science in Action
ST 1, 2; HNS 1; SPSP 5

START-UP ACTIVITY
MATERIALS

FOR EACH GROUP
- cup, paper
- paper towels
- tub, wide plastic
- water

Teacher's Notes: Food coloring may be added to the water so that students will see the water better. Furthermore, the activity can be done outdoors to minimize cleanup.

To reduce the mess, have students fill the cups only half full. Spread plenty of newspapers on the floor.

Answers

1. In Trial 1, students should see the water coming out of the hole and falling to the ground. In Trial 2, they should not see any water coming out of the hole as the cup falls.

2. The cup and the water fall at the same rate. Students may not know that both are accelerating, and students may say that both fell with the same velocity, or speed.

3. Sample answer: My prediction was wrong because I thought the water would come out of the cup faster, but no water came out at all.

START-UP ACTIVITY

Falling Water

Gravity is one of the most important forces in your life. In this activity, you will observe the effect of gravity on a falling object.

Procedure

1. Place a **wide plastic tub** on the floor. Punch a small hole in the side of a **paper cup,** near the bottom.

2. Hold your finger over the hole, and fill the cup with **water.** Keep your finger over the hole, and hold the cup waist-high above the tub.

3. Uncover the hole. Record your observations as Trial 1.

4. Predict what will happen to the water if you drop the cup at the same time you uncover the hole.

5. Cover the hole, and refill the cup with water.

6. Uncover the hole, and drop the cup at the same time. Record your observations as Trial 2.

7. Clean up any spilled water with **paper towels.**

Analysis

1. What differences did you observe in the behavior of the water during the two trials?

2. In Trial 2, how fast did the cup fall compared with how fast the water fell?

3. How did the results of Trial 2 compare with your prediction?

Chapter Starter Transparency
Use this transparency to help students begin thinking about forces and motion.

CHAPTER RESOURCES

Technology

Transparencies
- Chapter Starter Transparency

READING SKILLS

Student Edition on CD-ROM

Guided Reading Audio CD
- English or Spanish

Classroom Videos
- Brain Food Video Quiz

Workbooks

Science Puzzlers, Twisters & Teasers
- Forces and Motion GENERAL

Focus

Overview

In this section, students learn how gravity and air resistance affect falling objects. Students also learn about orbiting and study the relationship between gravity and projectile motion. You may wish to review the concepts of velocity, acceleration, and net force with your students before starting this section.

🔊 Bellringer

Have students write an answer to the following question: "If Wile E. Coyote and a boulder fall off a cliff at the same time, which do you think will hit the ground first?"

Motivate

Demonstration —— GENERAL

Falling Objects Have students examine a 12 in. softball and a women's-sized shot. Then, discuss the objects' similar sizes and different masses. Place a protective board on the floor, and stand on a sturdy table. Tell students that you will drop both objects from the same height. Hold the objects above the board, and ask students to predict which will land first. Drop the objects *at the same time*. Ask students for their observations, and repeat as necessary. **LS** Visual

What You Will Learn

● Explain the effect of gravity and air resistance on falling objects.
● Explain why objects in orbit are in free fall and appear to be weightless.
● Describe how projectile motion is affected by gravity.

Vocabulary

terminal velocity
free fall
projectile motion

READING STRATEGY

Reading Organizer As you read this section, create an outline of the section. Use the headings from the section in your outline.

Gravity and Motion

Suppose you dropped a baseball and a marble at the same time from the top of a tall building. Which do you think would land on the ground first?

In ancient Greece around 400 BCE, a philosopher named Aristotle (AR is TAWT uhl) thought that the rate at which an object falls depended on the object's mass. If you asked Aristotle whether the baseball or the marble would land first, he would have said the baseball. But Aristotle never tried dropping objects with different masses to test his idea about falling objects.

Gravity and Falling Objects

In the late 1500s, a young Italian scientist named Galileo Galilei (GAL uh LAY oh GAL uh LAY) questioned Aristotle's idea about falling objects. Galileo argued that the mass of an object does not affect the time the object takes to fall to the ground. According to one story, Galileo proved his argument by dropping two cannonballs of different masses from the top of the Leaning Tower of Pisa in Italy. The people watching from the ground below were amazed to see the two cannonballs land at the same time. Whether or not this story is true, Galileo's work changed people's understanding of gravity and falling objects.

Gravity and Acceleration

Objects fall to the ground at the same rate because the acceleration due to gravity is the same for all objects. Why is this true? Acceleration depends on both force and mass. A heavier object experiences a greater gravitational force than a lighter object does. But a heavier object is also harder to accelerate because it has more mass. The extra mass of the heavy object exactly balances the additional gravitational force. **Figure 1** shows objects that have different masses falling with the same acceleration.

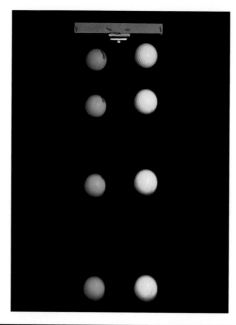

Figure 1 *This stop-action photo shows that a table-tennis ball and a golf ball fall at the same rate even though they have different masses.*

SCIENTISTS AT ODDS

Velocities of Falling Objects When Galileo attended the University of Pisa in the 1500s, scholars generally accepted Aristotle's theory that bodies fall to Earth at different velocities depending on their mass. It is said that Galileo questioned Aristotle's teachings after observing different-sized hailstones hitting the ground at the same time.

Acceleration Due to Gravity

Acceleration is the rate at which velocity changes over time. So, the acceleration of an object is the object's change in velocity divided by the amount of time during which the change occurs. All objects accelerate toward Earth at a rate of 9.8 meters per second per second. This rate is written as 9.8 m/s/s, or 9.8 m/s². So, for every second that an object falls, the object's downward velocity increases by 9.8 m/s, as shown in **Figure 2**.

Reading Check What is the acceleration due to gravity? *(See the Appendix for answers to Reading Checks.)*

Velocity of Falling Objects

You can calculate the change in velocity (Δ*v*) of a falling object by using the following equation:

$$\Delta v = g \times t$$

In this equation, *g* is the acceleration due to gravity on Earth (9.8 m/s²), and *t* is the time the object takes to fall (in seconds). The change in velocity is the difference between the final velocity and the starting velocity. If the object starts at rest, this equation yields the velocity of the object after a certain time period.

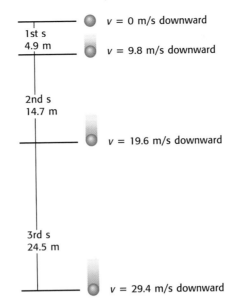

Figure 2 *A falling object accelerates at a constant rate. The object falls faster and farther each second than it did the second before.*

Calculating the Velocity of Falling Objects A stone at rest is dropped from a cliff, and the stone hits the ground after a time of 3 s. What is the stone's velocity when it hits the ground?

Step 1: Write the equation for change in velocity.

$$\Delta v = g \times t$$

Step 2: Replace *g* with its value and *t* with the time given in the problem, and solve.

$$\Delta v = 9.8 \frac{m/s}{s} \times 3 s$$
$$= 29.4 \text{ m/s}$$

To rearrange the equation to find time, divide by the acceleration due to gravity:

$$t = \frac{\Delta v}{g}$$

Now It's Your Turn

1. A penny at rest is dropped from the top of a tall stairwell. What is the penny's velocity after it has fallen for 2 s?
2. The same penny hits the ground in 4.5 s. What is the penny's velocity as it hits the ground?
3. A marble at rest is dropped from a tall building. The marble hits the ground with a velocity of 98 m/s. How long was the marble in the air?
4. An acorn at rest falls from an oak tree. The acorn hits the ground with a velocity of 14.7 m/s. How long did it take the acorn to land?

Answer to Reading Check
The acceleration due to gravity is 9.8 m/s².

CONNECTION ACTIVITY
Social Studies — ADVANCED

Greek Letters The triangle in the symbol for change in velocity is actually the Greek letter delta (Δ). In science, Δ often means "change in." When used in front of a variable, such as velocity, it indicates the result of subtracting the initial value of the variable from the final value of the variable. So, $\Delta v = v_{final} - v_{initial}$. Have students research how other Greek letters are used as symbols in science. Students should summarize their findings in a poster. **LS Verbal**

Figure 3 Effect of Air Resistance on a Falling Object

ⓐ The **force of gravity** is pulling down on the apple. If gravity were the only force acting on the apple, the apple would accelerate at a rate of 9.8 m/s².

ⓑ The **force of air resistance** is pushing up on the apple. This force is subtracted from the force of gravity to yield the net force.

ⓒ The **net force** on the apple is equal to the force of air resistance subtracted from the force of gravity. Because the net force is not 0 N, the apple accelerates downward. But the apple does not accelerate as fast as it would without air resistance.

Air Resistance and Falling Objects

Try dropping two sheets of paper—one crumpled in a tight ball and the other kept flat. What happened? Does this simple experiment seem to contradict what you just learned about falling objects? The flat paper falls more slowly than the crumpled paper because of *air resistance*. Air resistance is the force that opposes the motion of objects through air.

The amount of air resistance acting on an object depends on the size, shape, and speed of the object. Air resistance affects the flat sheet of paper more than the crumpled one. The larger surface area of the flat sheet causes the flat sheet to fall slower than the crumpled one. **Figure 3** shows the effect of air resistance on the downward acceleration of a falling object.

✓ Reading Check Will air resistance have more effect on the acceleration of a falling leaf or the acceleration of a falling acorn?

Acceleration Stops at the Terminal Velocity

As the speed of a falling object increases, air resistance increases. The upward force of air resistance continues to increase until it is equal to the downward force of gravity. At this point, the net force is 0 N and the object stops accelerating. The object then falls at a constant velocity called the **terminal velocity.**

Terminal velocity can be a good thing. Every year, cars, buildings, and vegetation are severely damaged in hailstorms. The terminal velocity of hailstones is between 5 and 40 m/s, depending on their size. If there were no air resistance, hailstones would hit the ground at velocities near 350 m/s! **Figure 4** shows another situation in which terminal velocity is helpful.

Figure 4 *The parachute increases the air resistance of this sky diver and slows him to a safe terminal velocity.*

terminal velocity the constant velocity of a falling object when the force of air resistance is equal in magnitude and opposite in direction to the force of gravity

Free Fall Occurs When There Is No Air Resistance

Sky divers are often described as being in free fall before they open their parachutes. However, that is an incorrect description, because air resistance is always acting on the sky diver.

An object is in **free fall** only if gravity is pulling it down and no other forces are acting on it. Because air resistance is a force, free fall can occur only where there is no air. Two places that have no air are in space and in a vacuum. A vacuum is a place in which there is no matter. **Figure 5** shows objects falling in a vacuum. Because there is no air resistance in a vacuum, the two objects are in free fall.

Orbiting Objects Are in Free Fall

Look at the astronaut in **Figure 6.** Why is the astronaut floating inside the space shuttle? You may be tempted to say that she is weightless in space. However, it is impossible for any object to be weightless anywhere in the universe.

Weight is a measure of gravitational force. The size of the force depends on the masses of objects and the distances between them. Suppose you traveled in space far away from all the stars and planets. The gravitational force acting on you would be very small because the distance between you and other objects would be very large. But you and all the other objects in the universe would still have mass. Therefore, gravity would attract you to other objects—even if just slightly—so you would still have weight.

Astronauts float in orbiting spacecrafts because of free fall. To better understand why astronauts float, you need to know what *orbiting* means.

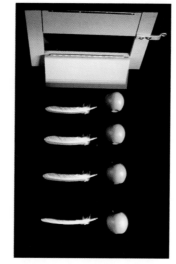

Figure 5 *Air resistance usually causes a feather to fall more slowly than an apple falls. But in a vacuum, a feather and an apple fall with the same acceleration because both are in free fall.*

free fall the motion of a body when only the force of gravity is acting on the body

Figure 6 *Astronauts appear to be weightless while they are floating inside the space shuttle— but they are not weightless!*

Using the Figure — GENERAL

How an Orbit is Formed Draw students' attention to **Figure 7.** Ask students why the shuttle does not fall to Earth if gravity is pulling downward on it. (The forward motion of the shuttle occurs together with free fall to produce a path that follows the curve of Earth's surface.) Ask what would happen if the shuttle started moving much faster or much slower. (If the shuttle moved fast enough, it would escape Earth's gravitational force and move off into space. If the shuttle moved more slowly, it would begin to fall toward Earth. **Note:** Tell students that the shuttle slows down to land in a controlled "fall" toward Earth. However, the shuttle continues to move forward so it spirals down toward Earth rather than falling straight down.) **LS** Visual

Cultural Awareness — GENERAL

An Astronaut First On September 12, 1992, Dr. Mae Jemison became the first African-American woman to orbit Earth. She was a science mission specialist on the space shuttle *Endeavour.* Dr. Jemison, who has degrees in chemical engineering and medicine, was in charge of many of the experiments conducted during the mission.

Answer to Reading Check

The word *centripetal* means "toward the center."

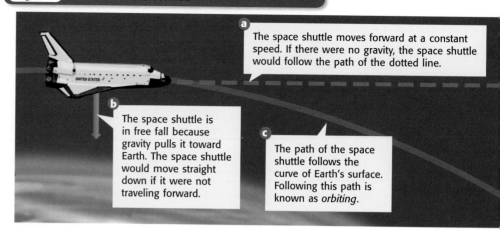

Figure 7 How an Orbit Is Formed

a The space shuttle moves forward at a constant speed. If there were no gravity, the space shuttle would follow the path of the dotted line.

b The space shuttle is in free fall because gravity pulls it toward Earth. The space shuttle would move straight down if it were not traveling forward.

c The path of the space shuttle follows the curve of Earth's surface. Following this path is known as *orbiting.*

Two Motions Combine to Cause Orbiting

An object is orbiting when it is traveling around another object in space. When a spacecraft orbits Earth, it is moving forward. But the spacecraft is also in free fall toward Earth. **Figure 7** shows how these two motions combine to cause orbiting.

As you can see in **Figure 7,** the space shuttle is always falling while it is in orbit. So why don't astronauts hit their heads on the ceiling of the falling shuttle? Because they are also in free fall—they are always falling, too. Because astronauts are in free fall, they float.

Orbiting and Centripetal Force

Besides spacecrafts and satellites, many other objects in the universe are in orbit. The moon orbits the Earth. Earth and the other planets orbit the sun. In addition, many stars orbit large masses in the center of galaxies. Many of these objects are traveling in a circular or nearly circular path. Any object in circular motion is constantly changing direction. Because an unbalanced force is necessary to change the motion of any object, there must be an unbalanced force working on any object in circular motion.

The unbalanced force that causes objects to move in a circular path is called a *centripetal force* (sen TRIP uht uhl FOHRS). Gravity provides the centripetal force that keeps objects in orbit. The word *centripetal* means "toward the center." As you can see in **Figure 8,** the centripetal force on the moon points toward the center of the moon's circular orbit.

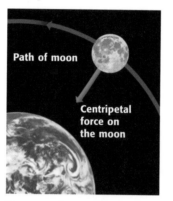

Figure 8 The moon stays in orbit around Earth because Earth's gravitational force provides a centripetal force on the moon.

Reading Check What does the word *centripetal* mean?

MISCONCEPTION ALERT

Shuttle Orbit The shuttle in **Figure 7** is shown in orbit facing forward and oriented right side up (called *airplane mode*). In orbit, the shuttle spends most of the time upside down and backward. It also orbits upside down and sideways (wing first), but it rarely orbits in airplane mode. It is only in airplane mode for landings.

CONNECTION ACTIVITY Astronomy — ADVANCED

Scale Drawing In **Figure 8,** the relative sizes of Earth and the moon and the distance between the two are not drawn to scale. Ask students to find average distance between Earth and the moon and the diameters of Earth and the moon. Then, have students use this information to make a poster of the moon in orbit around Earth that is drawn to scale. **LS** Logical/Visual

Projectile Motion and Gravity

The motion of a hopping grasshopper is an example of projectile motion (proh JEK tuhl MOH shuhn). **Projectile motion** is the curved path an object follows when it is thrown or propelled near the surface of the Earth. Projectile motion has two components—horizontal motion and vertical motion. The two components are independent, so they have no effect on each other. When the two motions are combined, they form a curved path, as shown in **Figure 9.** Some examples of projectile motion include the following:

- a frog leaping
- water sprayed by a sprinkler
- a swimmer diving into water
- balls being juggled
- an arrow shot by an archer

Horizontal Motion

When you throw a ball, your hand exerts a force on the ball that makes the ball move forward. This force gives the ball its horizontal motion, which is motion parallel to the ground.

After you release the ball, no horizontal forces are acting on the ball (if you ignore air resistance). Even gravity does not affect the horizontal component of projectile motion. So, there are no forces to change the ball's horizontal motion. Thus, the horizontal velocity of the ball is constant after the ball leaves your hand, as shown in **Figure 9.**

projectile motion the curved path that an object follows when thrown, launched, or otherwise projected near the surface of Earth

---

Figure 9 Projectile Motion

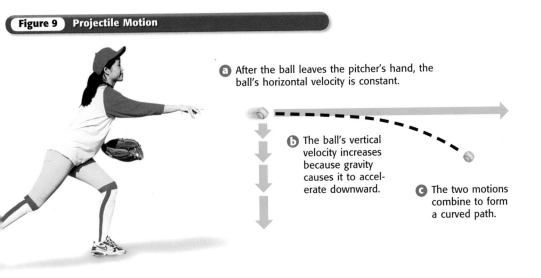

a After the ball leaves the pitcher's hand, the ball's horizontal velocity is constant.

b The ball's vertical velocity increases because gravity causes it to accelerate downward.

c The two motions combine to form a curved path.

CHAPTER RESOURCES

Technology

Transparencies
- P22 How an Orbit Is Formed; Projectile Motion

Close

Answer to Reading Check

Gravity gives vertical motion to an object in projectile motion.

Reteaching — BASIC

Horizontal Velocity Give students photocopies of **Figure 10** and ask them to use a ruler to draw vertical lines through the centers of the yellow balls. Then, have students measure the distance between the lines. Students should find that the distances are equal. Explain that this fact shows that the horizontal velocity is constant. **LS Visual**

Quiz — GENERAL

1. Why do you have to aim above a target that you want to hit with a thrown object? (The thrown object will be in projectile motion and will therefore accelerate downward.)

2. When does an object reach its terminal velocity? (when the upward force of air resistance equals the downward force of gravity)

Alternative Assessment — GENERAL

Making Models Give each group a plastic bag, string, tape, a washer, scissors, and a stopwatch. Have each group design a parachute. Challenge the groups to make the parachute that descends the slowest. How does the design of a parachute affect its rate of fall? **LS Kinesthetic**

INTERNET ACTIVITY

For another activity related to this chapter, go to **go.hrw.com** and type in the keyword **HP5FORW.**

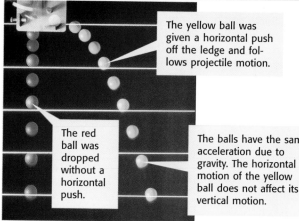

Figure 10 Projectile Motion and Acceleration Due to Gravity

The yellow ball was given a horizontal push off the ledge and follows projectile motion.

The red ball was dropped without a horizontal push.

The balls have the same acceleration due to gravity. The horizontal motion of the yellow ball does not affect its vertical motion.

Vertical Motion

Gravity pulls everything on Earth downward toward the center of Earth. A ball in your hand is prevented from falling by your hand. After you throw the ball, gravity pulls it downward and gives the ball vertical motion. Vertical motion is motion that is perpendicular to the ground. Gravity pulls objects in projectile motion down at an acceleration of 9.8 m/s^2 (if air resistance is ignored). This rate is the same for all falling objects. **Figure 10** shows that the downward acceleration of a thrown object and a falling object are the same.

Because objects in projectile motion accelerate downward, you always have to aim above a target if you want to hit it with a thrown or propelled object. That's why when you aim an arrow directly at a bull's-eye, your arrow strikes the bottom of the target rather than the middle of the target.

Reading Check What gives an object in projectile motion its vertical motion?

Penny Projectile Motion

1. Position a **flat ruler** and **two pennies** on a **desk or table** as shown below.

2. Hold the ruler by the end that is on the desk. Move the ruler quickly in the direction shown so that the ruler knocks the penny off the table and so that the other penny also drops. Repeat this step several times.

3. Which penny travels with projectile motion? In what order do the pennies hit the ground? Record and explain your answers.

QUICK Lab

MATERIALS

FOR EACH GROUP
- pennies (2)
- ruler, flat

Teacher's Notes: Make sure students have plenty of room. The penny in projectile motion may travel 1–2 m from its starting point. If the Quick Lab is done in a room without a carpet, students can listen for the sound of the pennies hitting the floor. Students should move the ruler quickly enough so that the penny on the ruler drops straight down.

Answers

3. The penny that was knocked off the table with the ruler was in projectile motion. The pennies should land at the same time because they have the same acceleration due to gravity. The horizontal motion does not affect the vertical motion.

SECTION Review

Summary

- Gravity causes all objects to accelerate toward Earth at a rate of 9.8 m/s^2.
- Air resistance slows the acceleration of falling objects. An object falls at its terminal velocity when the upward force of air resistance equals the downward force of gravity.
- An object is in free fall if gravity is the only force acting on it.
- Objects in orbit appear to be weightless because they are in free fall.

- A centripetal force is needed to keep objects in circular motion. Gravity acts as a centripetal force to keep objects in orbit.
- Projectile motion is the curved path an object follows when thrown or propelled near the surface of Earth.
- Projectile motion has two components—horizontal motion and vertical motion. Gravity affects only the vertical motion of projectile motion.

Using Key Terms

1. Use each of the following terms in a separate sentence: *terminal velocity* and *free fall*.

Understanding Key Ideas

2. Which of the following is in projectile motion?
   a. a feather falling in a vacuum
   b. a cat leaping on a toy
   c. a car driving up a hill
   d. a book laying on a desk

3. How does air resistance affect the acceleration of falling objects?

4. How does gravity affect the two components of projectile motion?

5. How is the acceleration of falling objects affected by gravity?

6. Why is the acceleration due to gravity the same for all objects?

Math Skills

7. A rock at rest falls off a tall cliff and hits the valley below after 3.5 s. What is the rock's velocity as it hits the ground?

Critical Thinking

8. **Applying Concepts** Think about a sport that uses a ball. Identify four examples from that sport in which an object is in projectile motion.

9. **Making Inferences** The moon has no atmosphere. Predict what would happen if an astronaut on the moon dropped a hammer and a feather at the same time from the same height.

Interpreting Graphics

10. Whenever Jon delivers a newspaper to the Zapanta house, the newspaper lands in the bushes, as shown below. What should Jon do to make sure the newspaper lands on the porch?

SC**LINKS**® **NSTA**
Developed and maintained by the
National Science Teachers Association

For a variety of links related to this chapter, go to www.scilinks.org
Topic: Gravity and Orbiting Objects; Projectile Motion
SciLinks code: HSM0692; HSM1223

Answers to Section Review

1. Sample answers: The sky diver stopped accelerating downward because she reached her terminal velocity. A feather dropped on the moon is in free fall.

2. b

3. Air resistance reduces the acceleration of falling objects and causes them to fall more slowly.

4. Gravity has no effect on the horizontal component of projectile motion. Gravity changes the vertical component of projectile motion by accelerating an object downward.

5. The acceleration due to gravity is the same for all objects. (Note: This is true only near the surface of Earth and when no air resistance acts on the objects.) Also acceptable: The force of gravity causes the acceleration of falling objects.

6. A heavier object experiences a greater gravitational force than a lighter object does. But a heavier object is also harder to accelerate because it has more mass. The greater gravitational force is exactly balanced by the greater mass. So, all objects fall with the same acceleration.

7. 3.5 s × 9.8 m/s^2 = 34.3 m/s

8. Sample answer: Basketball: a player jumping to dunk the ball, a ball passed between players, a ball shot toward the basket, and a ball bounced on the floor before it hits the floor

9. The feather and the hammer would hit the moon's surface at the same time because there is no air resistance. The feather and the hammer are in free fall.

10. Jon should either aim higher when throwing the newspaper or he should throw the newspaper with a greater horizontal velocity.

CHAPTER RESOURCES

Chapter Resource File

- • Section Quiz GENERAL
- • Section Review GENERAL
- • Vocabulary and Section Summary GENERAL
- • Reinforcement Worksheet BASIC
- • Datasheet for Quick Lab

Technology

- Interactive Explorations CD-ROM
  • Extreme Skiing GENERAL

Focus

Overview

This section introduces students to Newton's laws of motion. Before teaching this section, you may wish to review the concepts of acceleration, force, net force, friction, and balanced and unbalanced forces with your students.

 Bellringer

Have students respond to the following question:

If you are sitting still in your seat on a bus that is traveling on a highway, is your body at rest or in motion? (in motion with respect to the ground)

Explain your answer. Use a diagram if it will help make your answer clear.

Motivate

Demonstration — GENERAL

Egg in a Buggy Place a hard-boiled egg in a small, wheeled cart. Apply a strong force to the cart so that it strikes a wall. Ask students to draw a series of pictures that show what happens to the egg as the cart moves across the floor and strikes the wall. Then, ask them to draw a picture of how the egg could be protected in the cart. Challenge students to explain what happened to the egg. Visual

---

What You Will Learn

- Describe Newton's first law of motion, and explain how it relates to objects at rest and objects in motion.
- State Newton's second law of motion, and explain the relationship between force, mass, and acceleration.
- State Newton's third law of motion, and give examples of force pairs.

Vocabulary

inertia

READING STRATEGY

Paired Summarizing Read this section silently. In pairs, take turns summarizing the material. Stop to discuss ideas that seem confusing.

Figure 1 *A golf ball will remain at rest on a tee until it is acted on by the unbalanced force of a moving club.*

Newton's Laws of Motion

Imagine that you are playing baseball. The pitch comes in, and—crack—you hit the ball hard! But instead of flying off the bat, the ball just drops to the ground. Is that normal?

You would probably say no. You know that force and motion are related. When you exert a force on a baseball by hitting it with a bat, the baseball should move. In 1686, Sir Isaac Newton explained this relationship between force and the motion of an object with his three laws of motion.

Newton's First Law of Motion

> *An object at rest remains at rest, and an object in motion remains in motion at constant speed and in a straight line unless acted on by an unbalanced force.*

Newton's first law of motion describes the motion of an object that has a net force of 0 N acting on it. This law may seem complicated when you first read it. But, it is easy to understand when you consider its two parts separately.

Part 1: Objects at Rest

An object that is not moving is said to be at rest. A chair on the floor and a golf ball balanced on a tee are examples of objects at rest. Newton's first law says that objects at rest will stay at rest unless they are acted on by an unbalanced force. For example, objects will not start moving until a push or a pull is exerted on them. So, a chair won't slide across the room unless you push the chair. And, a golf ball won't move off the tee unless the ball is struck by a golf club, as shown in **Figure 1.**

Unbalanced force

Object at rest

Object in motion

CHAPTER RESOURCES

Chapter Resource File

- Lesson Plan
- Directed Reading A **BASIC**
- Directed Reading B **SPECIAL NEEDS**

Technology

- Transparencies
  - Bellringer

Workbooks

- Interactive Textbook **Struggling Readers**

CONNECTION to History — GENERAL

Sir Isaac Newton Long before Newton, others had observed relationships between forces and motion, rest, and acceleration. When Newton extended their work with his three laws of motion, he said, "If I have seen further it is by standing on the shoulders of Giants." Newton's genius was that he combined previous discoveries plus his own observations into a unified picture of how the universe worked.

Part 2: Objects in Motion

The second part of Newton's first law is about objects moving with a certain velocity. Such objects will continue to move forever with the same velocity unless an unbalanced force acts on them.

Think about driving a bumper car at an amusement park. Your ride is pleasant as long as you are driving in an open space. But the name of the game is bumper cars! Sooner or later you are likely to run into another car, as shown in **Figure 2.** Your bumper car stops when it hits another car. But, you continue to move forward until the force from your seat belt stops you.

Friction and Newton's First Law

An object in motion will stay in motion forever unless it is acted on by an unbalanced force. So, you should be able to give your desk a push and send it sliding across the floor. If you push your desk, the desk quickly stops. Why?

There must be an unbalanced force that acts on the desk to stop its motion. That unbalanced force is friction. The friction between the desk and the floor works against the motion of the desk. Because of friction, observing the effects of Newton's first law is often difficult. For example, friction will cause a rolling ball to slow down and stop. Friction will also make a car slow down if the driver lets up on the gas pedal. Because of friction, the motion of objects changes.

✓ Reading Check When you ride a bus, why do you fall forward when the bus stops moving? (*See the Appendix for answers to Reading Checks.*)

a An unbalanced force from another car acts on your car and changes your car's motion.

b The collision changes your car's motion, not your motion. Your motion continues with the same velocity.

c Another unbalanced force, from your seat belt, changes your motion.

Figure 2 *Bumper cars let you have fun with Newton's first law.*

First Law Skateboard

1. Place an **empty soda can** on top of a **skateboard.**
2. Ask a friend to catch the skateboard after you push it. Now, give the skateboard a quick, firm push. What happened to the soda can?
3. Put the can on the skateboard again. Push the skateboard gently so that the skateboard moves quickly but so that the can does not fall.
4. Ask your friend to stop the skateboard after he or she allows it to travel a short distance. What happened to the can?
5. Explain how Newton's first law applies to what happened.

Answer to Reading Check
When the bus is moving, both you and the bus are in motion. When the bus stops moving, no unbalanced force acts on your body, so your body continues to move forward.

Is That a Fact!
Antilock braking systems (ABS) controlled by a computer prevent skidding by sensing when the wheels are about to lock. They release and reapply the brakes up to 25 times a second. Instead of skidding out of control, the car slows down and stops safely.

Section 2 • Newton's Laws of Motion **45**

MATERIALS

FOR EACH STUDENT
• paper towel or construction paper
• plastic cup, empty
• water

Teacher's Notes: Cups should be large (12 oz or more), or 500 mL plastic beakers can be used.

Make sure that students don't fill the cups more than halfway. This will reduce spills, but it still makes the cup noticeably more massive.

Instruct students to keep the outer surfaces of the cups dry. A wet paper towel may break when pulled.

Beans or popcorn kernels can be substituted for the water, if desired.

Be sure to have extra paper towels on hand to clean up any spilled water.

Answers

2. Students will quickly learn that they have to jerk the paper towel out from under the cup, as in a magic trick.

5. It should be easier for students to do the trick with water in the cup because the cup has more mass and therefore more inertia. When the cup has more inertia, it is harder to move. It is therefore easier to move the paper towel out from under it.

inertia the tendency of an object to resist being moved or, if the object is moving, to resist a change in speed or direction until an outside force acts on the object

First-Law Magic

1. On a **table or desk**, place a **large, empty plastic cup** on top of a **paper towel.**

2. Without touching the cup or tipping it over, remove the paper towel from under the cup. How did you accomplish this? Repeat this step.

3. Fill the cup half full with **water,** and place the cup on the paper towel.

4. Once again, remove the paper towel from under the cup. Was it easier or harder to do this time?

5. Explain your observations in terms of mass, inertia, and Newton's first law of motion.

Inertia and Newton's First Law

Newton's first law of motion is sometimes called the *law of inertia.* **Inertia** (in UHR shuh) is the tendency of all objects to resist any change in motion. Because of inertia, an object at rest will remain at rest until a force makes it move. Likewise, inertia is the reason a moving object stays in motion with the same velocity unless a force changes its speed or direction. For example, because of inertia, you slide toward the side of a car when the driver turns a corner. Inertia is also why it is impossible for a plane, car, or bicycle to stop immediately.

Mass and Inertia

Mass is a measure of inertia. An object that has a small mass has less inertia than an object that has a large mass. So, changing the motion of an object that has a small mass is easier than changing the motion of an object that has a large mass. For example, a softball has less mass and therefore less inertia than a bowling ball. Because the softball has a small amount of inertia, it is easy to pitch a softball and to change its motion by hitting it with a bat. Imagine how difficult it would be to play softball with a bowling ball! **Figure 3** further shows the relationship between mass and inertia.

Figure 3 *Inertia makes it harder to accelerate a car than to accelerate a bicycle. Inertia also makes it easier to stop a moving bicycle than a car moving at the same speed.*

CHAPTER RESOURCES

Technology

Transparencies
• P23 Mass, Force, and Acceleration

Newton's Second Law of Motion

The acceleration of an object depends on the mass of the object and the amount of force applied.

Newton's second law describes the motion of an object when an unbalanced force acts on the object. As with Newton's first law, you should consider the second law in two parts.

Part 1: Acceleration Depends on Mass

Suppose you are pushing an empty cart. You have to exert only a small force on the cart to accelerate it. But, the same amount of force will not accelerate the full cart as much as the empty cart. Look at the first two photos in **Figure 4.** They show that the acceleration of an object decreases as its mass increases and that its acceleration increases as its mass decreases.

Part 2: Acceleration Depends on Force

Suppose you give the cart a hard push, as shown in the third photo in **Figure 4.** The cart will start moving faster than if you gave it only a soft push. So, an object's acceleration increases as the force on the object increases. On the other hand, an object's acceleration decreases as the force on the object decreases.

The acceleration of an object is always in the same direction as the force applied. The cart in **Figure 4** moved forward because the push was in the forward direction.

Reading Check What is the relationship between the force on an object and the object's acceleration?

Figure 4 Mass, Force, and Acceleration

Acceleration

Acceleration

Acceleration

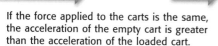

If the force applied to the carts is the same, the acceleration of the empty cart is greater than the acceleration of the loaded cart.

Acceleration will increase when a larger force is exerted.

Answer to Reading Check

The acceleration of an object increases as the force exerted on the object increases. (**Note:** this assumes that the mass of the object is constant.)

SCIENCE HUMOR

There once was a trucker from Nome,
Whose rig was loaded with foam.
Its very small mass
Made him able to pass
The other trucks all the way home.

Discussion ——— ADVANCED

Rearranging Newton's Second Law Discuss with students how the equation $F = m \times a$ can be used to find the mass of an object. Have them imagine that they hit an object of unknown mass with a force of 15 N and that the object accelerates at 5 m/s². What is the mass of the object? (3 kg) **LS** Logical

CONNECTION to Math ——— BASIC

Evaluating the Equation When you introduce the equation for Newton's second law, point out to students that acceleration and force are directly proportional (as force increases, acceleration increases) and that acceleration and mass are inversely proportional (as mass increases, acceleration decreases). These relationships are explained qualitatively, but students may not see the connection on their own. Also remind students of the definition of a newton:

1 newton = 1 kilogram-meter per second per second

OR

$1 \text{ N} = 1 \text{ kg•m/s}^2$

This is important for helping students through the unit cancellation in the Math Focus and in **Figure 5.**

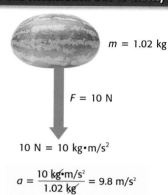

Figure 5 Newton's Second Law and Acceleration Due to Gravity

$m = 0.102$ kg

$F = 1$ N

$1 \text{ N} = 1 \text{ kg•m/s}^2$

$a = \dfrac{1 \text{ kg•m/s}^2}{0.102 \text{ kg}} = 9.8 \text{ m/s}^2$

$m = 1.02$ kg

$F = 10$ N

$10 \text{ N} = 10 \text{ kg•m/s}^2$

$a = \dfrac{10 \text{ kg•m/s}^2}{1.02 \text{ kg}} = 9.8 \text{ m/s}^2$

The apple has less mass than the watermelon does. So, less force is needed to give the apple the same acceleration that the watermelon has.

Expressing Newton's Second Law Mathematically

The relationship of acceleration (a) to mass (m) and force (F) can be expressed mathematically with the following equation:

$$a = \frac{F}{m}, \text{ or } F = m \times a$$

Notice that the equation can be rearranged to find the force applied. Both forms of the equation can be used to solve problems.

Newton's second law explains why objects fall to Earth with the same acceleration. In **Figure 5,** you can see how the large force of gravity on the watermelon is offset by its large mass. Thus, you find that the accelerations of the watermelon and the apple are the same when you solve for acceleration.

MATH FOCUS

Second-Law Problems What is the acceleration of a 3 kg mass if a force of 14.4 N is used to move the mass? (Note: 1 N is equal to 1 kg•m/s²)

Step 1: Write the equation for acceleration.

$$a = \frac{F}{m}$$

Step 2: Replace F and m with the values given in the problem, and solve.

$$a = \frac{14.4 \text{ kg•m/s}^2}{3 \text{ kg}} = 4.8 \text{ m/s}^2$$

Now It's Your Turn

1. What is the acceleration of a 7 kg mass if a force of 68.6 N is used to move it toward Earth?
2. What force is necessary to accelerate a 1,250 kg car at a rate of 40 m/s²?
3. Zookeepers carry a stretcher that holds a sleeping lion. The total mass of the lion and the stretcher is 175 kg. The lion's forward acceleration is 2 m/s². What is the force necessary to produce this acceleration?

CONNECTION ACTIVITY
Math ——— GENERAL

More Second Law Problems Have students do the following problems:

• Calculate the gravitational force acting on your 6 kg backpack. (This force is the weight of your backpack.)
($F = 6 \text{ kg} \times 9.8 \text{ m/s}^2 = 58.8 \text{ N}$)

• A 50 kg skater pushes off from a wall with a force of 200 N. What is the skater's acceleration? ($a = 200 \text{ N} \div 50 \text{ kg} = 200 \text{ kg•m/s}^2 \div 50 \text{ kg} = 4 \text{ m/s}^2$)
LS Logical

Answers to Math Focus

1. $a = F \div m = 68.6 \text{ N} \div 7 \text{ kg} = 9.8 \text{ m/s}^2$ (This is acceleration due to gravity.)
2. $F = m \times a = 1,250 \text{ kg} \times 40 \text{ m/s}^2 = 50,000 \text{ N}$
3. $F = m \times a = 175 \text{ kg} \times 2 \text{ m/s}^2 = 350 \text{ N}$

Newton's Third Law of Motion

Whenever one object exerts a force on a second object, the second object exerts an equal and opposite force on the first.

Newton's third law can be simply stated as follows: All forces act in pairs. If a force is exerted, another force occurs that is equal in size and opposite in direction. The law itself addresses only forces. But the way that force pairs interact affects the motion of objects.

How do forces act in pairs? Study **Figure 6** to learn how one force pair helps propel a swimmer through water. Action and reaction force pairs are present even when there is no motion. For example, you exert a force on a chair when you sit on it. Your weight pushing down on the chair is the action force. The reaction force is the force exerted by the chair that pushes up on your body. The force is equal to your weight.

Reading Check How are the forces in each force pair related?

Force Pairs Do Not Act on the Same Object

A force is always exerted by one object on another object. This rule is true for all forces, including action and reaction forces. However, action and reaction forces in a pair do not act on the same object. If they did, the net force would always be 0 N and nothing would ever move! To understand how action and reaction forces act on objects, look at **Figure 6** again. The action force was exerted on the water by the swimmer's hands. But the reaction force was exerted on the swimmer's hands by the water. The forces did not act on the same object.

Figure 6 *The action force and reaction force are a pair. The two forces are equal in size but opposite in direction.*

The action force is the swimmer's hands pushing on the water.

The reaction force is the water pushing on the hands. The reaction force moves the swimmer forward.

CHAPTER RESOURCES

Workbooks

Math Skills for Science
• Newton: Force and Motion **GENERAL**

CONNECTION to Real World — GENERAL

Artillery Recoil Newton's third law explains that when a shell is fired from an artillery piece, the force opposite to that which propels the shell forward causes the gun to recoil, or move backward. Because the mass of the gun is so much greater than the mass of the shell, the shell moves forward with a far greater velocity than the gun moves backward. This same law applies to the human cannonball at the circus!

Close

Reteaching ——— BASIC

Second-Law Practice Have students demonstrate the relationships between mass, force, and acceleration by pushing a wheeled cart with different forces. Change the mass of the cart by placing heavy books on the cart. Ask the class to describe the accelerations they observed.
LS Kinesthetic

Quiz ——————— GENERAL

1. How does Newton's second law explain why it is easier to push a bicycle than to push a car with the same acceleration? (The bicycle has a smaller mass, so a smaller force is required to give it the same acceleration as the car.)

2. Use Newton's third law to explain how a rocket accelerates. (The hot gases expelled from the back of the rocket produce a reaction force on the rocket that accelerates it.)

Alternative Assessment ——— GENERAL

Writing **Story** Have students write a story about an astronaut who spacewalks to fix a satellite. The only items she is carrying are her tools. As she completes the job, her backpack rocket fails. In the story, students should explain how the astronaut returns to the spacecraft. (Using Newton's third law, she could move toward the spacecraft by throwing her tools away from the spacecraft.) **LS Verbal**

Figure 7 **Examples of Action and Reaction Force Pairs**

The rabbit's legs exert a force on Earth. Earth exerts an equal force on the rabbit's legs and causes the rabbit to accelerate upward.

The space shuttle's thrusters push the exhaust gases downward as the gases push the shuttle upward with an equal force.

The bat exerts a force on the ball and sends the ball flying. The ball exerts an equal force on the bat, but the bat does not move backward because the batter is exerting another force on the bat.

All Forces Act in Pairs—Action and Reaction

Newton's third law says that all forces act in pairs. When a force is exerted, there is always a reaction force. A force never acts by itself. **Figure 7** shows some examples of action and reaction force pairs. In each example, the action force is shown in yellow and the reaction force is shown in red.

The Effect of a Reaction Can Be Difficult to See

Another example of a force pair is shown in **Figure 8**. Gravity is a force of attraction between objects that is due to their masses. If you drop a ball, gravity pulls the ball toward Earth. This force is the action force exerted by Earth on the ball. But gravity also pulls Earth toward the ball. The force is the reaction force exerted by the ball on Earth.

It's easy to see the effect of the action force—the ball falls to Earth. Why don't you notice the effect of the reaction force—Earth being pulled upward? To find the answer to this question, think about Newton's second law. It states that the acceleration of an object depends on the force applied to it and on the mass of the object. The force on Earth is equal to the force on the ball. But the mass of Earth is much larger than the mass of the ball. Thus, the acceleration of Earth is much smaller than the acceleration of the ball. The acceleration of the Earth is so small that you can't see or feel the acceleration. So, it is difficult to observe the effect of Newton's third law on falling objects.

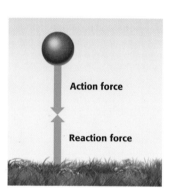

Figure 8 *The force of gravity between Earth and a falling object is a force pair.*

 **Reading Check** Why do objects fall toward Earth?

Answer to Reading Check
Objects accelerate toward Earth because the force of gravity pulls them toward Earth.

Cultural Awareness GENERAL

Gunpowder The Chinese invented gunpowder by the 10th century and used it in rockets for fireworks. These rockets were later adapted to warfare. In the 13th century, Chinese armies launched rockets over enemy troops.

SECTION Review

Summary

- Newton's first law of motion states that the motion of an object will not change if no unbalanced forces act on it.
- Objects at rest will not move unless acted upon by an unbalanced force.
- Objects in motion will continue to move at a constant speed and in a straight line unless acted upon by an unbalanced force.
- Inertia is the tendency of matter to resist a change in motion. Mass is a measure of inertia.

- Newton's second law of motion states that the acceleration of an object depends on its mass and on the force exerted on it.
- Newton's second law is represented by the following equation: $F = m \times a$.
- Newton's third law of motion states that whenever one object exerts a force on a second object, the second object exerts an equal and opposite force on the first object.

Using Key Terms

1. In your own words, write a definition for the term *inertia*.

Understanding Key Ideas

2. Which of the following will increase the acceleration of an object that is pushed by a force?
   a. decreasing the mass of the object
   b. increasing the mass of the object
   c. increasing the force pushing the object
   d. Both (a) and (c)

3. Give three examples of force pairs that occur when you do your homework.

4. What does Newton's first law of motion say about objects at rest and objects in motion?

5. Use Newton's second law to describe the relationship between force, mass, and acceleration.

Math Skills

6. What force is necessary to accelerate a 70 kg object at a rate of 4.2 m/s²?

Critical Thinking

7. **Applying Concepts** When a truck pulls a trailer, the trailer and truck accelerate forward even though the action and reaction forces are the same size but are in opposite directions. Why don't these forces balance each other?

8. **Making Inferences** Use Newton's first law of motion to explain why airbags in cars are important during head-on collisions.

Interpreting Graphics

9. Imagine you accidentally bumped your hand against a table, as shown in the photo below. Your hand hurts after it happens. Use Newton's third law of motion to explain what caused your hand to hurt.

SCiLINKS®

Developed and maintained by the National Science Teachers Association

For a variety of links related to this chapter, go to www.scilinks.org

Topic: Newton's Laws of Motion
SciLinks code: HSM1028

CHAPTER RESOURCES

Chapter Resource File

- Section Quiz GENERAL
- Section Review GENERAL
- Vocabulary and Section Summary GENERAL
- SciLinks Activity GENERAL
- Datasheet for Quick Lab

Answers to Section Review

1. Sample answer: Inertia is the tendency of an object to resist changes in motion.

2. d

3. Accept all reasonable answers. Students should list three examples of force pairs. Partial sample answer: using a pencil or pen (action: hand pushing on pencil; reaction: pencil pushing back on hand OR action: pencil pushing on paper; reaction: paper pushing on pencil).

4. Newton's first law states that objects at rest stay at rest and objects in motion stay in motion unless acted on by an unbalanced force.

5. Newton's second law states that the acceleration of an object increases as the force acting on it increases but the acceleration decreases as the mass of the object increases.

6. $F = 70$ kg $\times$ 4.2 m/s² $= 294$ N

7. The action and reaction forces do not balance each other because the forces are acting on two different objects. Because they act on two different objects, you cannot combine them to determine a net force.

8. Sample answer: During a head-on collision, an unbalanced force stops the motion of the car. But no unbalanced force immediately acts on the people inside the car. The people continue to move forward. Airbags are important because they provide unbalanced forces to stop the motion of the people in the car. The airbags prevent the people from hitting the dashboard or windshield of the car.

9. Your hand hit the table with a certain amount of force. According to Newton's third law of motion, the table exerts an equal and opposite force on your hand. The force exerted by the table causes your hand to hurt.

SECTION

3

Focus

Overview

In this section, students learn about momentum and perform calculations with the equation for momentum. Students also study the law of conservation of momentum and learn how it relates to Newton's third law of motion.

🔊 Bellringer

Tell students that this section is about momentum. Then, ask students to make a list of five things that they think have momentum and five things that don't have momentum.

Motivate

Group ACTiViTy — GENERAL

Testing Momentum Give each group of students two balls that have different masses. Have students take turns rolling the balls to each other with the same velocity. Ask the students to compare the forces needed to stop the balls. (More force is needed to stop the ball with more mass.) Ask students to explain why different forces are needed. (The ball that has more mass has more momentum. Therefore, it is harder to stop.) **LS** Kinesthetic

What You Will Learn

● Calculate the momentum of moving objects.
● Explain the law of conservation of momentum.

Vocabulary

momentum

READING STRATEGY

Prediction Guide Before reading this section, write the title of each heading in this section. Next, under each heading, write what you think you will learn.

momentum a quantity defined as the product of the mass and velocity of an object

Momentum

Imagine a compact car and a large truck traveling with the same velocity. The drivers of both vehicles put on the brakes at the same time. Which vehicle will stop first?

You would probably say that the compact car will stop first. You know that smaller objects are easier to stop than larger objects. But why? The answer is momentum (moh MEN tuhm).

Momentum, Mass, and Velocity

The **momentum** of an object depends on the object's mass and velocity. The more momentum an object has, the harder it is to stop the object or change its direction. In the example above, the truck has more mass and more momentum than the car has. So, a larger force is needed to stop the truck. Similarly, a fast-moving car has a greater velocity and thus more momentum than a slow-moving car of the same mass. So, a fast-moving car is harder to stop than a slow-moving car. **Figure 1** shows another example of an object that has momentum.

Calculating Momentum

Momentum (*p*) can be calculated with the equation below:

$$p = m \times v$$

In this equation, *m* is the mass of an object in kilograms and *v* is the object's velocity in meters per second. The units of momentum are kilograms multiplied by meters per second, or kg•m/s. Like velocity, momentum has a direction. Its direction is always the same as the direction of the object's velocity.

Figure 1 *The teen on the right has less mass than the teen on the left. But, the teen on the right can have a large momentum by moving quickly when she kicks.*

CHAPTER RESOURCES

Chapter Resource File

• Lesson Plan
• Directed Reading A **BASIC**
• Directed Reading B **SPECIAL NEEDS**

Technology

Transparencies
• Bellringer

Workbooks

Interactive Textbook Struggling Readers

Math Skills for Science
• Momentum **GENERAL**

MATH FOCUS

Momentum Calculations What is the momentum of an ostrich with a mass of 120 kg that runs with a velocity of 16 m/s north?

Step 1: Write the equation for momentum.

$$p = m \times v$$

Step 2: Replace m and v with the values given in the problem, and solve.

$$p = 120 \text{ kg} \times 16 \text{ m/s north}$$
$$p = 19{,}200 \text{ kg}\bullet\text{m/s north}$$

Now It's Your Turn

1. What is the momentum of a 6 kg bowling ball that is moving at 10 m/s down the alley toward the pins?
2. An 85 kg man is jogging with a velocity of 2.6 m/s to the north. Nearby, a 65 kg person is skateboarding and is traveling with a velocity of 3 m/s north. Which person has greater momentum? Show your calculations.

The Law of Conservation of Momentum

When a moving object hits another object, some or all of the momentum of the first object is transferred to the object that is hit. If only some of the momentum is transferred, the rest of the momentum stays with the first object.

Imagine that a cue ball hits a billiard ball so that the billiard ball starts moving and the cue ball stops, as shown in **Figure 2.** The white cue ball had a certain amount of momentum before the collision. During the collision, all of the cue ball's momentum was transferred to the red billiard ball. After the collision, the billiard ball moved away with the same amount of momentum the cue ball had. This example shows the *law of conservation of momentum*. The law of conservation of momentum states that any time objects collide, the total amount of momentum stays the same. The law of conservation of momentum is true for any collision if no other forces act on the colliding objects. This law applies whether the objects stick together or bounce off each other after they collide.

Reading Check What can happen to momentum when two objects collide? (*See the Appendix for answers to Reading Checks.*)

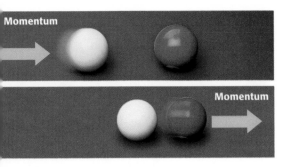

Figure 2 *The momentum before a collision is equal to the momentum after the collision.*

Answer to Reading Check

When two objects collide, some or all of the momentum of each object can be transferred to the other object.

Answers to Math Focus

1. $p = 6 \text{ kg} \times 10 \text{ m/s down the alley} = 60 \text{ kg}\bullet\text{m/s down the alley}$
2. The man jogging has greater momentum.

   $p = 85 \text{ kg} \times 2.6 \text{ m/s north} = 221 \text{ kg}\bullet\text{m/s north (man jogging)}$

   $p = 65 \text{ kg} \times 3 \text{ m/s north} = 195 \text{ kg}\bullet\text{m/s north (person skateboarding)}$

Close

Reteaching ——— BASIC

Velocity and Momentum Tell students that slow-moving objects that have large masses can have more momentum than fast-moving objects that have smaller masses. For example, a large cruise ship moving slowly into port has more momentum than a person running very fast. Have students describe other slow-moving objects that have a large momentum. **LS** Verbal

Quiz ——— GENERAL

1. What is the equation for momentum? ($p = m \times v$)

2. Give an example of an object with a small mass that has a large momentum. Explain your answer. (Sample answer: A fastball pitched by a baseball pitcher has a small mass but a large velocity. Therefore, the ball has a large momentum.)

Alternative Assessment ——— ADVANCED

Writing **Momentum Analysis**
Have students choose a sport that they participate in or that they can watch. Then, ask students to write a one-page paper describing how conservation of momentum affects the movement of the players or the objects used in the game. **LS** Verbal

---

CONNECTION TO Language Arts

WRITING SKILL **Momentum and Language**
The word *momentum* is often used in everyday language. For example, a sports announcer may say that the momentum of a game has changed. Or you may read that an idea is gaining momentum. In your **science journal**, write a paragraph that explains how the everyday use of the word *momentum* differs from momentum in science.

Objects Sticking Together

Sometimes, objects stick together after a collision. The footba[ll] players shown in **Figure 3** are an example of such a collisio[n.] A dog leaping and catching a ball and a teen jumping on [a] skateboard are also examples. After two objects stick togethe[r,] they move as one object. The mass of the combined objec[t] is equal to the masses of the two objects added together. In [a] head-on collision, the combined objects move in the directio[n] of the object that had the greater momentum before the colli[i]sion. But together, the objects have a velocity that differs fro[m] the velocity of either object before the collision. The objec[t] have a different velocity because momentum is conserved an[d] depends on mass and velocity. So, when mass changes, th[e] velocity must change, too.

Objects Bouncing Off Each Other

In some collisions, the objects bounce off each other. Th[e] bowling ball and bowling pins shown in **Figure 3** are example[s] of objects that bounce off each other after they collide. Bi[l]liard balls and bumper cars are other examples. During thes[e] types of collisions, momentum is usually transferred from on[e] object to another object. The transfer of momentum cause[s] the objects to move in different directions at different speed[s.] However, the total momentum of all the objects will remai[n] the same before and after the collision.

✓ **Reading Check** What are two ways that objects may interact after a collision?

Figure 3 **Examples of Conservation of Momentum**

When football players tackle another player, they stick together. The velocity of each player changes after the collision because of conservation of momentum.

Although the bowling ball and bowling pins bounc[e] off each other and move in different directions afte[r] a collision, momentum is neither gained nor lost.

Answer to Reading Check
After a collision, objects can stick together or can bounce off each other.

Conservation of Momentum and Newton's Third Law

Conservation of momentum can be explained by Newton's third law of motion. In the example of the billiard ball, the cue ball hit the billiard ball with a certain amount of force. This force was the action force. The reaction force was the equal but opposite force exerted by the billiard ball on the cue ball. The action force made the billiard ball start moving, and the reaction force made the cue ball stop moving, as shown in **Figure 4.** Because the action and reaction forces are equal and opposite, momentum is neither gained nor lost.

Figure 4 *The action force makes the billiard ball begin moving, and the reaction force stops the cue ball's motion.*

SECTION Review

Summary

- Momentum is a property of moving objects.
- Momentum is calculated by multiplying the mass of an object by the object's velocity.
- When two or more objects collide, momentum may be transferred, but the total amount of momentum does not change. This is the law of conservation of momentum.

Using Key Terms

1. Use the following term in a sentence: *momentum.*

Understanding Key Ideas

2. Which of the following has the smallest amount of momentum?
   a. a loaded truck driven at highway speeds
   b. a track athlete running a race
   c. a baby crawling on the floor
   d. a jet airplane being towed toward an airport

3. Explain the law of conservation of momentum.

4. How is Newton's third law of motion related to the law of conservation of momentum?

Math Skills

5. Calculate the momentum of a 2.5 kg puppy that is running with a velocity of 4.8 m/s south.

Critical Thinking

6. **Applying Concepts** A car and a train are traveling with the same velocity. Do the two objects have the same momentum? Explain your answer.

7. **Analyzing Ideas** When you catch a softball, your hand and glove move in the same direction that the ball is moving. Analyze the motion of your hand and glove in terms of momentum.

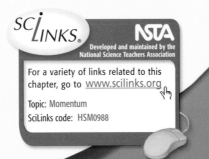

For a variety of links related to this chapter, go to www.scilinks.org

Topic: Momentum
SciLinks code: HSM0988

Answers to Section Review

1. Sample answer: To calculate the momentum of an object, multiply the mass of the object by its velocity.

2. c

3. The law of conservation of momentum states that any time objects collide, the total amount of momentum stays the same. The law of conservation of momentum is true when no other forces act on the objects.

4. Newton's third law can explain the law of conservation of momentum. Because the action and reaction forces are equal and opposite, momentum is neither gained nor lost.

5. p = 2.5 kg × 4.8 m/s south = 12 kg•m/s south

6. No, although the train and the car have the same velocity, the train has more mass than the car, so the train has greater momentum.

7. The softball has momentum as it travels toward your glove. When the ball hits your glove, some of its momentum is transferred to your glove and your hand. As a result, your glove and hand move in the direction that the ball was moving before the catch.

CHAPTER RESOURCES

Chapter Resource File

- Section Quiz **GENERAL**
- Section Review **GENERAL**
- Vocabulary and Section Summary **GENERAL**
- Critical Thinking **ADVANCED**

Inertia-Rama!

Teacher's Notes

Time Required
Two 45-minute class periods

Lab Ratings

EASY ———————————→ HARD

Teacher Prep 🧪🧪
Student Set-Up 🧪
Concept Level 🧪🧪
Clean Up 🧪

MATERIALS

1. Be sure to have a few extra raw and hard-boiled eggs on hand. Having students spin their eggs in a box may reduce the chance that an egg will break.
2. Use a relatively large coin, such as a quarter or 50-cent piece. Or you may have students try the Station 2 procedure with coins of different sizes and compare the results.
3. The mass used at Station 3 should be at least 1 kg. A larger mass will give better results.

Safety Caution
Remind students to review all safety cautions and icons before beginning this lab activity.

Preparation Notes
This lab may be done in one class period if enough supplies are available to avoid changing stations.

Skills Practice Lab

OBJECTIVES

Observe several effects of inertia.

Describe the motion of objects in terms of inertia.

MATERIALS

Station 1
• egg, hard-boiled
• egg, raw
Station 2
• card, index
• coin
• cup
Station 3
• mass, hanging, 1 kg
• meterstick
• scissors
• thread, spool

SAFETY

Inertia-Rama!

Inertia is a property of all matter, from small particles of dust to enormous planets and stars. In this lab, you will investigate the inertia of various shapes and kinds of matter. Keep in mind that each investigation requires you to either overcome or use the object's inertia.

Station 1: Magic Eggs

Procedure

1 There are two eggs at this station—one is hard-boiled (solid all the way through) and the other is raw (liquid inside). The masses of the two eggs are about the same. The eggs are not marked. You should not be able to tell them apart by their appearance. Without breaking them open, how can you tell which egg is raw and which egg is hard-boiled?

2 Before you do anything to either egg, make some predictions. Will there be any difference in the way the two eggs spin? Which egg will be the easier to stop?

3 First, spin one egg. Then, place your finger on it gently to make it stop spinning. Record your observations.

4 Repeat step 3 with the second egg.

5 Compare your predictions with your observations. (Repeat steps 3 and 4 if necessary.)

6 Which egg is hard-boiled and which one is raw? Explain.

Analyze the Results

1 **Explaining Events** Explain why the eggs behave differently when you spin them even though they should have the same inertia. (Hint: Think about what happens to the liquid inside the raw egg.)

Draw Conclusions

2 **Drawing Conclusions** Explain why the eggs react differently when you try to stop them.

 Holt Lab Generator CD-ROM

Search for any lab by topic, standard, difficulty level, or time. Edit any lab to fit your needs, or create your own labs. Use the Lab Materials QuickList software to customize your lab materials list.

Vicky Farland
Crane Junior High
Yuma, Arizona

CHAPTER RESOURCES

Chapter Resource File

• **Datasheet for Chapter Lab**
• **Lab Notes and Answers**

Technology

 Classroom Videos
• Lab Video

LabBook

• A Marshmallow Catapult
• Blast Off!
• Quite a Reaction

Station 2: Coin in a Cup

Procedure

1. At this station, you will find a coin, an index card, and a cup. Place the card over the cup. Then, place the coin on the card over the center of the cup, as shown below.

2. Write down a method for getting the coin into the cup without touching the coin and without lifting the card.

3. Try your method. If it doesn't work, try again until you find a method that does work.

Analyze the Results

1. **Describing Events** Use Newton's first law of motion to explain why the coin falls into the cup if you remove the card quickly.

Draw Conclusions

2. **Defending Conclusions** Explain why pulling on the card slowly will not work even though the coin has inertia. (Hint: Friction is a force.)

Station 3: The Magic Thread

Procedure

1. At this station, you will find a spool of thread and a mass hanging from a strong string. Cut a piece of thread about 40 cm long. Tie the thread around the bottom of the mass, as shown at right.

2. Pull gently on the end of the thread. Observe what happens, and record your observations.

3. Stop the mass from moving. Now hold the end of the thread so that there is a lot of slack between your fingers and the mass.

4. Give the thread a quick, hard pull. You should observe a very different event. Record your observations. Throw away the thread.

Analyze the Results

1. **Analyzing Results** Use Newton's first law of motion to explain why the result of a gentle pull is different from the result of a hard pull.

Draw Conclusions

2. **Applying Conclusions** Both moving and nonmoving objects have inertia. Explain why throwing a bowling ball and catching a thrown bowling ball are hard.

3. **Drawing Conclusions** Why is it harder to run with a backpack full of books than to run with an empty backpack?

Station 2
Analyze the Results

1. The coin remains at rest, so when the card is removed quickly, there is not enough friction to move the coin. So, the coin falls into the cup when the card is removed.

Draw Conclusions

2. When you pull slowly, there is enough time for the friction between the card and the coin to move the coin. So, the coin remains on the card.

Station 3
Analyze the Results

1. The mass tends to stay at rest. A gentle pull exerts a small force over a longer time and moves the mass, but a hard pull breaks the thread before the mass moves.

Draw Conclusions

2. It is just as hard to catch the bowling ball as it is to throw the bowling ball because the bowling ball has the same inertia in both cases.

3. Accept all reasonable answers that take into account the added inertia of the objects in the backpack. Sample answer: Starting and stopping will be harder because the extra mass increases your inertia. In addition, the books in the backpack act as the liquid inside a raw egg does. As you bounce up, they resist your upward movement. As you bounce down, they are still moving upward.

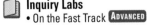
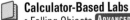

Station 1
Analyze the Results

1. The liquid inside the raw egg sloshes, it doesn't spin smoothly as the hard-boiled egg does.

Draw Conclusions

2. When you stop the eggs, the hard-boiled egg stops as a whole, while the shell of the raw egg can be stopped and the liquid inside keeps spinning.

Chapter Review

Assignment Guide

SECTION	QUESTIONS
1	2–3, 5, 7, 11–12, 15
2	1, 6, 8–9, 13, 16, 18
3	4, 10, 17, 19
1 and 3	14

ANSWERS

Using Key Terms

1. inertia
2. terminal velocity
3. Projectile motion
4. Momentum
5. Free fall

Understanding Key Ideas

6. b
7. d
8. d
9. b
10. b

USING KEY TERMS

Complete each of the following sentences by choosing the correct term from the word bank.

free fall	projectile motion
inertia	terminal velocity
momentum	

1 An object in motion has ___, so it tends to stay in motion.

2 An object is falling at its ___ if it falls at a constant velocity.

3 ___ is the path that a thrown object follows.

4 ___ is a property of moving objects that depends on mass and velocity.

5 ___ occurs only when air resistance does not affect the motion of a falling object.

UNDERSTANDING KEY IDEAS

Multiple Choice

6 When a soccer ball is kicked, the action and reaction forces do not cancel each other out because
  a. the forces are not equal in size.
  b. the forces act on different objects.
  c. the forces act at different times.
  d. All of the above

7 An object is in projectile motion if it
  a. is thrown with a horizontal push.
  b. is accelerated downward by gravity.
  c. does not accelerate horizontally.
  d. All of the above

8 Newton's first law of motion applies
  a. moving objects.
  b. objects that are not moving.
  c. objects that are accelerating.
  d. Both (a) and (b)

9 To accelerate two objects at the same rate, the force used to push the object that has more mass should be
  a. smaller than the force used to push the object that has less mass.
  b. larger than the force used to push the object that has less mass.
  c. the same as the force used to push the object that has less mass.
  d. equal to the object's weight.

10 A golf ball and a bowling ball are moving at the same velocity. Which of the two has more momentum?
  a. The golf ball has more momentum because it has less mass.
  b. The bowling ball has more momentum because it has more mass.
  c. They have the same momentum because they have the same velocity.
  d. There is not enough information to determine the answer.

hort Answer

1. Give an example of an object that is in free fall.

2. Describe how gravity and air resistance are related to an object's terminal velocity.

3. Why can friction make observing Newton's first law of motion difficult?

ath Skills

4. A 12 kg rock falls from rest off a cliff and hits the ground in 1.5 s.

a. Without considering air resistance, what is the rock's velocity just before it hits the ground?

b. What is the rock's momentum just before it hits the ground?

CRITICAL THINKING

5. **Concept Mapping** Use the following terms to create a concept map: *gravity, free fall, terminal velocity, projectile motion,* and *air resistance.*

6. **Identifying Relationships** During a space shuttle launch, about 830,000 kg of fuel is burned in 8 min. The fuel provides the shuttle with a constant thrust, or forward force. How does Newton's second law of motion explain why the shuttle's acceleration increases as the fuel is burned?

17. **Analyzing Processes** When using a hammer to drive a nail into wood, you have to swing the hammer through the air with a certain velocity. Because the hammer has both mass and velocity, it has momentum. Describe what happens to the hammer's momentum after the hammer hits the nail.

18. **Applying Concepts** Suppose you are standing on a skateboard or on in-line skates and you toss a backpack full of heavy books toward your friend. What do you think will happen to you? Explain your answer in terms of Newton's third law of motion.

INTERPRETING GRAPHICS

19. The picture below shows a common desk toy. If you pull one ball up and release it, it hits the balls at the bottom and comes to a stop. In the same instant, the ball on the other side swings up and repeats the cycle. How does conservation of momentum explain how this toy works?

Critical Thinking

15. An answer to this exercise can be found at the end of this book.

16. Newton's second law: a = F / m. During takeoff, the shuttle burns fuel and therefore loses mass. However, the forward force on the shuttle remains the same. So, the shuttle's acceleration increases because its mass constantly decreases during takeoff.

17. When the hammer hits the nail, the hammer stops. Its momentum is transferred to the nail, driving it into the wood. Momentum is also transferred from the hammer to your hand and from the nail to the wood and to the work bench or table top.

18. You will move away from your friend (in the direction opposite from where you threw the backpack). The action force is you pushing the backpack toward your friend. The reaction force is the backpack pushing you away from your friend.

Interpreting Graphics

19. The law of conservation of momentum: when two or more objects interact, the total amount of momentum must stay the same. The ball moving in the air has a certain amount of momentum, and the balls at rest have no momentum. When the moving ball hits the balls at rest, all of its momentum is transferred to them, and it comes to a stop. The momentum is transferred from ball to ball until it reaches the ball on the other end. The ball on the other end keeps all the momentum, and it moves away from the other balls.

11. Accept all reasonable answers. Sample answers: A feather falling inside a vacuum chamber is in free fall. An object dropped on the moon is in free fall.

12. Gravity and air resistance combine to give a net force on a falling object. When gravity and air resistance are the same size but in opposite directions, the object stops accelerating downward and has reached its terminal velocity.

13. Friction is a force that opposes the motion of objects. Friction slows the motion of moving objects so you don't see objects moving forever in a straight line.

CHAPTER RESOURCES

Chapter Resource File

- Chapter Review GENERAL
- Chapter Test A GENERAL
- Chapter Test B ADVANCED
- Chapter Test C SPECIAL NEEDS
- Vocabulary Activity GENERAL

Workbooks

Study Guide
- Study Guide is also available in Spanish.

Teacher's Note

To provide practice under more realistic testing conditions, give students 20 minutes to answer all of the questions in this Standardized Test Preparation.

MISCONCEPTION ALERT

Answers to the standardized test preparation can help you identify student misconceptions and misunderstandings.

Passage 1

1. A

2. H

3. D

✚ TEST DOCTOR

Question 3: Some students may pick answer choice A because the passage states that astronauts train underwater. However, the passage also states that astronauts train in a modified KC-135 airplane. Students should recognize that the training on this airplane is not done underwater, so the statement that astronauts always have to train underwater is incorrect.

READING

Read each of the passages below. Then, answer the questions that follow each passage.

Passage 1 How do astronauts prepare for trips in the space shuttle? One method is to use simulations on Earth that mimic the conditions in space. For example, underwater training lets astronauts experience reduced gravity. They can also ride on NASA's modified KC-135 airplane. NASA's KC-135 simulates how it feels to be in a space shuttle. How does this airplane work? It flies upward at a steep angle and then flies downward at a 45° angle. When the airplane flies downward, the effect of reduced gravity is produced. As the plane falls, the astronauts inside the plane can float like astronauts in the space shuttle do!

1. What is the purpose of this passage?

  A to explain how astronauts prepare for missions in space

  B to convince people to become astronauts

  C to show that space is similar to Earth

  D to describe what it feels like to float in space

2. What can you conclude about NASA's KC-135 from the passage?

  F NASA's KC-135 is just like other airplanes.

  G All astronauts train in NASA's KC-135.

  H NASA's KC-135 simulates the space shuttle by reducing the effects of gravity.

  I Being in NASA's KC-135 is not very much like being in the space shuttle.

3. Based on the passage, which of the following statements is a fact?

  A Astronauts always have to train underwater.

  B Flying in airplanes is similar to riding in the space shuttle.

  C People in NASA's KC-135 float at all times.

  D Astronauts use simulations to learn what reduced gravity is like.

Passage 2 There once was a game that could be played by as few as 5 or as many as 1,000 players. The game could be played on a small field for a few hours or on a huge tract of land for several days. The game was not just for fun—in fact, it was often used as a <u>substitute</u> for war. One of the few rules was that the players couldn't touch the ball with their hands—they had to use a special stick with webbing on one end. Would you believe that this game is the same as the game of lacrosse that is played today?

Lacrosse is a game that was originally played by Native Americans. They called the game *baggataway*, which means "little brother of war." Although lacrosse has changed and is now played all over the world, it still requires special, webbed sticks.

1. What is the purpose of this passage?

  A to explain the importance of rules in lacrosse

  B to explain why sticks are used in lacrosse

  C to describe the history of lacrosse

  D to describe the rules of lacrosse

2. Based on the passage, what does the word *substitute* mean?

  F something that occurs before war

  G something that is needed to play lacrosse

  H something that is of Native American origin

  I something that takes the place of something else

Passage 2

1. C

2. I

✚ TEST DOCTOR

Question 1: Although some of the rules of lacrosse are mentioned in the passage, the main purpose of the article is not to explain the importance of lacrosse rules or to describe lacrosse rules. Instead, the passage focuses on how and why the game that is now known as lacrosse was originally played. Therefore, the purpose of the passage is to describe the history of lacrosse.

Read each question below, and choose the best answer.

1. Which of the following images shows an object with no momentum that is about to be set in motion by an unbalanced force?

A

B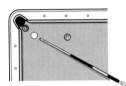

C

D

2. During a laboratory experiment, liquid was collected in a graduated cylinder. What is the volume of the liquid?

F 30 mL
G 35 mL
H 40 mL
I 45 mL

MATH

Read each question below, and choose the best answer.

1. The table below shows the accelerations produced by different forces for a 5 kg mass. Assuming that the pattern continues, use this data to predict what acceleration would be produced by a 100 N force.

Force	Acceleration
25 N	5 m/s^2
50 N	10 m/s^2
75 N	15 m/s^2

A 10 m/s^2
B 20 m/s^2
C 30 m/s^2
D 100 m/s^2

2. The average radius of the moon is 1.74×10^6 m. What is another way to express the radius of the moon?

F 0.00000174 m
G 0.000174 m
H 174,000 m
I 1,740,000 m

3. The half price bookstore is selling 4 paperback books for a total of $5.75. What would the price of 20 paperback books be?

A $23.00
B $24.75
C $28.75
D $51.75

4. A 75 kg speed skater is moving with a velocity of 16 m/s east. What is the speed skater's momentum? (Momentum is calculated with the equation: *momentum = mass × velocity*.)

F 91 kg•m/s
G 91 kg•m/s east
H 1,200 kg•m/s east
I 1,200 kg•m/s^2 east

---

1. B
2. G

TEST DOCTOR

Question 1: To answer this question, students must remember that momentum is equal to the product of mass and velocity. Because all objects have mass, the only way an object can have no momentum is if its velocity is 0 m/s. Only answer choices B and D have objects with no momentum. However, answer choice D does not show any impending unbalanced force. Answer choice B shows that the cue stick is moving and is about to exert an unbalanced force on the cue ball (that has no momentum). Therefore, B is the correct answer.

MATH

1. B
2. I
3. C
4. H

TEST DOCTOR

Question 4: The product of 75 and 16 is 1,200. Some students may have difficulty selecting between answer choices H and I because both choices appear to have the correct answer. However, answer choice I has units of kilograms-meters per second squared (kg•m/s^2) and the correct units for momentum are kilograms-meters per second (kg•m/s). Answer choice H is correct.

Standardized Test Preparation

CHAPTER RESOURCES

Chapter Resource File

 • Standardized Test Preparation GENERAL

State Resources

For specific resources for your state, visit **go.hrw.com** and type in the keyword **HSMSTR**.

Scientific Discoveries

Background

The Millennium Bridge swayed because the people walking on the bridge subconsciously started to walk in-step. The steps of the people matched the resonant frequency of the bridge, which caused the bridge to sway even more. This phenomenon has been observed on a few other bridges. In fact, marching soldiers are often instructed to "break step" when crossing bridges to avoid the possibility of marching at the bridge's resonant frequency.

The engineers who built the Millennium Bridge installed dampers and shock absorbers to stop the swaying of the bridge. The bridge reopened on February 22, 2003.

Science, Technology, and Society

Discussion —————— GENERAL

Lead a discussion about the benefits of the power suit. (Sample answers: The power suit will make nurses' jobs easier. The power suit will prevent back injuries.) Ask students to describe other situations or jobs that may benefit from the use of the power suit. (Sample answer: Construction workers and people who move furniture could benefit from the power suit.)

Science in Action

Scientific Discoveries

The Millennium Bridge

You may have heard the children's song, "London Bridge is falling down . . .". London Bridge never fell. But some people who walked on the Millennium Bridge thought that it might fall instead! The Millennium Bridge is a pedestrian bridge in London, England. The bridge opened on June 10, 2000, and more than 80,000 people crossed it that day. Immediately, people noticed something wrong—the bridge was swaying! The bridge was closed after two days so that engineers could determine what was wrong. After much research, the engineers learned that the force of the footsteps of the people crossing the bridge caused the bridge to sway.

Language Arts ACTIVITY

WRITING SKILL Imagine that you were in London on June 10, 2000 and walked across the Millennium Bridge. Write a one-page story about what you think it was like on the bridge that day.

Science, Technology, and Society

Power Suit for Lifting Patients

Imagine visiting a hospital and seeing someone who looked half human and half robot. No, it isn't a scene from a science fiction movie—it is a new invention that may some day help nurses lift patients easily. The invention, called a power suit, is a metal framework that a nurse would wear on his or her back. The suit calculates how much force a nurse needs to lift a patient, and then the robotic joints on the suit help the nurse exert the right amount of force. The suit will also help nurses avoid injuring their backs.

Math ACTIVITY

The pound (symbol £) is the currency in England. The inventor of the suit thinks that it will be sold for £1200. How much will the suit cost in dollars if $1 is equal to £0.60?

Answer to Language Arts Activity

Accept all reasonable answers. Students may describe the motion of the bridge or how they felt when the bridge started to sway. Students may also describe the reaction of the other people on the bridge.

Answer to Math Activity

£1200 × $1 ÷ £0.60 = $2,000

The answer to this Math Activity may vary as the rate of exchange between the dollar and the pound changes. As an extension, you may ask your students to research the current exchange rate and find the current price of the power suit.

Steve Okamoto

Roller Coaster Designer Roller coasters have fascinated Steve Okamoto ever since his first ride on one. "I remember going to Disneyland as a kid. My mother was always

upset with me because I kept looking over the sides of the rides, trying to figure out how they worked," he says. To satisfy his curiosity, Okamoto became a mechanical engineer. Today he uses his scientific knowledge to design and build machines, systems, and buildings. But his specialty is roller coasters.

Roller coasters really do coast along the track. A motor pulls the cars up a high hill to start the ride. After that, the cars are powered by only gravity. Designing a successful roller coaster is not a simple task. Okamoto has to calculate the cars' speed and acceleration on each part of the track. He must also consider the safety of the ride and the strength of the structure that supports the track.

Social Studies ACTIVITY

Research the history of roller coasters to learn how roller coaster design has changed over time. Make a poster to summarize your research.

go.hrw.com

To learn more about these Science in Action topics, visit go.hrw.com and type in the keyword **HP5FORF**.

Current Science

Check out Current Science® articles related to this chapter by visiting go.hrw.com. Just type in the keyword **HP5CS06**.

Background

Steve Okamoto has a degree in product design. He studied both mechanical engineering and studio art. Product designers consider an object's form as well as its function and take into account the interests and abilities of the product's consumer.

Two of Okamoto's first coasters were the Ninjas at Six Flags Over Mid-America, in St. Louis, Missouri, and Six Flags Magic Mountain, in Los Angeles, California.

When designing a ride, Okamoto studies site maps of the location, then goes to the amusement park to look at the actual site. Because most rides he designs are for older parks, fitting a coaster around, above, and between existing rides and buildings is one of his biggest challenges. Most rides and parks also have some kind of theme, so marketing goals and concerns figure into his designs as well. (As an example, Okamoto designed a roller coaster named the *Mamba*. The coaster is named for one of the fastest snakes in Africa and is designed around this theme.)

Answer to Social Studies Activity
Accept all reasonable answers. Student posters may show different types of roller coasters including old-fashioned wooden roller coasters and modern steel-tube roller coasters. You may wish to challenge students to learn when the first roller coaster was built or to learn when the first roller coaster with a loop was built.

3

Forces in Fluids
Chapter Planning Guide

Compression guide:
To shorten instruction because of time limitations, omit Section 3.

OBJECTIVES	LABS, DEMONSTRATIONS, AND ACTIVITIES	TECHNOLOGY RESOURCES
PACING • 90 min pp. 64–71 **Chapter Opener**	**SE** Start-up Activity, p. 65 GENERAL	**OSP** Parent Letter ■ **CD** Student Edition on CD-ROM **CD** Guided Reading Audio CD ■ **TR** Chapter Starter Transparency* **VID** Brain Food Video Quiz
Section 1 Fluids and Pressure • Describe how fluids exert pressure. • Analyze how atmospheric pressure varies with depth. • Explain how depth and density affect water pressure. • Give examples of fluids flowing from high to low pressure.	**TE** Demonstration Building Pressure, p. 67 GENERAL **TE** Connection Activity Language Arts, p. 67 GENERAL **TE** Connection Activity Earth Science, p. 68 GENERAL **SE** Quick Lab Blown Away, p. 70 GENERAL **CRF** Datasheet for Quick Lab* **LB** Whiz-Bang Demonstrations The Rise and Fall of Raisins,* Going Against the Flow* GENERAL	**OSP** Lesson Plans (also in print) **TR** Bellringer Transparency* **TR** LINK TO LIFE SCIENCE L6 Math Focus Surface Area-to-Volume Ratio* **TR** P24 Exhaling, Pressure, and Fluid Flow* **CD** Science Tutor
PACING • 90 min pp. 72–77 **Section 2 Buoyant Force** • Explain the relationship between fluid pressure and buoyant force. • Predict whether an object will float or sink in a fluid. • Analyze the role of density in an object's ability to float. • Explain how the overall density of an object can be changed.	**TE** Demonstration Density Layers, p. 72 GENERAL **SE** School-to-Home Activity Floating Fun, p. 73 GENERAL **TE** Connection Activity Math, p. 73 ADVANCED **TE** Activity Making Models, p. 74 GENERAL **TE** Connection Activity Math, p. 74 ADVANCED **SE** Connection to Geology Floating Rocks, p. 75 GENERAL **TE** Group Activity Buoyancy and Scuba Diving, p. 75 GENERAL **SE** Quick Lab Ship Shape, p. 76 GENERAL **CRF** Datasheet for Quick Lab* **SE** Skills Practice Lab Fluids, Force, and Floating, p. 84 GENERAL **CRF** Datasheet for Chapter Lab* **SE** Skills Practice Lab Density Diver, p. 200 GENERAL **CRF** Datasheet for LabBook*	**OSP** Lesson Plans (also in print) **TR** Bellringer Transparency* **TR** P25 Shape and Overall Density* **TR** P26 Controlling Density Using Ballast Tanks* **SE** Internet Activity, p. 75 GENERAL **CRF** SciLinks Activity* GENERAL **VID** Lab Videos for Physical Science **CD** Interactive Explorations CD-ROM Sea the Light GENERAL **CD** Science Tutor
PACING • 45 min pp. 78–83 **Section 3 Fluids and Motion** • Describe the relationship between pressure and fluid speed. • Analyze the roles of lift, thrust, and wing size in flight. • Describe drag, and explain how it affects lift. • Explain Pascal's principle.	**TE** Demonstration Magic Water, p. 78 GENERAL **TE** Activity Pressure Analogy, p. 79 BASIC **TE** Activity Wing Shape, p. 79 ADVANCED **TE** Demonstration Flying Ball, p. 79 GENERAL **SE** Connection to Social Studies The First Flight, p. 80 GENERAL **TE** Activity Wind Tunnels, p. 80 ADVANCED **TE** Connection Activity Language Arts, p. 81 GENERAL **TE** Group Activity Floating Bubbles, p. 81 ◆ GENERAL **SE** Science in Action Math, Social Studies, and Language Arts Activities, pp. 90–91 GENERAL **LB** EcoLabs & Field Activities What's the Flap All About?* BASIC **LB** Long-Term Projects & Research Ideas Scuba Dive* ADVANCED	**OSP** Lesson Plans (also in print) **TR** Bellringer Transparency* **TR** P27 Wing Design and Lift* **TR** P28 Bernoulli's Principle and the Screwball* **CD** Science Tutor

PACING • 90 min

CHAPTER REVIEW, ASSESSMENT, AND STANDARDIZED TEST PREPARATION

CRF Vocabulary Activity* GENERAL
SE Chapter Review, pp. 86–87 GENERAL
CRF Chapter Review* ■ GENERAL
CRF Chapter Tests A* ■ GENERAL, B* ADVANCED, C* SPECIAL NEEDS
SE Standardized Test Preparation, pp. 88–89 GENERAL
CRF Standardized Test Preparation* GENERAL
CRF Performance-Based Assessment* GENERAL
OSP Test Generator, Test Item Listing

Online and Technology Resources

Holt Online Learning

Visit go.hrw.com for access to Holt Online Learning, or enter the keyword **HP7 Home** for a variety of free online resources.

One-Stop Planner® CD-ROM

This CD-ROM package includes:
• Lab Materials QuickList Software
• Holt Calendar Planner
• Customizable Lesson Plans
• Printable Worksheets
• ExamView® Test Generator
• Interactive Teacher's Edition
• Holt PuzzlePro®
• Holt PowerPoint® Resources

SKILLS DEVELOPMENT RESOURCES

SECTION REVIEW AND ASSESSMENT

CORRELATIONS

SE Pre-Reading Activity, p. 64 GENERAL
OSP Science Puzzlers, Twisters & Teasers GENERAL

National Science Education Standards

SAI 1, 2; ST 2

CRF Directed Reading A* ■ BASIC, B* SPECIAL NEEDS
IT Interactive Textbook* Struggling Readers
CRF Vocabulary and Section Summary* ■ GENERAL
SE Reading Strategy Brainstorming, p. 66 GENERAL
SE Math Focus Pressure, Force, and Area, p. 67 GENERAL
TE Inclusion Strategies, p. 69
TE Support for English Language Learners, p. 69
MS Math Skills for Science The Pressure Is On!* GENERAL
MS Math Skills for Science Density* GENERAL

SE Reading Checks, pp. 67, 68, 70 GENERAL
TE Homework, p. 67 ADVANCED
TE Homework, p. 68 GENERAL
TE Reteaching, p. 70 BASIC
TE Quiz, p. 70 GENERAL
TE Alternative Assessment, p. 70 ADVANCED
SE Section Review,* p. 71 GENERAL
CRF Section Quiz* ■ GENERAL

SAI 1; ST 2; PS 1a

CRF Directed Reading A* ■ BASIC, B* SPECIAL NEEDS
IT Interactive Textbook* Struggling Readers
CRF Vocabulary and Section Summary* ■ GENERAL
SE Reading Strategy Discussion, p. 72 GENERAL
TE Reading Strategy Prediction Guide, p. 73 GENERAL
SE Math Focus Finding Density, p. 74 GENERAL
TE Support for English Language Learners, p. 75

SE Reading Checks, pp. 73, 74, 76 GENERAL
TE Homework, p. 73 GENERAL
TE Reteaching, p. 76 BASIC
TE Quiz, p. 76 GENERAL
TE Alternative Assessment, p. 77 GENERAL
SE Section Review,* p. 77 ■ GENERAL
CRF Section Quiz* ■ GENERAL

SAI 1; ST 2; HNS 3; PS 1a, 2c;
Chapter Lab: SAI 1; *LabBook:*
SAI 1

CRF Directed Reading A* ■ BASIC, B* SPECIAL NEEDS
IT Interactive Textbook* Struggling Readers
CRF Vocabulary and Section Summary* ■ GENERAL
SE Reading Strategy Reading Organizer, p. 78 GENERAL
TE Inclusion Strategies, p. 80
TE Support for English Language Learners, p. 81
CRF Reinforcement Worksheet Building Up Pressure* BASIC
CRF Critical Thinking Build a Better Submarine* ADVANCED

SE Reading Checks, pp. 79, 81, 82 GENERAL
TE Homework, p. 81 GENERAL
TE Reteaching, p. 82 BASIC
TE Quiz, p. 82 GENERAL
TE Alternative Assessment, p. 82 GENERAL
SE Section Review,* p. 83 GENERAL
CRF Section Quiz* ■ GENERAL

UCP 5; SAI 1; ST 2; SPSP 5;
HNS 3

---

www.scilinks.org
Maintained by the **National Science Teachers Association.** See Chapter Enrichment pages that follow for a complete list of topics.

Check out *Current Science* articles and activities by visiting the HRW Web site at **go.hrw.com.** Just type in the keyword **HP5CS07T.**

 Classroom Videos

- **Lab Videos** demonstrate the chapter lab.
- **Brain Food Video Quizzes** help students review the chapter material.

 Classroom CD-ROMs

- **Guided Reading Audio CD** (Also in Spanish)
- **Interactive Explorations**
- **Virtual Investigations**
- **Visual Concepts**
- **Science Tutor**

Holt Lab Generator CD-ROM

Search for any lab by topic, standard, difficulty level, or time. Edit any lab to fit your needs, or create your own labs. Use the Lab Materials QuickList software to customize your lab materials list.

Chapter Resources

Visual Resources

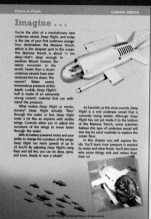

Section: Fluids and Pressure

Imagine the following situation:

One afternoon, you go outside to find your younger sister standing by her bike with a nail in her hand. The bike has a flat tire. She wants to know why the air came out of the tire when she pulled the nail out.

Write a few sentences in your **science journal** to explain why air rushes out of a hole in a tire.

Section: Buoyant Force

Identify which of the following objects will float in water: a rock, an orange, a screw, a quarter, a candle, a plastic-foam "peanut," and a chalkboard eraser.

Write a hypothesis in your **science journal** about why an aircraft carrier, which weighs thousands of tons, does not sink.

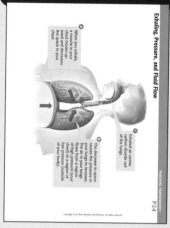

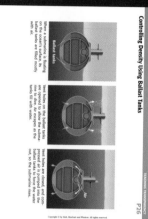

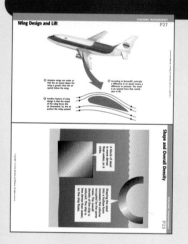

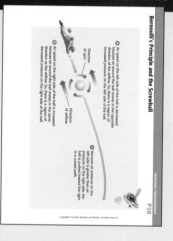

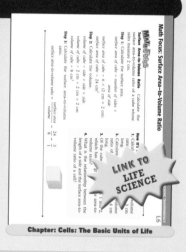

Chapter: Cells: The Basic Units of Life

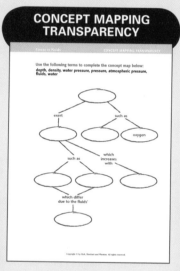

Use the following terms to complete the concept map below: depth, density, water pressure, pressure, atmospheric pressure, fluids, water

Planning Resources

Lesson Plan   SAMPLE

Section: Waves

Pacing

Regular Schedule: with lab(s):2 days   without lab(s):0 days
Block Schedule: with lab(s):1 1/2 days   without lab(s):1 day

Objectives

1. Relate seven properties of life to a living organism.
2. Describe seven themes that can help you to organize what you learn about biology.
3. Identify the tiny structures that make up all living organisms.
4. Differentiate between reproduction and heredity and between metabolism and homeostasis.

National Science Education Standards Covered

LS1Interi:Cells have particular structures that underlie their functions.
LS5Mat1:Most cell functions involve chemical reactions.
LS5Beh1:Cells store and use information to guide their functions.
UCP1:Cell functions are regulated.
SI1: Cells can differentiate and form complete multicellular organisms.
PS1: Species evolve over time.
ESS1: The great diversity of organisms is the result of more than 3.5 billion years of evolution.
ESS2: Natural selection and its evolutionary consequences provide a scientific explanation for the fossil record of ancient life forms as well as for the striking molecular similarities observed among the diverse species of living organisms.
ST1: The millions of different species of plants, animals, and microorganisms that live on Earth today are related by descent from common ancestors.
ST2: The energy for life primarily comes from the sun.
SPSP1: The complexity and organization of organisms accommodates the need for obtaining, transforming, transporting, releasing, and eliminating the matter and energy used to sustain the organism.
SPSP6: As matter and energy flows through different levels of organization of living systems—cells, organs, communities—and between living systems and the physical environment, chemical elements are recombined in different ways.
HNS1: Organisms have behavioral responses to internal changes and to external stimuli.

Dear Parent,   SAMPLE

Your son's or daughter's science class will soon begin exploring the chapter entitled "The World of Physical Science." In this chapter, students will learn about how the scientific method applies to the world of physical science and the role of physical science in the world. By the end of the chapter, students should demonstrate a clear understanding of the chapter's main ideas and be able to discuss the following topics:

1. physical science as the study of energy and matter (Section 1)
2. the role of physical science in the world around them (Section 1)
3. careers that rely on physical science (Section 1)
4. the steps used in the scientific method (Section 2)
5. examples of technology (Section 2)
6. how the scientific method is used to answer questions and solve problems (Section 2)
7. how our knowledge of science changes over time (Section 2)
8. how models represent real objects or systems (Section 3)
9. examples of different ways models are used in science (Section 3)
10. the importance of the International System of Units (Section 4)
11. the appropriate units to use for particular measurements (Section 4)
12. how area and density are derived quantities (Section 4)

Questions to Ask Along the Way

You can help your son or daughter learn about these topics by asking interesting questions such as the following:

- What are some surprising careers that use physical science?
- What is a characteristic of a good hypothesis?
- When is it a good idea to use a model?
- Why do Americans measure things in terms of inches and feet and meters?

ALSO IN SPANISH

TEST ITEM LISTING
The World of Science   SAMPLE

MULTIPLE CHOICE

1. A limitation of models is that
   a. they are large enough to use.
   b. they do not act exactly like the things that they model.
   c. they are smaller than the things that they model.
   d. they model unfamiliar things.
   Answer: B   Difficulty: 1   Section: 3   Objective: 2

2. The length 10 m is equal to
   a. 100 cm.   c. 10,000 mm.
   b. 1,000 cm.   d. Both (a) and (c)
   Answer: B   Difficulty: 1   Section: 3   Objective: 2

3. To be valid, a hypothesis must be
   a. testable.   c. made into a law.
   b. supported by evidence   d. Both (a) and (b)
   Answer: B   Difficulty: 1   Section: 2   Objective: 1

4. The statement "Sheila has a stain on her shirt" is an example of a(n)
   a. law.   c. observation.
   b. hypothesis.   d. prediction.
   Answer: B   Difficulty: 1   Section: 2   Objective: 2

5. A hypothesis is often developed out of
   a. observations.   c. laws.
   b. experiments.   d. Both (a) and (b)
   Answer: B   Difficulty: 1   Section: 2   Objective: 1

6. How many milliliters are in 3.5 kL?
   a. 3,500 ml.   c. 3,500, 000 ml.
   b. 0.0035 ml.   d. 35,000 ml.
   Answer: B   Difficulty: 1   Section: 3   Objective: 2

7. A map of Seattle is an example of a
   a. time.   c. model.
   b. theory.   d. unit.
   Answer: B   Difficulty: 1   Section: 3   Objective: 2

8. A lab has the safety icons shown below. These icons mean that you should wear
   a. only safety goggles   c. safety goggles and a lab apron.
   b. only a lab apron.   d. safety goggles, a lab apron, and gloves
   Answer: B   Difficulty: 1   Section: 3   Objective: 2

9. The law of conservation of mass says the to of at mass before a chemical change is
   a. more than the total mass after the change.
   b. less than the total mass after the change.
   c. the same as the total mass after the change.
   d. not the same as the total mass after the change.
   Answer: B   Difficulty: 1   Section: 3   Objective: 2

10. In which of the following areas might you find a geochemist at work?
   a. studying the chemistry of rocks   c. studying forestry
   b. studying forestry   d. studying the atmosphere
   Answer: B   Difficulty: 1   Section: 3   Objective: 2

One-Stop Planner® CD-ROM

This CD-ROM includes all of the resources shown here and the following time-saving tools:

- **Lab Materials QuickList Software**
- **Customizable lesson plans**
- **Holt Calendar Planner**
- **The powerful ExamView® Test Generator**

Meeting Individual Needs

DIRECTED READING A
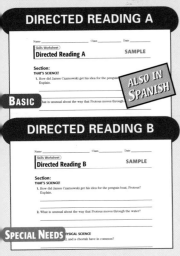
BASIC · ALSO IN SPANISH

DIRECTED READING B
SPECIAL NEEDS

VOCABULARY ACTIVITY
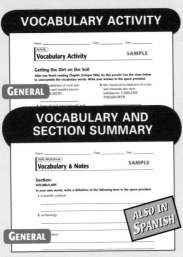
GENERAL

VOCABULARY AND SECTION SUMMARY
GENERAL · ALSO IN SPANISH

REINFORCEMENT
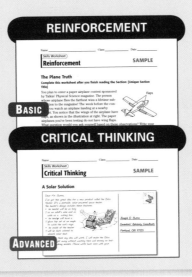
BASIC

CRITICAL THINKING
ADVANCED

SCILINKS ACTIVITY

GENERAL

SCIENCE PUZZLERS, TWISTERS & TEASERS
GENERAL

Labs and Activities

ECOLABS & FIELD ACTIVITIES
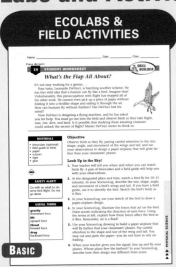
BASIC

LONG-TERM PROJECTS & RESEARCH IDEAS

ADVANCED

WHIZ-BANG DEMONSTRATIONS
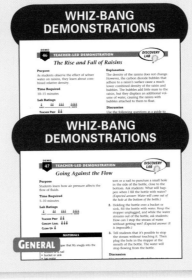

WHIZ-BANG DEMONSTRATIONS
GENERAL

DATASHEETS FOR QUICK LABS

DATASHEETS FOR CHAPTER LABS

DATASHEETS FOR LABBOOK

Review and Assessments

SECTION QUIZ

GENERAL · ALSO IN SPANISH

SECTION REVIEW
GENERAL · ALSO IN SPANISH

CHAPTER REVIEW
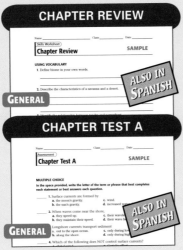
GENERAL · ALSO IN SPANISH

CHAPTER TEST A
GENERAL · ALSO IN SPANISH

CHAPTER TEST B
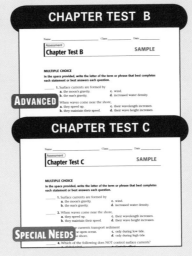
ADVANCED

CHAPTER TEST C
SPECIAL NEEDS

STANDARDIZED TEST PREPARATION
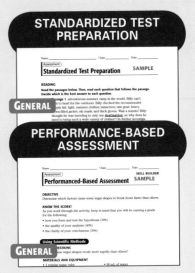
GENERAL

PERFORMANCE-BASED ASSESSMENT
GENERAL

This Chapter Enrichment provides relevant and interesting information to expand and enhance your presentation of the chapter material.

Section 1

Fluids and Pressure

Refresher on Gas Laws

- Nearly all materials expand when they are heated and contract when they are cooled. Gases are not an exception. A gas expands as it gets hotter because the kinetic energy of its particles increases. When the kinetic energy increases, the particles move faster and bounce against each other harder. This movement causes the gas particles to move farther apart, and the gas expands. If the pressure does not change, the volume of the gas will increase as the temperature increases. This property of gases is known as *Charles's law.*

- The air pressure inside the tires of an automobile can be much greater than the pressure outside the tires. The pressure can be greater inside an enclosed container because air, like all gases, is compressible. If the temperature does not change, the pressure of a gas will increase as the volume decreases. This property of gases is known as *Boyle's law.*

Is That a Fact!

- ◆ The water pressure at the bottom of a small, deep pond is greater than the pressure at the bottom of a large, shallow lake because water pressure is determined by the depth of the water, not the volume of the water.

Section 2

Buoyant Force

Archimedes (287–212 BCE)

- Archimedes, a Greek mathematician, inventor, and physicist, lived in the ancient city of Syracuse from 287 to 212 BCE. He is famous for his work in geometry, physics, mechanics, and water pressure.

Diving and Water Pressure

- Scuba diving relies in part on the principles of buoyancy and fluid pressure. Some of the effects of water pressure can be felt even in a swimming pool. Just a few meters under water, your ears begin to hurt from the pressure of the water on your eardrums.

- As a diver descends deeper into the water with scuba gear, the diver's lungs hold more air because the air is compressed by the water pressure. As a diver rises to the surface, the air expands again. Under certain circumstances, the air in a diver's lungs could expand enough to rupture the air sacs in the diver's lungs.

Is That a Fact!

- ◆ Humans have built underwater vessels for hundreds of years. In 1620, the Dutch inventor Cornelis Drebbel built what is thought to be the first submarine. His vessel was not much more than a rowboat covered with greased leather. It traveled at a depth of 4 to 5 m under water in the Thames River, in London, England. King James I of England is said to have taken a short ride in this vessel.

Neutral Buoyancy

- Scuba divers use weights to compensate for the buoyancy of their body and diving gear. When a diver weighs exactly the same as an equal volume of the surrounding water, the diver can swim to any depth and remain there effortlessly. This state is called *neutral buoyancy.*

Section 3

Fluids and Motion

Daniel Bernoulli (1700–1782)

- Daniel Bernoulli was born in the Netherlands in 1700. For most of his life, he lived in Basel, Switzerland.

- Bernoulli was born into a family distinguished for accomplishments in science and mathematics. His father, Johann, was famous for his work in calculus, trigonometry, and the study of geodesics. Bernoulli's uncle Jacob was integral in the development of calculus. Bernoulli's brothers, Nicolaus and Johann II, were also noted mathematicians and physicists.

- Bernoulli's greatest work was *Hydrodynamica,* which was published in 1738. It included the concept now known as Bernoulli's principle. He also made important contributions to probability theory and studied astronomy, botany, physiology, gravity, and magnetism.

Examples of Bernoulli's Principle

- Even on a calm night, air moves across the top of a chimney. This air movement causes the pressure at the top of the chimney to be lower than the pressure in the house. According to Bernoulli's principle, the smoke in the fireplace is pushed up the chimney by the greater air pressure in the house.

- Bernoulli's principle also explains why a soft convertible top on a car bulges when the car travels at high speeds. The air moving over the top causes an area of low pressure, and the higher pressure inside the car pushes the soft top up.

Is That a Fact!

- Water flowing in a stream speeds up when it flows through a narrow part of the stream bed. According to Bernoulli's principle, the water pressure decreases as the speed increases.

Blaise Pascal

- Blaise Pascal (1623–1662) was a famous French scientist, mathematician, philosopher, and writer of prose. He had no formal schooling but pursued his interests under his father's guidance. Pascal's father forbade him to study mathematics until he was 15 years old, but Pascal's curiosity led him to begin studying geometry in secret at the age of 12. By the time he was 14, Pascal was regularly attending sessions with the leading geometricians of his time. Pascal presented his first mathematics paper at the age of 16. The SI unit for pressure, the pascal, is named after Blaise Pascal.

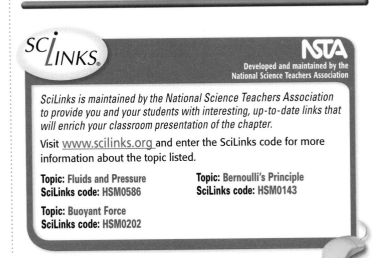

SciLinks is maintained by the National Science Teachers Association to provide you and your students with interesting, up-to-date links that will enrich your classroom presentation of the chapter.

Visit www.scilinks.org and enter the SciLinks code for more information about the topic listed.

Topic: Fluids and Pressure
SciLinks code: HSM0586

Topic: Bernoulli's Principle
SciLinks code: HSM0143

Topic: Buoyant Force
SciLinks code: HSM0202

Overview

Tell students that this chapter will help them learn about fluids and the forces caused by fluids, including buoyant force, lift, and drag. Students also learn about pressure and the factors that affect flight.

Assessing Prior Knowledge

Students should be familiar with the following topics:
- forces and net force
- motion and speed
- SI units

Identifying Misconceptions

As students learn the material in this chapter, some of them may have difficulties understanding that gases, such as oxygen and air, are fluids. This confusion may result from the common usage of the word *fluid*. In everyday language, fluids usually refer to liquids only.

Forces in Fluids

The Big Idea Forces in fluids are related to pressure and density and can affect the motion of objects in the fluid.

About the PHOTO

As you race downhill on your bicycle, the air around you pushes on your body and slows you down. "What a drag!" you say. Well, actually, it is a drag. When designing bicycle gear and clothing, manufacturers consider more than just looks and comfort. They also try to decrease drag, a fluid force that opposes motion. This photo shows cyclists riding their bikes in a wind tunnel in a study of how a fluid—air—affects their ride.

PRE-READING ACTIVITY

FOLDNOTES **Booklet** Before you read the chapter, create the FoldNote entitled "Booklet" described in the **Study Skills** section of the Appendix. Label each page of the booklet with a main idea from the chapter. As you read the chapter, write what you learn about each main idea on the appropriate page of the booklet.

Standards Correlations

National Science Education Standards

The following codes indicate the National Science Education Standards that correlate to this chapter. The full text of the standards is at the front of the book.

Chapter Opener
SAI 1, 2; ST 2

Section 1 Fluids and Pressure
SAI 1; ST 2; PS 1a

Section 2 Buoyant Force
SAI 1; ST 2; HNS 3; PS 1a, 2c; *LabBook:* SAI 1

Section 3 Fluids and Motion
UCP 5; SAI 1; ST 2; SPSP 5; HNS 3; *LabBook:* SAI 1

Chapter Lab
SAI 1

Chapter Review
SAI 1

Science in Action
SPSP 5

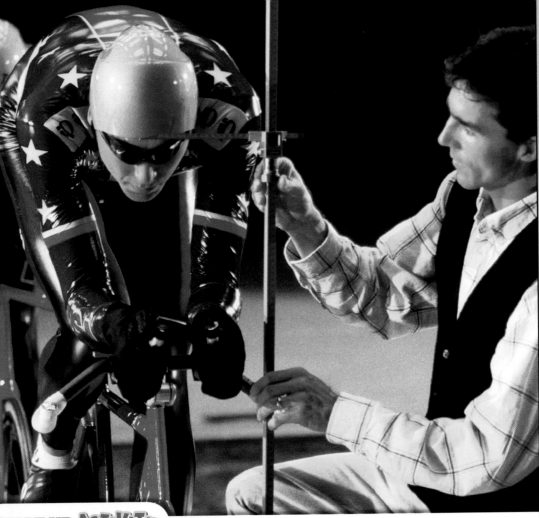

START-UP ACTIVITY

MATERIALS

FOR EACH STUDENT
• paper, sheet

Teacher's Notes: Tell students that this activity is an exception to the usual rules about flying paper planes in class.

Answers

1. Sample answer: The plane did not stay in the air as long. To get a longer flight, I had to throw much harder.

2. Sample answer: I gave the plane its forward motion when I threw the plane.

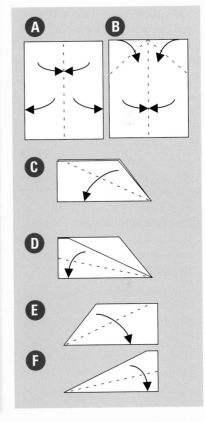

START-UP ACTIVITY

Taking Flight

In this activity, you will build a model airplane to learn how wing size affects flight.

Procedure

1. Fold a **sheet of paper** in half lengthwise. Then, open it. Fold the top corners toward the center crease. Keep the corners folded down, and fold the entire sheet in half along the center crease.

2. With the plane on its side, fold the top front edge down so that it meets the bottom edge. Fold the top edge down again so that it meets the bottom edge. Turn the plane over, and repeat.

3. Raise the wings so that they are perpendicular to the body.

4. Point the plane slightly upward, and gently throw it. Repeat several times. Describe what you see.

5. Make the wings smaller by folding them one more time. Gently throw the plane. Repeat several times. Describe what you see.

6. Using the smaller wings, try to achieve the same flight path you saw when the wings were bigger.

Analysis

1. What happened to the plane's flight when you reduced the size of its wings? What did you have to do to achieve the same flight path as when the wings were bigger?

2. What gave your plane its forward motion?

Chapter Starter Transparency
Use this transparency to help students begin thinking about fluids and pressure.

CHAPTER RESOURCES

Technology

Transparencies
• Chapter Starter Transparency

READING SKILLS

Student Edition on CD-ROM

Guided Reading Audio CD
• English or Spanish

Classroom Videos
• Brain Food Video Quiz

Workbooks

Science Puzzlers, Twisters & Teasers
• Forces in Fluids GENERAL

Chapter 3 • Forces in Fluids **65**

Focus

Overview

In this section, students learn about the properties of fluids. Students also learn how pressure is related to depth and density and how fluids flow from areas of high pressure to areas of low pressure.

Bellringer

Have your students imagine the following situation: "One afternoon, you go outside to find your younger sister standing by her bike holding a nail in her hand. The bike has a flat tire. She wants to know why the air came out of the tire when she pulled the nail out." Have students write a few sentences to explain why air rushes out of a hole in a tire.

MISCONCEPTION ///ALERT\\\

Pressure and Weight
Students might assume that pressure calculations will always involve the force of a fluid. Explain that because weight is a measure of gravitational force, anything that has weight exerts pressure. Thus, a crate on a floor exerts pressure on the floor.

What You Will Learn
- Describe how fluids exert pressure.
- Analyze how atmospheric pressure varies with depth.
- Explain how depth and density affect water pressure.
- Give examples of fluids flowing from high to low pressure.

Vocabulary
fluid
pressure
pascal
atmospheric pressure

READING STRATEGY

Brainstorming The key idea of this section is pressure. Brainstorm words and phrases related to pressure.

fluid a nonsolid state of matter in which the atoms or molecules are free to move past each other, as in a gas or liquid

pressure the amount of force exerted per unit area of a surface

pascal the SI unit of pressure (symbol, Pa)

atmospheric pressure the pressure caused by the weight of the atmosphere

Figure 1 *The force of the air particles hitting the inner surface of the tire creates pressure, which keeps the tire inflated.*

Fluids and Pressure

What does a dolphin have in common with a sea gull? What does a dog have in common with a fly? What do you have in common with all these living things?

One answer to these questions is that you and all these other living things spend a lifetime moving through fluids. A **fluid** is any material that can flow and that takes the shape of its container. Fluids include liquids and gases. Fluids can flow because the particles in fluids move easily past each other.

Fluids Exert Pressure

You probably have heard the terms *air pressure* and *water pressure*. Air and water are fluids. All fluids exert pressure. So what is pressure? Think about this example. When you pump up a bicycle tire, you push air into the tire. And like all matter, air is made of tiny particles that are constantly moving.

Look at **Figure 1.** Inside the tire, the air particles collide with each other and with the walls of the tire. Together, these collisions create a force on the tire. The amount of force exerted on a given area is **pressure.**

Calculating Pressure

Pressure can be calculated by using the following equation:

$$pressure = \frac{force}{area}$$

The SI unit for pressure is the **pascal.** One pascal (1 Pa) is the force of one newton exerted over an area of one square meter (1 N/m^2).

CHAPTER RESOURCES

Chapter Resource File
- Lesson Plan
- Directed Reading A BASIC, B SPECIAL NEEDS

Technology
Transparencies
- Bellringer
- *LINK TO LIFE SCIENCE* L6 Math Focus: Surface Area-to-Volume Ratio

Workbooks
Interactive Textbook Struggling Readers
Math Skills for Science
- The Pressure Is On! GENERAL

Is That a Fact!

The air in a large room in your house weighs about as much as an average adult male (about 736 N)!

MATH FOCUS

Pressure, Force, and Area What is the pressure exerted by a book that has an area of 0.2 m² and a weight of 10 N?

Step 1: Write the equation for pressure.

$$pressure = \frac{force}{area}$$

Step 2: Replace *force* and *area* with the values given, and solve. (Hint: Weight is a measure of gravitational force.)

$$pressure = \frac{10\ N}{0.2\ m^2} = 50\ N/m^2 = 50\ Pa$$

The equation for pressure can be rearranged to find force or area, as shown below.

$$force = pressure \times area \quad \text{(Rearrange by multiplying by area.)}$$

$$area = \frac{force}{pressure} \quad \text{(Rearrange by multiplying by area and then dividing by pressure.)}$$

Now It's Your Turn

1. Find the pressure exerted by a 3,000 N crate that has an area of 2 m².
2. Find the weight of a rock that has an area of 10 m² and that exerts a pressure of 250 Pa.

Pressure and Bubbles

When you blow a soap bubble, you blow in only one direction. So, why does the bubble get rounder instead of longer as you blow? The shape of the bubble partly depends on an important property of fluids: Fluids exert pressure evenly in all directions. The air you blow into the bubble exerts pressure evenly in all directions. So, the bubble expands in all directions to create a sphere.

Atmospheric Pressure

The *atmosphere* is the layer of nitrogen, oxygen, and other gases that surrounds Earth. Earth's atmosphere is held in place by gravity, which pulls the gases toward Earth. The pressure caused by the weight of the atmosphere is called **atmospheric pressure.** *at the ocean*

Atmospheric pressure is exerted on everything on Earth, including you. At sea level, the atmosphere exerts a pressure of about 101,300 N on every square meter, or 101,300 Pa. So, there is a weight of about 10 N (about 2 lbs) on every square centimeter of your body. Why don't you feel this crushing pressure? Like the air inside a balloon, the fluids inside your body exert pressure. **Figure 2** can help you understand why you don't feel the pressure.

Reading Check Name two gases in the atmosphere. *(See the Appendix for answers to Reading Checks.)*

Atmospheric pressure

Air pressure inside the balloon

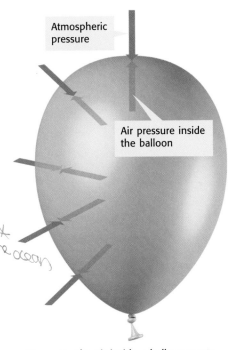

Figure 2 *The air inside a balloon exerts pressure that keeps the balloon inflated against atmospheric pressure. Similarly, fluid inside your body exerts pressure that works against atmospheric pressure.*

Answer to Math Focus

1. *pressure* = 3,000 N ÷ 2 m² = 1,500 Pa
2. *force* = 250 Pa × 10 m² = 2,500 N

Answer to Reading Check

Two gases in the atmosphere are nitrogen and oxygen.

CONNECTION to Life Science — GENERAL

Surface Area-to-Volume Ratio Use the teaching transparency titled "Math Focus: Surface Area-to-Volume Ratio" to help students understand how objects, including the human body, can withstand atmospheric pressure.

Motivate

Demonstration — GENERAL

Safety Caution: Have students wear protective goggles during this demonstration.

Building Pressure Place two plastic soda bottles filled halfway with water in front of the classroom. Add some fizzing powder or crushed fizzing tablets to each bottle. Immediately, place a cork snugly in one of the bottles. Stretch the mouth of a balloon over the other bottle, sealing the opening of the bottle. Have the class observe what happens. Ask students to explain what happened in each bottle. (Sample answer: The fizzing tablet created gas. The gas created pressure inside the bottle with the cork, and the pressure forced the cork off. The balloon on the other bottle was filled by the gas created by the tablet.) **LS** Visual

Teach

CONNECTION ACTIVITY
Language Arts — GENERAL

 Writing **Fluid Poem** Have students write a short poem describing something about fluids. Some possible topics include water, mixing liquids, air, steam, clouds, or fog. **LS** Verbal

Homework — ADVANCED

Comparing Pressure Have students calculate the pressure exerted by their bodies on the floor. Students should estimate the area of their feet as a rectangle. Ask students to compare the pressure exerted when their feet are flat on the floor with the pressure exerted when students are standing on their toes. **LS** Logical

Section 1 • Fluids and Pressure **67**

Teach, continued

CONNECTION ACTIVITY
Earth Science ——— GENERAL

Weather and Pressure Have students research the effects of atmospheric pressure on weather. Have students make a poster or concept map to display their results. [LS] Visual

BRAIN FOOD

Mount Everest The high altitude of Mount Everest can be hazardous to visitors' health. Most of the mountain's base camps are more than 4,000 m above sea level. Altitude sickness can affect people who reach that elevation. Climbers must use oxygen masks above 5,500 m because, at that elevation, there is not enough oxygen to sustain normal body functions.

Homework ——— GENERAL

Pressure Essay Have students write an essay describing how they are affected by fluid pressure on a typical day. Students should include examples such as weather, transportation, plumbing, breathing, and so on. [LS] Verbal

Answer to Reading Check
Pressure increases as depth

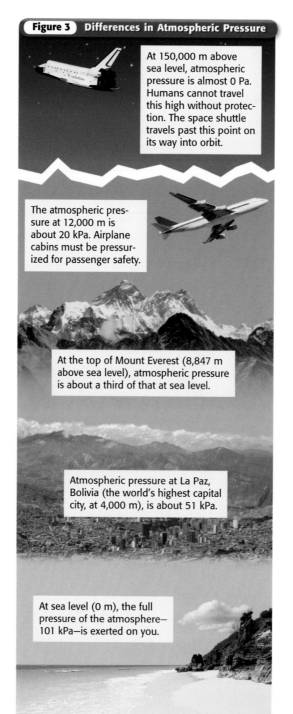

Figure 3 Differences in Atmospheric Pressure

At 150,000 m above sea level, atmospheric pressure is almost 0 Pa. Humans cannot travel this high without protection. The space shuttle travels past this point on its way into orbit.

The atmospheric pressure at 12,000 m is about 20 kPa. Airplane cabins must be pressurized for passenger safety.

At the top of Mount Everest (8,847 m above sea level), atmospheric pressure is about a third of that at sea level.

Atmospheric pressure at La Paz, Bolivia (the world's highest capital city, at 4,000 m), is about 51 kPa.

At sea level (0 m), the full pressure of the atmosphere—101 kPa—is exerted on you.

Variation of Atmospheric Pressure

The atmosphere stretches about 150 km above Earth's surface. However, about 80% of the atmosphere's gases are found within 10 km of Earth's surface. At the top of the atmosphere, pressure is almost nonexistent. The pressure is close to 0 Pa because the gas particles are far apart and rarely collide. Mount Everest in south-central Asia is the highest point on Earth. At the top of Mount Everest, atmospheric pressure is about 33,000 Pa, or 33 kilopascals (33 kPa). (Remember that the prefix *kilo-* means 1,000. So, 1 kPa is equal to 1,000 Pa.) At sea level, atmospheric pressure is about 101 kPa.

Atmospheric Pressure and Depth

Take a look at **Figure 3.** Notice how atmospheric pressure changes as you travel through the atmosphere. The further down through the atmosphere you go, the greater the pressure is. In other words, the pressure increases as the atmosphere gets "deeper." An important point to remember about fluids is that pressure varies depending on depth. At lower levels of the atmosphere, there is more fluid above that is being pulled by Earth's gravitational force. So, there is more pressure at lower levels of the atmosphere.

✓ Reading Check Describe how pressure changes with depth.

Pressure Changes and Your Body

So, what happens to your body when atmospheric pressure changes? If you travel to higher or lower points in the atmosphere, the fluids in your body have to adjust to maintain equal pressure. You may have experienced this adjustment if your ears have "popped" when you were in a plane taking off or in a car traveling down a steep mountain road. The "pop" happens because of pressure changes in pockets of air behind your eardrums.

MISCONCEPTION ALERT

Variation of Air Density The relationship between pressure and depth in the atmosphere is not the same as in the ocean. Air is less dense at higher altitudes. So, the pressure in the upper atmosphere varies less with depth than pressure in the lower atmosphere does. But water density in the ocean remains approximately constant with depth. So, the rate of change in pressure remains relatively constant as you go deeper underwater.

Water Pressure

Water is a fluid. So, it exerts pressure like the atmosphere does. Water pressure also increases as depth increases, as shown in **Figure 4**. The deeper a diver goes in the water, the greater the pressure is. The pressure increases because more water above the diver is being pulled by Earth's gravitational force. In addition, the atmosphere presses down on the water, so the total pressure on the diver includes water pressure and atmospheric pressure.

Water Pressure and Depth

Like atmospheric pressure, water pressure depends on depth. Water pressure does not depend on the total amount of fluid present. A swimmer would feel the same pressure swimming at 3 m below the surface of a small pond and at 3 m below the surface of an ocean. Even though there is more water in the ocean than in the pond, the pressure on the swimmer in the pond would be the same as the pressure on the swimmer in the ocean.

Density Making a Difference

Water is about 1,000 times more dense than air. *Density* is the amount of matter in a given volume, or mass per unit volume. Because water is more dense than air, a certain volume of water has more mass—and weighs more—than the same volume of air. So, water exerts more pressure than air.

For example, if you climb a 10 m tree, the decrease in atmospheric pressure is too small to notice. But if you dive 10 m underwater, the pressure on you increases to 201 kPa, which is almost twice the atmospheric pressure at the surface!

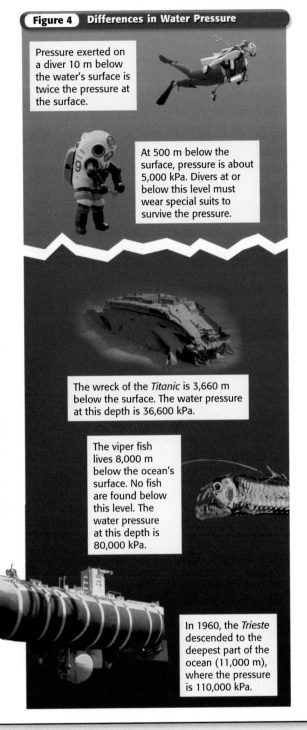

Figure 4 Differences in Water Pressure

Pressure exerted on a diver 10 m below the water's surface is twice the pressure at the surface.

At 500 m below the surface, pressure is about 5,000 kPa. Divers at or below this level must wear special suits to survive the pressure.

The wreck of the *Titanic* is 3,660 m below the surface. The water pressure at this depth is 36,600 kPa.

The viper fish lives 8,000 m below the ocean's surface. No fish are found below this level. The water pressure at this depth is 80,000 kPa.

In 1960, the *Trieste* descended to the deepest part of the ocean (11,000 m), where the pressure is 110,000 kPa.

CONNECTION to Real World — GENERAL

Pressure and Diving The pressure on a diver's body increases as the diver goes deeper underwater. The increased pressure on the diver's chest makes breathing more difficult. Scuba divers use a pressure regulator to solve this problem. As they go deeper, the regulator increases the pressure of the air released from the diver's air tanks. The pressure of the released air equals the pressure of the water on the diver, making breathing easier.

Cultural Awareness GENERAL

Pearl Diving Have students research Japanese pearl divers. Students should investigate the techniques these deep divers use to cope with the effects of water pressure. Ask students to make a poster that illustrates what they learn. **LS** Visual

INCLUSION Strategies

- *Attention Deficit Disorder*
- *Developmentally Delayed*
- *Hearing Impaired*

Many students benefit from hands-on activities. Give students a hands-on opportunity to clarify the meaning of the word *density*. Working in small groups, have students gather a kilogram of each of the following items: marshmallows, popcorn kernels, and measuring masses (the metal "weights" used with two-pan balances). Have each student handle the items to feel their masses and compare their volumes. Ask each group to write a paragraph comparing the volumes and masses of the different items and indicating the order of the items from highest to lowest. **LS** Kinesthetic

SUPPORT FOR

English Language Learners

Pressure and Depth To check comprehension of the relationship between air pressure and depth as well as water pressure and depth, ask students to summarize what they have learned after reading the text and the graphics on these pages. Have students write a brief summary explaining how pressure changes with depth and what that means for the human body in each environment. Evaluate the summaries based on accuracy of information, clarity of organization, and grammar and spelling. **LS** Verbal

CHAPTER RESOURCES

Workbooks

 Math Skills for Science
- Density GENERAL

Section 1 • Fluids and Pressure **69**

Reteaching — BASIC

How Droppers Work Give each pair of students a plastic dropper and a small cup of water. Ask students to write a paragraph describing how the dropper works. Students should address why water goes up into the dropper and why the water can be forced out. Students may experiment with the droppers as they write their paragraphs. (Both events can be explained by the fact that fluids flow from areas of high pressure to areas of low pressure.) **LS Verbal/Kinesthetic**

Quiz — GENERAL

1. What do liquids and gases have in common? (They are both fluids.)

2. Why does pressure increase with depth? (As depth increases, the weight of the fluid above increases, which increases pressure.)

Alternative Assessment — ADVANCED

Airflow Tracking Have students make a poster showing the air-flow in their home. Have them write a short description of the circulation of the air by using the concept of fluid pressure. Students should also describe how they tracked the airflow in their home. **LS Visual**

Answer to Reading Check

You decrease pressure inside a straw by removing some of the air inside the straw.

Blown Away

1. Lay an **empty plastic soda bottle** on its side.
2. Wad a **small piece of paper** (about 4 × 4 cm) into a ball.
3. Place the paper ball just inside the bottle's opening.
4. Blow straight into the opening.
5. Record your observations.
6. Explain your results in terms of high and low fluid pressures.

Pressure Differences and Fluid Flow

When you drink through a straw, you remove some of the air in the straw. Because there is less air inside the straw, the pressure in the straw is reduced. But the atmospheric pressure on the surface of the liquid remains the same. Thus, there is a difference between the pressure inside the straw and the pressure outside the straw. The outside pressure forces the liquid up the straw and into your mouth. So, just by drinking through a straw, you can observe an important property of fluids: Fluids flow from areas of high pressure to areas of low pressure.

✓ **Reading Check** When drinking through a straw, how do you decrease the pressure inside the straw?

Pressure Differences and Breathing

Take a deep breath—fluid is flowing from high to low pressure! When you inhale, a muscle increases the space in your chest and gives your lungs room to expand. This expansion decreases the pressure in your lungs. The pressure in your lungs becomes lower than the air pressure outside your lungs. Air then flows into your lungs—from high to low pressure. This air carries oxygen that you need to live. **Figure 5** shows how exhaling also causes fluids to flow from high to low pressure. You can see a similar flow of fluid when you open a carbonated beverage or squeeze toothpaste onto your toothbrush.

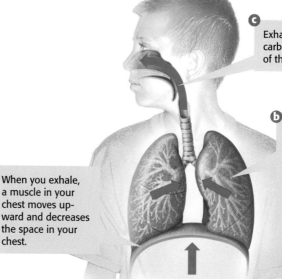

Figure 5   Exhaling, Pressure, and Fluid Flow

c — Exhaled air carries carbon dioxide out of the lungs.

b — The decrease in space causes the pressure in your lungs to increase. The air in your lungs flows from a region of high pressure (your chest) to a region of low pressure (outside of your body).

a — When you exhale, a muscle in your chest moves upward and decreases the space in your chest.

MATERIALS

FOR EACH STUDENT
• bottle, soda, plastic
• paper, 4 × 4 cm square

Answers

5. Students should observe that the paper wad flies out of the bottle.

6. By blowing into the bottle, one increases the air pressure inside the bottle. Fluids flow from high pressure to low pressure, so the air inside flows out of the bottle and carries the paper wad with it.

Pressure Differences and Tornadoes

Look at the tornado in **Figure 6.** Some of the damaging winds caused by tornadoes are the result of pressure differences. The air pressure inside a tornado is very low. Because the air pressure outside of the tornado is higher than the pressure inside, air pushes into the tornado. The rushing air causes the tornado to be like a giant vacuum cleaner—objects are pushed into the tornado. The winds created are usually very strong and affect the area around the tornado. So, objects, such as trees and buildings, can be severely damaged by wind even if they are not in the direct path of a tornado.

Figure 6 *Tornadoes are like giant vacuum cleaners because of pressure differences.*

SECTION Review

Summary

- A fluid is any material that flows and takes the shape of its container.
- Pressure is force exerted on a given area.
- Moving particles of matter create pressure by colliding with one another and with the walls of their container.
- The pressure caused by the weight of the atmosphere is called *atmospheric pressure.*
- Fluid pressure increases as depth increases.
- As depth increases, water pressure increases faster than atmospheric pressure does because water is denser than air.
- Fluids flow from areas of high pressure to areas of low pressure.

Using Key Terms

1. In your own words, write a definition for each of the following terms: *fluid* and *atmospheric pressure.*

2. Use the following terms in the same sentence: *pressure* and *pascal.*

Understanding Key Ideas

3. Which of the following statements about fluids is true?
   a. Fluids rarely take the shape of their container.
   b. Fluids include liquids and gases.
   c. Fluids flow from low pressure to high pressure.
   d. Fluids exert the most pressure in the downward direction.

4. How do fluids exert pressure on a container?

5. Why are you not crushed by atmospheric pressure?

6. Explain why atmospheric pressure changes as depth changes.

7. Give three examples of fluids flowing from high pressure to low pressure in everyday life.

Math Skills

8. The water in a glass has a weight of 2.4 N. The bottom of the glass has an area of 0.012 m². What is the pressure exerted by the water on the bottom of the glass?

Critical Thinking

9. **Identifying Relationships** Mercury is a liquid that has a density of 13.5 g/mL. Water has a density of 1.0 g/mL. Equal volumes of mercury and water are in identical containers. Explain why the pressures exerted on the bottoms of the containers are different.

10. **Making Inferences** Why do airplanes need to be pressurized for passenger safety when flying high in the atmosphere?

Developed and maintained by the National Science Teachers Association

For a variety of links related to this chapter, go to www.scilinks.org

Topic: Fluids and Pressure
SciLinks code: HSM0586

Focus

Overview

This section describes how differences in fluid pressure create buoyant force. Students are introduced to Archimedes' principle and learn how to find the buoyant force on an object. Finally, students learn the factors that determine whether an object floats or sinks in a fluid.

 Bellringer

Ask your students to identify which of the following objects will float in water: a rock, an orange, a screw, a quarter, a candle, a plastic-foam "peanut," and a chalkboard eraser. Ask students to write a hypothesis about why an aircraft carrier, which weighs thousands of tons, does not sink.

Motivate

Demonstration — GENERAL

Density Layers Layer 20 mL each of corn syrup, water, and cooking oil in a 100 mL graduated cylinder. Have students observe as you drop in objects that will float on the different layers. You might also try adding droplets of alcohol. Use the results of the demonstration to launch a discussion about buoyant force. **LS** Visual

---

What You Will Learn

- Explain the relationship between fluid pressure and buoyant force.
- Predict whether an object will float or sink in a fluid.
- Analyze the role of density in an object's ability to float.
- Explain how the overall density of an object can be changed.

Vocabulary

buoyant force
Archimedes' principle

READING STRATEGY

Discussion Read this section silently. Write down questions that you have about this section. Discuss your questions in a small group.

---

buoyant force the upward force that keeps an object immersed in or floating on a liquid

Archimedes' principle the principle that states that the buoyant force on an object in a fluid is an upward force equal to the weight of the volume of fluid that the object displaces

---

Figure 1 *There is more pressure at the bottom of an object because pressure increases with depth. This results in an upward buoyant force on the object.*

Buoyant Force

Why does an ice cube float on water? Why doesn't it sink to the bottom of your glass?

Imagine that you use a straw to push an ice cube under water. Then, you release the cube. A force pushes the ice back to the water's surface. The force, called **buoyant force** (BOY uhnt FAWRS), is the upward force that fluids exert on all matter.

Buoyant Force and Fluid Pressure

Look at **Figure 1.** Water exerts fluid pressure on all sides of an object. The pressure exerted horizontally on one side of the object is equal to the pressure exerted on the opposite side. These equal pressures cancel one another. So, the only fluid pressures affecting the net force on the object are at the top and at the bottom. Pressure increases as depth increases. So, the pressure at the bottom of the object is greater than the pressure at the top. The water exerts a net upward force on the object. This upward force is buoyant force.

Determining Buoyant Force

Archimedes (AHR kuh MEE deez), a Greek mathematician who lived in the third century BCE, discovered how to determine buoyant force. **Archimedes' principle** states that the buoyant force on an object in a fluid is an upward force equal to the weight of the fluid that the object takes the place of, or displaces. Suppose the object in **Figure 1** displaces 250 mL of water. The weight of that volume of displaced water is about 2.5 N. So, the buoyant force on the object is 2.5 N. Notice that only the weight of the displaced fluid determines the buoyant force on an object. The weight of the object does not affect buoyant force.

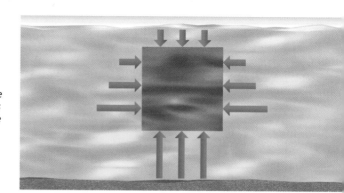

CHAPTER RESOURCES

Chapter Resource File

- **Lesson Plan**
- **Directed Reading A** BASIC
- **Directed Reading B** SPECIAL NEEDS

Technology

 Transparencies
- Bellringer

Workbooks

 Interactive Textbook Struggling Readers

Q: Why did the banker jump into the swimming pool?

A: He needed to float a loan.

Weight Versus Buoyant Force

An object in a fluid will sink if its weight is greater than the buoyant force (the weight of the fluid it displaces). An object floats only when the buoyant force on the object is equal to the object's weight.

Sinking

The rock in **Figure 2** weighs 75 N. It displaces 5 L of water. Archimedes' principle says that the buoyant force is equal to the weight of the displaced water—about 50 N. The rock's weight is greater than the buoyant force. So, the rock sinks.

Floating

The fish in **Figure 2** weighs 12 N. It displaces a volume of water that weighs 12 N. Because the fish's weight is equal to the buoyant force, the fish floats in the water. In fact, the fish is suspended in the water as it floats. Now, look at the duck. The duck does not sink. So, the buoyant force on the duck must be equal to the duck's weight. But the duck isn't all the way underwater! Only the duck's feet, legs, and stomach have to be underwater to displace 9 N of water, which is equal to the duck's weight. So, the duck floats on the surface of the water.

Buoying Up

If the duck dove underwater, it would displace more than 9 N of water. So, the buoyant force on the duck would be greater than the duck's weight. When the buoyant force on an object is greater than the object's weight, the object is *buoyed up* (pushed up) in water. An object is buoyed up until the part of the object underwater displaces an amount of water that equals the object's entire weight. Thus, an ice cube pops to the surface when it is pushed to the bottom of a glass of water.

Reading Check What causes an object to buoy up? (*See the Appendix for answers to Reading Checks.*)

Figure 2 *Will an object sink or float? That depends on whether the buoyant force is less than or equal to the object's weight.*

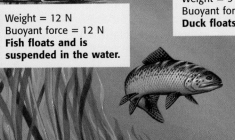

Weight = 12 N
Buoyant force = 12 N
Fish floats and is suspended in the water.

Weight = 9 N
Buoyant force = 9 N
Duck floats on the surface.

Weight = 75 N
Buoyant force = 50 N
Rock sinks.

Teach, continued

ACTIVITY — GENERAL

Making Models Have students make a model of a hot-air balloon. Before they begin, discuss how heating the air inside the balloon changes the balloon's overall density and therefore changes its buoyancy. Provide students with tissue paper, tape, glue, string, and other materials to make a model balloon. Fill the completed models with hot air from a hair dryer. Release the model to see if it floats. Have students evaluate their balloon's performance.

LS Kinesthetic

CONNECTION ACTIVITY
Math — ADVANCED

Rearranging the Density Equation Have students rearrange the equation for density to solve for mass and volume. (*mass = density × volume*; *volume = mass ÷ density*) Then, have students solve the following problems:

1. The density of the liquid mercury is 13.5 g/mL. What is the mass of a 2.4 mL sample of mercury? (32.4 g)

2. The density of aluminum is 2.7 g/cm³. What is the volume of a 9.45 g sample of aluminum? (3.5 cm³)

LS Logical

Figure 3 *Helium in a balloon floats in air for the same reason an ice cube floats on water—helium is less dense than the surrounding fluid.*

Floating, Sinking, and Density

Think again about the rock in the lake. The rock displaces 5 L of water. But volumes of solids are measured in cubic centimeters (cm³). Because 1 mL is equal to 1 cm³, the volume of the rock is 5,000 cm³. But 5,000 cm³ of rock weighs more than an equal volume of water. So, the rock sinks.

Because mass is proportional to weight, you can say that the rock has more mass per volume than water has. Mass per unit volume is density. The rock sinks because it is more dense than water is. The duck floats because it is less dense than water is. The density of the fish is equal to the density of the water.

More Dense Than Air

Why does an ice cube float on water but not in air? An ice cube floats on water because it is less dense than water. But most substances are *more* dense than air. So, there are few substances that float in air. The ice cube is more dense than air, so the ice cube doesn't float in air.

Less Dense Than Air

One substance that is less dense than air is helium, a gas. In fact, helium has one-seventh the density of air under normal conditions. A given volume of helium displaces an equal volume of air that is much heavier than itself. So, helium floats in air. Because helium floats in air, it is used in parade balloons, such as the one shown in **Figure 3.**

✓ **Reading Check** Name a substance that is less dense than air.

MATH FOCUS

Finding Density Find the density of a rock that has a mass of 10 g and a volume of 2 cm³.

Step 1: Write the equation for density. Density is calculated by using this equation:

$$density = \frac{mass}{volume}$$

Step 2: Replace *mass* and *volume* with the values in the problem, and solve.

$$density = \frac{10\ g}{2\ cm^3} = 5\ g/cm^3$$

Now It's Your Turn

1. What is the density of a 20 cm³ object that has a mass of 25 g?

2. A 546 g fish displaces 420 mL of water. What is the density of the fish? (Note: 1 mL = 1 cm³)

3. A beaker holds 50 mL of a slimy green liquid. The mass of the liquid is 163 g. What is the density of the liquid?

Answer to Reading Check

Helium is less dense than air.

Answers to Math Focus

1. 1.25 g/cm³
2. 1.3 g/cm³
3. 3.26 g/mL

Is That a Fact!

Before plastics can be recycled, they must first be separated by type. Most containers display a number that identifies the type of plastic used. Containers that do not display number codes can be separated by density by being floated in liquids of different densities.

Changing Overall Density

Steel is almost 8 times denser than water. And yet huge steel ships cruise the oceans with ease. But hold on! You just learned that substances that are more dense than water will sink in water. So, how does a steel ship float?

Changing Shape

The secret of how a ship floats is in the shape of the ship. What if a ship were just a big block of steel, as shown in **Figure 4**? If you put that block into water, the block would sink because it is more dense than water. So, ships are built with a hollow shape. The amount of steel in the ship is the same as in the block. But the hollow shape increases the volume of the ship. Remember that density is mass per unit volume. So, an increase in the ship's volume leads to a decrease in its density. Thus, ships made of steel float because their *overall density* is less than the density of water.

Most ships are built to displace more water than is necessary for the ship to float. Ships are made this way so that they won't sink when people and cargo are loaded on the ship.

CONNECTION TO Geology

Floating Rocks The rock that makes up Earth's continents is about 15% less dense than the molten (melted) mantle rock below it. Because of this difference in density, the continents are floating on the mantle. Research the structure of Earth, and make a poster that shows Earth's interior layers.

ACTIVITY

Figure 4 Shape and Overall Density

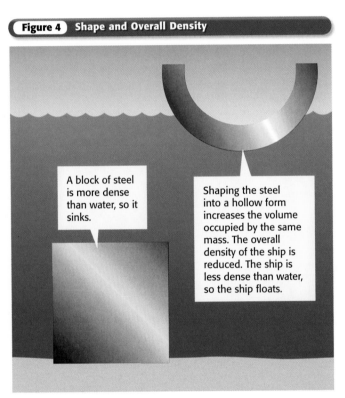

A block of steel is more dense than water, so it sinks.

Shaping the steel into a hollow form increases the volume occupied by the same mass. The overall density of the ship is reduced. The ship is less dense than water, so the ship floats.

INTERNET ACTIVITY

For another activity related to this chapter, go to **go.hrw.com** and type in the keyword **HP5FLUW.**

Close

Reteaching — BASIC

Rubber Ducky   Place a rubber duck in a large, clear container of water. Explain to students that the overall density of the rubber and the air allows the duck to float. Then, cut the duck in two and put the pieces in the water. Explain that the pieces sink because there is no air trapped inside the duck and the rubber is more dense than water. **LS Visual**

Quiz — GENERAL

1. How can you determine the buoyant force acting on an object? (Determine the weight of the volume of fluid displaced by the object.)

2. Who discovered how to determine buoyant force? (Archimedes)

3. How can a scuba diver keep from floating back to the surface of the water? (The diver can add weights.)

Answer to Reading Check

Crew members control the density of a submarine by controlling the amount of water in the ballast tanks.

Ship Shape

1. Roll a **piece of clay** into a ball the size of a golf ball, and drop it into a **container of water.** Record your observations.

2. With your hands, flatten the ball of clay until it is a bit thinner than your little finger, and press it into the shape of a bowl or canoe.

3. Place the clay boat gently in the water. How does the change of shape affect the buoyant force on the clay? How is that change related to the overall density of the clay boat? Record your answers.

Changing Mass

A submarine is a special kind of ship that can travel both on the surface of the water and underwater. Submarines have *ballast tanks* that can be opened to allow sea water to flow in. As water is added, the submarine's mass increases, but its volume stays the same. The submarine's overall density increases so that it can dive under the surface. Crew members control the amount of water taken in. In this way, they control how dense the submarine is and how deep it dives. Compressed air is used to blow the water out of the tanks so that the submarine can rise. Study **Figure 5** to learn how ballast tanks work.

✓ Reading Check How do crew members control the density of a submarine?

Figure 5   Controlling Density Using Ballast Tanks

When a submarine is floating on the ocean's surface, its ballast tanks are filled mostly with air.

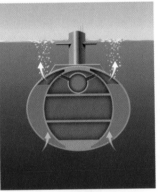

Vent holes on the ballast tanks are opened to allow the submarine to dive. Air escapes as the tanks fill with water.

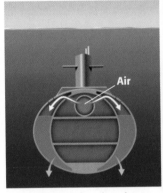

Vent holes are closed, and compressed air is pumped into the ballast tanks to force the water out, so the submarine rises.

Quick Lab

MATERIALS

FOR EACH STUDENT
- bowl or pail, medium, one for every two or three students
- clay, modeling, golf-ball-sized piece
- water

Answer

3. Forming the clay into a boat shape causes the clay to displace more water, which increases the buoyant force. The change in shape causes the overall density of the clay boat to decrease so that the clay boat is less dense than the water. Therefore, the clay boat floats.

Changing Volume

[li]ke a submarine, some fish adjust their over-[al]l density to stay at a certain depth in the [w]ater. Most bony fishes have an organ called a *swim bladder,* shown in **Figure 6.** This swim blad[d]er is filled with gases produced in a fish's blood. [T]he inflated swim bladder increases the fish's [vo]lume and thereby decreases the fish's overall [d]ensity, which keeps the fish from sinking in [t]he water. The fish's nervous system controls the [am]ount of gas in the bladder. Some fish, such as [sh]arks, do not have a swim bladder. These fish [m]ust swim constantly to keep from sinking.

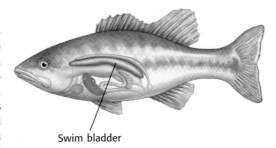

Figure 6 *Most bony fishes have an organ called a* swim bladder *that allows them to adjust their overall density.*

SECTION Review

Summary

- All fluids exert an upward force called *buoyant force.*
- Buoyant force is caused by differences in fluid pressure.
- Archimedes' principle states that the buoyant force on an object is equal to the weight of the fluid displaced by the object.
- Any object that is more dense than the surrounding fluid will sink. An object that is less dense than the surrounding fluid will float.
- The overall density of an object can be changed by changing the object's shape, mass, or volume.

Using Key Terms

1. Use the following terms in the same sentence: *buoyant force* and *Archimedes' principle.*

Understanding Key Ideas

2. Which of the following changes increases the overall density of the object?
   a. A block of iron is formed into a hollow shape.
   b. A submarine fills its ballast tanks with water.
   c. A submarine fills its ballast tanks with air.
   d. A fish increases the amount of gas in its swim bladder.

3. Explain how differences in fluid pressure create buoyant force on an object.

4. How does an object's density determine whether the object will sink or float in water?

5. Name three methods that can be used to change the overall density of an object.

Math Skills

6. What is the density of an object that has a mass of 184 g and a volume of 50 cm^3?

Critical Thinking

7. **Applying Concepts** An object weighs 20 N. It displaces a volume of water that weighs 15 N.
   a. What is the buoyant force on the object?
   b. Will this object float or sink? Explain your answer.

8. **Predicting Consequences** Iron has a density of 7.9 g/cm^3. Mercury is a liquid that has a density of 13.5 g/cm^3. Will iron float or sink in mercury? Explain your answer.

9. **Evaluating Hypotheses** Imagine that your brother tells you that all heavy objects sink in water. Explain why you agree or disagree with his statement.

SCILINKS

Developed and maintained by the National Science Teachers Association

For a variety of links related to this chapter, go to www.scilinks.org

Topic: Buoyant Force
SciLinks code: HSM0202

Alternative Assessment ——— GENERAL

Life Jackets Ask students to make a poster that explains how a life jacket helps a person float. (Most life jackets are made from porous material filled with air.) (A life jacket keeps a person from sinking because the air inside the life jacket increases the person's volume but does not increase his or her weight by very much. The person's overall density decreases, and the person floats.) **LS** Visual

Answers to Section Review

1. Sample answer: Archimedes' principle is about the relationship between the buoyant force of an object and the amount of water the object displaces.

2. b

3. Water pressure is exerted on all sides of an object. The pressures exerted horizontally on the sides cancel each other out. The pressure exerted at the bottom is greater than that exerted at the top because pressure increases with depth. This creates an overall upward force on the object—the buoyant force.

4. An object will float in water if its density is less than the density of water. An object will sink in water if its density is greater than the density of water.

5. The density of an object can be changed by changing the shape, mass, or volume of an object.

6. 184 g ÷ 50 cm^3 = 3.68 g/cm^3

7. a. 15 N
   b. It will sink because its weight is greater than the buoyant force acting on it.

8. Iron will float in mercury because iron is less dense than mercury.

9. Sample answer: I disagree with this statement because steel ships are heavy but they float in water. The ships float because the overall density of the steel and the air inside the ship is less than the density of water.

Focus

Overview

In this section, students learn about Bernoulli's principle. They then explore how objects that are heavier than air can achieve flight. Students also learn about the basic aspects of flight. Finally, students learn about Pascal's principle.

📶 Bellringer

Pose the following problem to your students: "You have been asked to design two kites. One kite will be flown in areas where there is almost always a good breeze. The other kite will be flown in areas with very little wind." What differences in design and materials are there between your two kites?

Motivate

Demonstration — GENERAL

Magic Water Place a straw upright in a glass of water. Hold a second straw at a right angle at the top of the first so that the straws are just touching. Blow very hard through the horizontal straw. Water will rise up in the vertical straw and form a spray. Tell students they will learn why this occurs after reading this section. Visual

What You Will Learn

- Describe the relationship between pressure and fluid speed.
- Analyze the roles of lift, thrust, and wing size in flight.
- Describe drag, and explain how it affects lift.
- Explain Pascal's principle.

Vocabulary

Bernoulli's principle
lift
thrust
drag
Pascal's principle

READING STRATEGY

Reading Organizer As you read this section, create an outline of the section. Use the headings from the section in your outline.

Bernoulli's principle the principle that states that the pressure in a fluid decreases as the fluid's velocity increases

Figure 1 *This ball is pushed by the higher pressure of the air into an area of reduced pressure—the water stream.*

Fluids and Motion

Hold two sheets of paper so that the edges are hanging in front of your face about 4 cm apart. The flat faces of the paper should be parallel to each other. Now, blow as hard as you can between the two sheets of paper.

What's going on? You can't separate the sheets by blowing between them. In fact, the sheets move closer together the harder you blow. You may be surprised that the explanation for this unusual occurrence also includes how wings help birds and planes fly and how pitchers throw screwballs.

Fluid Speed and Pressure

The strange reaction of the paper is caused by a property of moving fluids. This property was first described in the 18th century by Daniel Bernoulli (ber NOO lee), a Swiss mathematician. **Bernoulli's principle** states that as the speed of a moving fluid increases, the fluid's pressure decreases. In the case of the paper, air speed between the two sheets increased when you blew air between them. Because air speed increased, the pressure between the sheets decreased. Thus, the higher pressure on the outside of the sheets pushed them together.

Science in a Sink

Bernoulli's principle is at work in **Figure 1**. A table-tennis ball is attached to a string and swung into a stream of water. Instead of being pushed out of the water, the ball is held in the water. Why? The water is moving faster than the air around it, so the water has a lower pressure than the surrounding air. The higher air pressure pushes the ball into the area of lower pressure—the water stream. Try this at home to see for yourself!

CHAPTER RESOURCES

Chapter Resource File
- Lesson Plan
- Directed Reading A BASIC
- Directed Reading B SPECIAL NEEDS

Technology
Transparencies
- Bellringer
- P27 Wing Design and Lift

Workbooks
Interactive Textbook Struggling Readers

Figure 2   Wing Design and Lift

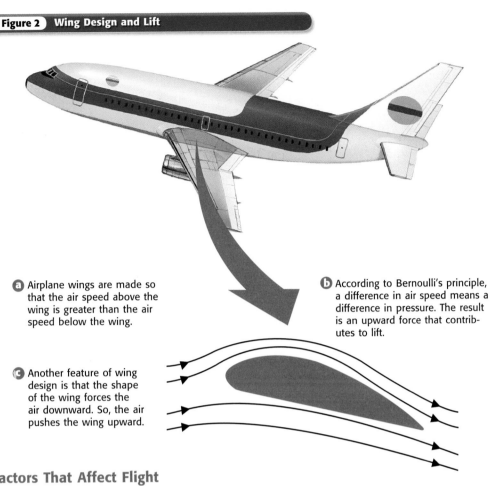

a Airplane wings are made so that the air speed above the wing is greater than the air speed below the wing.

b According to Bernoulli's principle, a difference in air speed means a difference in pressure. The result is an upward force that contributes to lift.

c Another feature of wing design is that the shape of the wing forces the air downward. So, the air pushes the wing upward.

Factors That Affect Flight

A common commercial airplane in the skies today is the Boeing 737 jet. Even without passengers, the plane weighs 250,000 N. How can something so big and heavy get off the ground and fly? Wing shape plays a role in helping these big planes—as well as smaller planes and birds—achieve flight, as shown in **Figure 2.**

According to Bernoulli's principle, the fast-moving air above the wing exerts less pressure than the slow-moving air below the wing. The greater pressure below the wing exerts an upward force. This upward force, known as **lift,** pushes the wings (and the rest of the airplane or bird) upward against the downward pull of gravity.

✏️ *airplane's speed)*

lift an upward force on an object that moves in a fluid

✓ **Reading Check**   What is lift? *(See the Appendix for answers to Reading Checks.)*

**MISCONCEPTION /// ALERT **

More Than Bernoulli When teaching about airplane flight, emphasize that there is more to understanding lift than can be explained by Bernoulli's principle. Newton's third law also plays a part. A tilted wing deflects horizontal airflow downward (the action force exerted by the wing on the air). The reaction force is the upward force the air exerts on the wing. This force also contributes to lift.

Answer to Reading Check
Lift is an upward force on an object that is moving in a fluid.

Teach

ACTIVITY ——————— BASIC

Pressure Analogy Before you discuss Bernoulli's principle, it may help some students to imagine the pressure of a fluid as the combined pressure of many particles striking a surface. Have students imagine a swarm of bees trapped in a short section of a long piece of pipe. As the bees fly around inside the pipe, they bounce off each other and off the walls of the pipe, creating pressure. Then, have students imagine that the bees are suddenly able to fly the entire length of the pipe. Explain that, because the bees have more room, they bounce against the walls of the pipe much less frequently, creating less pressure inside the pipe. **LS** Verbal/Logical

ACTIVITY ——————— ADVANCED

Wing Shape Ask students to examine the wing shape shown in **Figure 2.** Have students use their knowledge of Bernoulli's principle to hypothesize about what type of wings might work in flight. Does the wing have to be curved? Is flight possible without wings? **LS** Logical/Visual

Demonstration —— GENERAL

Flying Ball Point the airflow of a portable hair dryer straight up, and suspend a table-tennis ball in the airstream. Change the direction of the airflow slightly to maneuver the ball. Have students speculate on the forces that are at work in this demonstration. **LS** Visual

INCLUSION Strategies

- *Hearing Impaired*
- *Learning Disabled*
- *Developmentally Delayed*

The concept of airplane lift is complicated for students with language delays to understand. Use this experiment to give them a chance to experience the idea of lift. Organize the students into small groups. Give each group an 8 1/2 in. × 11 in. sheet of paper and an 11 in. × 17 in. sheet of paper. Ask each team to make two paper airplanes that are alike except that one has much larger wings. Ask students to note the lift of each plane as they do the following: Throw the two planes with the same force. Throw the short-winged plane with light force and then with heavy force. Throw the long-winged plane with light force and then with heavy force.

LS Kinesthetic

English Language Learners

ACTIVITY — ADVANCED

Wind Tunnels Have students research how engineers use wind tunnels to test the design of airplane wings. Then, have students use what they have learned to build their own wings and wind tunnel, and show the class how to test the wing designs.

LS Kinesthetic

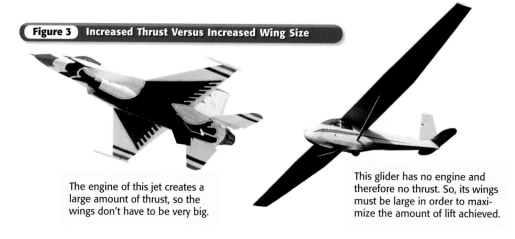

Figure 3 Increased Thrust Versus Increased Wing Size

The engine of this jet creates a large amount of thrust, so the wings don't have to be very big.

This glider has no engine and therefore no thrust. So, its wings must be large in order to maximize the amount of lift achieved.

thrust the pushing or pulling force exerted by the engine of an aircraft or rocket

CONNECTION TO Social Studies

The First Flight The first successful flight of an engine-driven machine that was heavier than air happened in Kitty Hawk, North Carolina, in 1903. Orville Wright was the pilot. The plane flew only 37 m (about the length of a 737 jet) before landing, and the entire flight lasted only 12 s. Research another famous pilot in the history of flight. Make a poster that includes information about the pilot as well as pictures of the pilot and his or her airplane.

Thrust and Lift

The amount of lift created by a plane's wing is determine partly by the speed at which air travels around the wing. Th speed of a plane is determined mostly by its thrust. **Thrust** the forward force produced by the plane's engine. In general, plane with a large amount of thrust moves faster than a plan that has less thrust does. This faster speed means air trave around the wing at a higher speed, which increases lift.

Wing Size, Speed, and Lift

The amount of lift also depends partly on the size of a plane wings. Look at the jet plane in **Figure 3.** This plane can fl with a relatively small wing size because its engine gives a larg amount of thrust. This thrust pushes the plane through the sk at great speeds. So, the jet creates a large amount of lift wit small wings by moving quickly through the air. Smaller wing keep a plane's weight low, which also helps it move faster.

Compared with the jet, the glider in **Figure 3** has a larg wing area. A glider is an engineless plane. It rides rising a currents to stay in flight. Without engines, gliders produc no thrust and move more slowly than many other kinds c planes. Thus, a glider must have large wings to create the lif it needs to stay in the air.

Bernoulli and Birds

Birds don't have engines, so birds must flap their wings to pus themselves through the air. A small bird must flap its wings a a fast pace to stay in the air. But a hawk flaps its wings onl occasionally because it has larger wings than the small bird has. A hawk uses its large wings to fly with very little effort Fully extended, a hawk's wings allow the hawk to glide o wind currents and still have enough lift to stay in the air.

Cultural Awareness — GENERAL

Boomerangs More than 8,000 years ago, Australian aborigines discovered the aerodynamic qualities of a type of hunting stick called a boomerang. Have students research boomerangs and compare a boomerang's flight with an airplane's flight. Ask students to present their findings in a poster. **LS** Visual

CHAPTER RESOURCES

Technology

Transparencies
- P28 Bernoulli's Principle and the Screwball

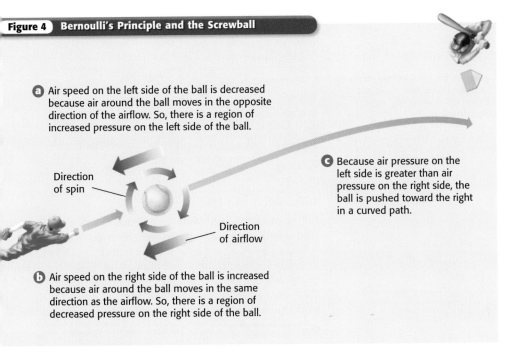

Figure 4 Bernoulli's Principle and the Screwball

a Air speed on the left side of the ball is decreased because air around the ball moves in the opposite direction of the airflow. So, there is a region of increased pressure on the left side of the ball.

Direction of spin

Direction of airflow

c Because air pressure on the left side is greater than air pressure on the right side, the ball is pushed toward the right in a curved path.

b Air speed on the right side of the ball is increased because air around the ball moves in the same direction as the airflow. So, there is a region of decreased pressure on the right side of the ball.

Bernoulli and Baseball

You don't have to look up at a bird or a plane flying through the sky to see Bernoulli's principle in your world. Any time fluids are moving, Bernoulli's principle is at work. **Figure 4** shows how a baseball pitcher can take advantage of Bernoulli's principle to throw a confusing screwball that is difficult for a batter to hit.

Drag and Motion in Fluids

Have you ever walked into a strong wind and noticed that the wind seemed to slow you down? It may have felt like the wind was pushing you backward. Fluids exert a force that opposes the motion of objects moving through the fluids. The force that opposes or restricts motion in a fluid is called **drag.**

In a strong wind, air "drags" on your body and makes it difficult for you to move forward. Drag also works against the forward motion of a plane or bird in flight. Drag is usually caused by an irregular flow of air. An irregular or unpredictable flow of fluids is known as *turbulence.*

WingFlaps

drag a force parallel to the velocity of the flow; it opposes the direction of an aircraft and, in combination with thrust, determines the speed of the aircraft

✓ **Reading Check** What is turbulence?

Reteaching ———— BASIC

Seeing Turbulence Give pairs of students a shallow pan of water and an index card. Tell students to slowly drag the index card through the water and to watch the water behind the card. Tell students that the ripples behind the card and the swirls that come off the edge of the card are examples of turbulence. **LS** Visual

Quiz ———————— GENERAL

1. What forces act on an aircraft? (lift, thrust, drag, and gravity)

2. When an airplane is flying, how does the air pressure above a wing compare with that below the wing? (Air pressure above the wing is lower.)

3. How is thrust related to the speed of an airplane? (The speed of an airplane increases as its thrust increases.)

Alternative Assessment ——— GENERAL

Aircraft Chart Display two or three photographs or models of different types of aircraft, such as a glider, a jet, a biplane, or even an airship. Ask students to select two of the aircraft and to make a chart that compares and contrasts the aircraft in terms of lift, drag, thrust, and gravity. **LS** Verbal

Figure 5 *The pilot of this airplane can move these flaps to adjust the amount of lift when the airplane lands or takes off.*

Turbulence and Lift

Lift is often reduced when turbulence causes drag. Drag can be a serious problem for airplanes moving at high speeds. So airplanes are equipped with ways to reduce turbulence as much as possible when in flight. For example, flaps like those shown in **Figure 5** can be used to change the shape or area of a wing. This change can reduce drag and increase lift. Similarly, birds can adjust their wing feathers in response to turbulence.

✓ **Reading Check** How do airplanes reduce turbulence?

Pascal's Principle

Imagine that the water-pumping station in your town increases the water pressure by 20 Pa. Will the water pressure be increased more at a store two blocks away or at a home 2 km away?

Believe it or not, the increase in water pressure will be the same at both locations. This equal change in water pressure is explained by Pascal's principle. **Pascal's principle** states that a change in pressure at any point in an enclosed fluid will be transmitted equally to all parts of that fluid. This principle was discovered by the 17th-century French scientist Blaise Pascal.

Pascal's principle the principle that states that a fluid in equilibrium contained in a vessel exerts a pressure of equal intensity in all directions

Pascal's Principle and Motion

Hydraulic (hie DRAW lik) devices use Pascal's principle to move or lift objects. Liquids are used in hydraulic devices because liquids cannot be easily compressed, or squeezed, into a smaller space. Cranes, forklifts, and bulldozers have hydraulic devices that help them lift heavy objects.

Hydraulic devices can multiply forces. Car brakes are a good example. In **Figure 6,** a driver's foot exerts pressure on a cylinder of liquid. This pressure is transmitted to all parts of the liquid-filled brake system. The liquid moves the brake pads. The pads press against the wheels, and friction stops the car. The force is multiplied because the pistons that push the brake pads are larger than the piston that is pushed by the brake pedal.

Answer to Reading Check
Airplanes can reduce turbulence by changing the shape or area of the wings.

Figure 6 *Because of Pascal's principle, the touch of a foot can stop tons of moving metal.*

① When the driver pushes the brake pedal, a small piston exerts pressure on the fluid inside the brake system.

② The change in pressure is transmitted to the large pistons that push on the brake pads.

SECTION Review

Summary

- Bernoulli's principle states that fluid pressure decreases as the speed of the fluid increases.
- Wing shape allows airplanes to take advantage of Bernoulli's principle to achieve flight.
- Lift on an airplane is determined by wing size and thrust.
- Drag opposes motion through fluids.
- Pascal's principle states that a change in pressure in an enclosed fluid is transmitted equally to all parts of the fluid.

Using Key Terms

For each pair of terms, explain how the meanings of the terms differ.

1. *Bernoulli's principle* and *Pascal's principle*

2. *thrust* and *drag*

Understanding Key Ideas

3. The shape of an airplane's wing helps it gain
   a. drag.   c. thrust.
   b. lift.   d. turbulence.

4. What is the relationship between pressure and fluid speed?

5. What is Pascal's principle?

6. What force opposes motion through a fluid? How does this force affect lift?

7. How do thrust and lift help an airplane achieve flight?

Critical Thinking

8. **Applying Concepts** Air moving around a speeding race car can create lift. Upside-down wings, or spoilers, are mounted on the rear of race cars. Use Bernoulli's principle to explain how spoilers reduce the danger of accidents.

9. **Making Inferences** When you squeeze a balloon, where is the pressure inside the balloon increased the most? Explain.

Interpreting Graphics

10. Look at the image below. When the space through which a fluid flows becomes narrow, fluid speed increases. Using this information, explain how the two boats could collide.

 SCILINKS

NSTA
Developed and maintained by the
National Science Teachers Association

For a variety of links related to this chapter, go to www.scilinks.org

Topic: Bernoulli's Principle
SciLinks code: HSM0143

CHAPTER RESOURCES

Chapter Resource File

- Section Quiz **GENERAL**
- Section Review **GENERAL**
- Vocabulary and Section Summary **GENERAL**
- Reinforcement Worksheet **BASIC**
- Critical Thinking **ADVANCED**

Answers to Section Review

1. Bernoulli's principle states that the pressure in a fluid decreases as the fluid's velocity increases. Pascal's principle states that a fluid in an enclosed container exerts pressure equally in all directions.

2. Thrust is the pushing or pulling force exerted by the engine of an airplane that moves the airplane forward. Drag is a force that opposes motion in a fluid.

3. b

4. As fluid speed increases, the pressure exerted by the fluid decreases.

5. Pascal's principle states that an enclosed fluid exerts pressure equally in all directions.

6. Drag is a force that opposes motion through a fluid. Lift is often reduced when turbulence causes drag.

7. Lift helps an airplane achieve flight by pushing the airplane up. Thrust helps an airplane achieve flight by causing the airplane to move faster through the air. The faster speed means that air travels faster around the wings, which increases lift.

8. Sample answer: Air traveling around the spoiler produces a downward force. This downward force pushes down on the rear of the car and helps keep the rear wheels of the cars in contact with the road. The cars travel more safely because the rear wheels stay in contact with the road.

9. The pressure inside the balloon increases equally in all directions. Squeezing a balloon demonstrates Pascal's principle.

10. As the fluid speed between the boats increases, the fluid pressure decreases. The pressure on the outer sides of the boats then becomes greater than the pressure between them. This increased pressure from the outside can push the boats together, causing them to collide.

Fluids, Force, and Floating

Teacher's Notes

Time Required

One to two 45-minute class periods

Lab Ratings

EASY ——————→ HARD

Teacher Prep 🧪
Student Set-Up 🧪🧪
Concept Level 🧪🧪🧪
Clean Up 🧪

MATERIALS

The supplies listed are for one group of 3–4 students. The tank or tub should have vertical sides. A small or medium-sized tub works best because changes in volume can be observed easily. Masses should be added near the center of the baking pan. A fish tank or aquarium works well for this activity.

Preparation Notes

If you use a tub or pan without vertical sides, the buoyant force and the weight of the pan and masses will not be equal. In most cases, the buoyant force will be greater than the weight. Have students measure the side of the baking pan and mark the one-quarter, one-half, and three-quarter levels. Analyze the results.

Lab Notes

Volumes of liquids are usually expressed in milliliters (mL). Here, the volume measurements for the water displaced are based on a rectangular container (the tank or tub), so cubic centimeters (cm^3) are used.

Skills Practice Lab

Fluids, Force, and Floating

Why do some objects sink in fluids but others float? In thi lab, you'll get a sinking feeling as you determine that an obje floats when its weight equals the buoyant force exerted b the surrounding fluid.

 OBJECTIVES

Calculate the buoyant force on an object.

Compare the buoyant force on an object with its weight.

MATERIALS

- balance
- mass set
- pan, rectangular baking
- paper towels
- ruler, metric
- tub, plastic, large rectangular
- water

SAFETY

Procedure

1 Copy the table shown below.

Measurement	Trial 1	Trial 2
Length (l), cm		
Width (w), cm		
Initial height (h_1), cm		
Initial volume (V_1), cm^3 $V_1 = l \times w \times h_1$		
New height (h_2), cm		
New total volume (V_2), cm^3 $V_2 = l \times w \times h_2$	*DO NOT WRITE IN BOOK*	
Displaced volume (ΔV), cm^3 $\Delta V = V_2 - V_1$		
Mass of displaced water, g $m = \Delta V \times 1 \ g/cm^3$		
Weight of displaced water, N (buoyant force)		
Weight of pan and masses, N		

2 Fill the tub half full with water. Measure (in centimeters the length, width, and initial height of the water. Record you measurements in the table.

3 Using the equation given in the table, determine the initia volume of water in the tub. Record your results in the table.

4 Place the pan in the water, and place masses in the par as shown on the next page. Keep adding masses until th pan sinks to about three-quarters of its height. Record th new height of the water in the table. Then, use this value t determine and record the new total volume of water plus th volume of water displaced by the pan.

---

5. Determine the volume of the water that was displaced by the pan and masses, and record this value in the table. The displaced volume is equal to the new total volume minus the initial volume.

6. Determine the mass of the displaced water by multiplying the displaced volume by its density (1 g/cm³). Record the mass in the table.

7. Divide the mass by 100. The value you get is the weight of the displaced water in newtons (N). This is equal to the buoyant force. Record the weight of the displaced water in the table.

8. Remove the pan and masses, and determine their total mass (in grams) using the balance. Convert the mass to weight (N), as you did in step 7. Record the weight of the masses and pan in the table.

9. Place the empty pan back in the tub. Perform a second trial by repeating steps 4–8. This time, add masses until the pan is just about to sink.

Analyze the Results

1. **Identifying Patterns** Compare the buoyant force (the weight of the displaced water) with the weight of the pan and masses for both trials.

2. **Examining Data** How did the buoyant force differ between the two trials? Explain.

Draw Conclusions

3. **Drawing Conclusions** Based on your observations, what would happen if you were to add even more mass to the pan than you did in the second trial? Explain your answer in terms of the buoyant force.

4. **Making Predictions** What would happen if you put the masses in the water without the pan? What difference does the pan's shape make?

Analyze the Results

1. In each trial, the buoyant force and the weight should be the same.

2. The buoyant force is larger in the second trial because more water is displaced.

Draw Conclusions

3. The pan would sink because its weight would be greater but the buoyant force (the weight of the water displaced) would be about the same.

4. The masses would sink. The shape of the pan allows the masses to displace more water than the masses alone displace.

Chapter Review

Assignment Guide

Section	Questions
1	1, 3, 7, 11–15, 20–21
2	5, 8–10, 18, 22–24
3	2, 4, 6, 17, 19
1 and 2	16

ANSWERS

Using Key Terms

1. replace *lift* with *pressure*
2. replace *drag* with *thrust*
3. replace *pascal* with *fluid*
4. replace *Archimedes' principle* with *Pascal's principle*
5. replace *Atmospheric pressure* with *Buoyant force*

Understanding Key Ideas

6. d
7. d
8. a
9. d
10. b
11. c

USING KEY TERMS

In each of the following sentences, replace the incorrect term with the correct term from the word bank.

thrust   pressure
drag   lift
buoyant force   fluid
Pascal's principle
Bernoulli's principle

1 Lift increases with the depth of a fluid.

2 A plane's engines produce drag to push the plane forward.

3 A pascal can be a liquid or a gas.

4 A hydraulic device uses Archimedes' principle to lift or move objects.

5 Atmospheric pressure is the upward force exerted on objects by fluids.

UNDERSTANDING KEY IDEAS

Multiple Choice

6 The design of a wing
a. causes the air above the wing to travel faster than the air below the wing.
b. helps create lift.
c. creates a low-pressure zone above the wing.
d. All of the above

7 Fluid pressure is always directed
a. up.   c. sideways.
b. down.   d. in all directions.

8 An object surrounded by a fluid will displace a volume of fluid that is
a. equal to its own volume.
b. less than its own volume.
c. greater than its own volume.
d. denser than itself.

9 If an object weighing 50 N displaces a volume of water that weighs 10 N, what is the buoyant force on the object?
a. 60 N   c. 40 N
b. 50 N   d. 10 N

10 A helium-filled balloon will float in air because
a. there is more air than helium.
b. helium is less dense than air.
c. helium is as dense as air.
d. helium is more dense than air.

11 Materials that can flow to fit their containers include
a. gases.
b. liquids.
c. both gases and liquids.
d. gases, liquids, and solids.

Short Answer

12 Where is water pressure greater, at a depth of 1 m in a large lake or at a depth of 2 m in a small pond? Explain your answer.

13 Why are bubbles round?

14 Why are tornadoes like giant vacuum cleaners?

Math Skills

15 Calculate the area of a 1,500 N object that exerts a pressure of 500 Pa (500 N/m^2). Then, calculate the pressure exerted by the same object over twice that area.

CRITICAL THINKING

16 Concept Mapping Use the following terms to create a concept map: *fluid, pressure, depth, density,* and *buoyant force.*

17 Forming Hypotheses Gases can be easily compressed into smaller spaces. Why would this property of gases make gases less useful than liquids in hydraulic brakes?

18 Making Comparisons Will a ship loaded with beach balls float higher or lower in the water than an empty ship? Explain your reasoning.

19 Applying Concepts Inside all vacuum cleaners is a high-speed fan. Explain how this fan causes the vacuum cleaner to pick up dirt.

20 Evaluating Hypotheses A 600 N girl on stilts says to two 600 N boys sitting on the ground, "I am exerting over twice as much pressure as the two of you are exerting together!" Could this statement be true? Explain your reasoning.

INTERPRETING GRAPHICS

Use the diagram of an iceberg below to answer the questions that follow.

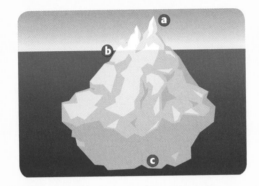

21 At what point (a, b, or c) is water pressure greatest on the iceberg?

22 How much of the iceberg has a weight equal to the buoyant force?

   a. all of it
   b. the section from a to b
   c. the section from b to c
   d. None of the above

23 How does the density of ice compare with the density of water?

24 Why do you think icebergs are dangerous to passing ships?

---

12. Water pressure is greater at a depth of 2 m in a small pond. Pressure increases with depth regardless of the amount of fluid present.

13. Bubbles are round because air, like all fluids, exerts pressure evenly in all directions. So, when you blow a bubble, the bubble expands in all directions to create a sphere.

14. Tornadoes are like giant vacuum cleaners because the air rushing into the tornado pushes objects into a tornado. This process is similar to the way dirt is pushed into a vacuum cleaner.

CHAPTER RESOURCES

Chapter Resource File

- Chapter Review `GENERAL`
- Chapter Test A `GENERAL`
- Chapter Test B `ADVANCED`
- Chapter Test C `SPECIAL NEEDS`
- Vocabulary Activity `GENERAL`

Workbooks

 Study Guide
 • Study Guide is also available in Spanish.

---

15. 3 m^2; 250 Pa

Critical Thinking

16. An answer to this exercise can be found at the end of this book.

17. If a gas were used in hydraulic brakes, the brakes would not work. When the brake pedal is pushed, the gas would compress and therefore would not push on the brake pads to stop the wheels.

18. The ship will float lower in the water because the beach balls will add to the total mass of the ship but will not increase the volume. Therefore, the overall density of the ship will increase, causing the ship to sink a little.

19. The fan causes the air inside the vacuum cleaner to move faster, which decreases pressure. The higher air pressure outside of the vacuum then pushes dirt into the vacuum cleaner.

20. Yes, the statement could be true. Pressure is equal to force divided by area. The girl on stilts is exerting force over a much smaller area than the two boys on the ground are. Therefore, it is possible that the girl is exerting twice as much pressure as the two boys are.

Interpreting Graphics

21. c

22. a

23. Ice is less dense than water.

24. Only a small portion of an iceberg floats above water, as shown in the image. A ship may actually be closer to running into a massive block of ice underwater than it would appear on the surface. If the ship is not turned or stopped in time, it could collide with the iceberg.

Standardized Test Preparation

Teacher's Note
To provide practice under more realistic testing conditions, give students 20 minutes to answer all of the questions in this Standardized Test Preparation.

Answers to the standardized test preparation can help you identify student misconceptions and misunderstandings.

Passage 1
1. C
2. I
3. B

Question 1: Although "overthrowing the government" is a meaning of the word *revolutionary*, it is not the correct meaning of the word in the passage. There is no mention of government in the passage. "Radically different" is also a meaning of the word *revolutionary* and is the correct answer.

Standardized Test Preparation

READING
Read each of the passages below. Then, answer the questions that follow each passage.

Passage 1 The Mariana Trench is about 11 km deep—that's deep enough to swallow Mount Everest, the tallest mountain in the world. Fewer than a dozen undersea vessels have ever ventured this deep into the ocean. Why? Water exerts tremendous pressure at this depth. A revolutionary new undersea vessel, *Deep Flight*, has a hull made of an extremely strong ceramic material that can withstand such pressure. Although *Deep Flight* has not made it to the bottom of the Mariana Trench, some scientists think this type of undersea vessel will one day be used routinely to explore the ocean floor.

1. What is the meaning of the word *revolutionary* in this passage?
   A strange
   B overthrowing the government
   C radically different
   D disgusting

2. Based on the name of the undersea vessel described in this passage, what does the vessel look like?
   F a robot
   G a house
   H a car
   I an airplane

3. Based on the passage, which of the following statements is a fact?
   A Scientists hope to fly *Deep Flight* to the top of Mount Everest.
   B *Deep Flight* can withstand very high pressures.
   C Scientists cannot explore the ocean without using *Deep Flight*.
   D *Deep Flight* has gone to the bottom of the Mariana Trench a dozen times.

Passage 2 Buoyancy is an object's ability to float. An object will float if the water it displaces has a mass greater than the object's mass. It will sink if the water it displaces has a mass less than its own mass. But if an object displaces its own mass in water, it will neither float nor sink. Instead, it will remain suspended in the water because of what is called *neutral buoyancy*.

A goldfish has neutral buoyancy. A goldfish has a sac in its body called a *swim bladder*. Gases from blood vessels can diffuse into and out of the swim bladder. When the goldfish needs to rise in the water, for example, gases diffuse into the swim bladder and cause it to inflate. The swim bladder helps the goldfish maintain neutral buoyancy.

1. What is the purpose of this passage?
   A to explain how a goldfish maintains neutral buoyancy
   B to explain how to change the buoyancy of an object
   C to convince people to buy goldfish
   D to describe objects that float and sink

2. What is the meaning of the word *suspended* in this passage?
   F not allowed to attend school
   G stopped for a period of time
   H weighed down
   I supported from sinking

3. What is buoyancy?
   A a sac in a goldfish's body
   B the ability to float
   C the mass of an object
   D an inflated balloon

Passage 2
1. A
2. I
3. B

Question 2: Answer choices F, G, and I are all correct meanings of the word *suspended*. However, both answer choices F and G can be eliminated because the passage does not discuss school attendance or mention stopping any activity for a period of time. The passage does discuss sinking and floating, and I is the correct answer.

The graph below shows the water pressure measured by a scientist at different depths in the ocean. Use the graph below to answer the questions that follow.

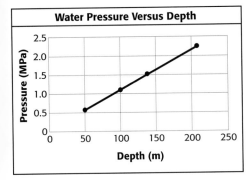

Water Pressure Versus Depth

1. What is the pressure on the object when it is 100 m underwater?
   A 1.0 MPa
   B 1.1 MPa
   C 1.5 MPa
   D 2.0 MPa

2. Based on the data in the graph, which of the following is the best estimate of the pressure at 250 m below the surface of the ocean?
   F 1.7 MPa
   G 2.2 MPa
   H 2.6 MPa
   I 5.0 MPa

3. Which of the following statements best describes the relationship between the water pressure on an object and the depth of the object in the ocean?
   A Water pressure increases as the depth increases.
   B Water pressure decreases as the depth increases.
   C Water pressure does not change as the depth increases.
   D Water pressure has no predictable relationship to the depth.

MATH

Read each question below, and choose the best answer.

1. Anna-Marie has a coil of wire. She uses a balance to find that the wire has a mass of 17.8 g. She uses water displacement to find that the volume of the wire is 2.0 cm^3. Density is equal to mass divided by volume. What is the density of the wire?
   A 0.11 g/cm^3
   B 8.9 g/cm^3
   C 19.8 g/cm^3
   D 35.6 g/cm^3

2. Hussain rode his bike 30 km this weekend. What is this distance expressed in meters?
   F 0.3 m
   G 300 m
   H 30,000 m
   I 300,000 m

3. Olivia purchased 21 tubes of oil paint at $3.95 per tube, which includes tax. What was the total cost of the 21 tubes of paint?
   A $65.15
   B $82.95
   C $89.10
   D $93.50

4. Javi filled a container halfway full with water. The container measures 2 m wide, 3 m long, and 1 m high. How many cubic meters of water are in the container?
   F 2 m^3
   G 3 m^3
   H 5 m^3
   I 6 m^3

5. Pressure is equal to force divided by area. Jenny pushes a door with a force of 12 N. The area of her hand is 96 cm^2. What is the pressure exerted by Jenny's hand on the door?
   A 0.125 N/cm
   B 0.125 N/cm^2
   C 8 N/cm
   D 8 N/cm^2

Standardized Test Preparation

1. B
2. H
3. A

 **TEST DOCTOR**

Question 2: To answer this question, students must extrapolate (or imagine) that the line in the graph continues up and to the right. Students should determine that the extrapolated line will cross the 250 m point somewhere just above 2.5 MPa. The only answer choice that is above and close to 2.5 MPa is H.

MATH
1. B
2. H
3. B
4. G
5. B

 **TEST DOCTOR**

Question 4: Students may be tempted to multiply the dimensions of the container to find the total volume of the container. However, the problem clearly states that the container is only halfway full with water. Therefore, students must multiply 2 m, 3 m, and 0.5 m to find the number of cubic meters in the container. The correct choice is G.

CHAPTER RESOURCES

Chapter Resource File

• Standardized Test Preparation GENERAL

State Resources

For specific resources for your state, visit **go.hrw.com** and type in the keyword **HSMSTR**.

Science, Technology, and Society

Teaching Strategy—GENERAL

Go to an open area with your students. Have students throw a Frisbee® with different amounts of thrust, or have them vary the angle of attack when they throw their disk. Discuss Bernoulli's principle and other aspects of lift. Have students attempt to throw a Frisbee without any spin (eliminating the angular momentum that gives the disk stability in flight). Compare a spinning Frisbee with a spinning top or a moving bicycle.

Science Fiction

Background

Sports and science fiction may seem like an unlikely combination, but Jack C. Haldeman II enjoys both. He has written science fiction stories, sports stories, and stories such as "Wet Behind the Ears," which is a bit of both! Before becoming a writer, Haldeman received a college degree in life science and worked as a research assistant, a medical technician, a statistician, a photographer, and an apprentice in a print shop.

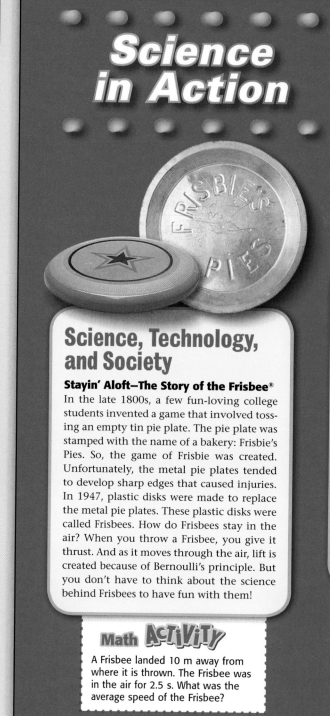

Science in Action

HOLT ANTHOLOGY OF
Science Fiction
HOLT, RINEHART AND WINSTON

Science, Technology, and Society

Stayin' Aloft—The Story of the Frisbee®
In the late 1800s, a few fun-loving college students invented a game that involved tossing an empty tin pie plate. The pie plate was stamped with the name of a bakery: Frisbie's Pies. So, the game of Frisbie was created. Unfortunately, the metal pie plates tended to develop sharp edges that caused injuries. In 1947, plastic disks were made to replace the metal pie plates. These plastic disks were called Frisbees. How do Frisbees stay in the air? When you throw a Frisbee, you give it thrust. And as it moves through the air, lift is created because of Bernoulli's principle. But you don't have to think about the science behind Frisbees to have fun with them!

Math ACTIVITY

A Frisbee landed 10 m away from where it is thrown. The Frisbee was in the air for 2.5 s. What was the average speed of the Frisbee?

Science Fiction

"Wet Behind the Ears" by Jack C. Haldeman II
Willie Joe Thomas cheated to get a swimming scholarship. Now, he is faced with a major swim meet, and his coach told him that he has to swim or be kicked off the team. Willie Joe could lose his scholarship.

One day, Willie Joe's roommate, Frank, announces that he has developed a new "sliding compound." And Frank also said something about using the compound to make ships go faster. So, Willie Joe thought, if it works for ships, it might work for swimming.

See what happens when Willie Joe tries to save his scholarship by using Frank's compound at the swim meet. Read "Wet Behind the Ears," by Jack C. Haldeman II in the *Holt Anthology of Science Fiction*.

Language Arts ACTIVITY

Analyze the story structure of "Wet Behind the Ears." In your analysis, identify the introduction, the rising action, the climax, and the denouement. Summarize your analysis in a chart.

Answer to Math Activity

The equation for average speed is:
average speed = distance ÷ time
average speed = 10 m ÷ 2.5 s = 4 m/s

Answer to Language Arts Activity

Accept all reasonable answers. Students should make a chart that analyzes the story structure of "Wet Behind the Ears." The first column of their chart should list the parts of the story (introduction, rising action, climax, and denouement). The second column should have a brief summary of what occurred in each part of the story.

Alisha Bracken

Scuba Instructor Alisha Bracken first started scuba diving in her freshman year of college. Her first dives were in a saltwater hot spring near Salt Lake City, Utah. "It was awesome," Bracken says. "There were nurse sharks, angelfish, puffer fish and brine shrimp!" Bracken enjoyed her experience so much that she wanted to share it with other people. The best way to do that was to become an instructor and teach other people to dive.

Bracken says one of the biggest challenges of being a scuba instructor is teaching people to adapt and function in a foreign environment. She believes that learning to dive properly is important not only for the safety of the diver but also for the protection of the underwater environment. She relies on science principles to help teach people how to control their movements and protect the natural environment. "Buoyancy is the foundation of teaching people to dive comfortably," she explains. "Without it, we cannot float on the surface or stay off the bottom. Underwater life can be damaged if students do not learn and apply the concepts of buoyancy."

Social Studies ACTIVITY

Scuba divers and other underwater explorers sometimes investigate shipwrecks on the bottom of the ocean. Research the exploration of a specific shipwreck. Make a poster showing what artifacts were retrieved from the shipwreck and what was learned from the exploration.

go.hrw.com

To learn more about these Science in Action topics, visit go.hrw.com and type in the keyword **HP5FLUF**.

Current Science

Check out Current Science® articles related to this chapter by visiting go.hrw.com. Just type in the keyword **HP5CS07**.

Careers

Background

The word *scuba* is an acronym that stands for *self-contained underwater breathing apparatus*. The first scuba breathing device, known as the aqualung, was invented by Jacques Cousteau and Emile Gagnan in 1943. This invention allowed divers to move freely underwater for long periods of time.

Scuba diving has become a popular form of recreation, with about one million people becoming certified divers every year. To rent scuba equipment, divers must be certified by an organization such as the Professional Association of Diving Instructors (PADI) or the National Association of Underwater Instructors (NAUI). Some organizations certify divers as young as 10 years old, while other groups have an age requirement of 12 years. In order to receive a certification, divers must take an open water diving course, which can last from three days to six weeks.

Answer to Social Studies Activity

Accept all reasonable answers. All students' posters should identify a shipwreck, list or show some of the artifacts collected from the shipwreck, and summarize what was learned by the exploration of the shipwreck.

Work and Machines
Chapter Planning Guide

Compression guide:
To shorten instruction because of time limitations, omit Section 3.

OBJECTIVES	LABS, DEMONSTRATIONS, AND ACTIVITIES	TECHNOLOGY RESOURCES
PACING • 135 min pp. 92–99 **Chapter Opener**	SE **Start-up Activity,** p. 93 GENERAL	OSP **Parent Letter** ■ CD **Student Edition on CD-ROM** CD **Guided Reading Audio CD** ■ TR **Chapter Starter Transparency*** VID **Brain Food Video Quiz**
Section 1 Work and Power • Determine when work is being done on an object. • Calculate the amount of work done on an object. • Explain the difference between work and power.	TE **Activity** Work in Sports, p. 94 GENERAL TE **Activity** Work Done on a Spring Scale, p. 96 GENERAL SE **Quick Lab** Get to Work!, p. 97 ◆ GENERAL CRF **Datasheet for Quick Lab*** SE **Skills Practice Lab** A Powerful Workout, p. 114 GENERAL CRF **Datasheet for Chapter Lab*** LB **Inquiry Labs** Get an Arm and an Egg Up* ADVANCED SE **Science in Action** Math, Social Studies, and Language Arts Activities, pp. 120–121 GENERAL	OSP **Lesson Plans** (also in print) TR **Bellringer Transparency*** TR P29 Work or Not Work?* TR P30 Force Times Distance* TR *LINK TO LIFE SCIENCE* L80 A Pair of Muscles in the Arm* CRF **SciLinks Activity*** GENERAL VID **Lab Videos for Physical Science** CD **Science Tutor**
PACING • 45 min pp. 100–105 **Section 2 What Is a Machine?** • Explain how a machine makes work easier. • Describe and give examples of the force-distance trade-off that occurs when a machine is used. • Calculate mechanical advantage. • Explain why machines are not 100% efficient.	TE **Connection Activity** Home Economics, p. 100 GENERAL TE **Activity** Machines as Solutions to Problems, p. 102 ADVANCED TE **Connection Activity** Math, p. 102 GENERAL TE **Connection Activity** Life Science, p. 103 GENERAL TE **Connection Activity** History, p. 103 GENERAL SE **School-to-Home Activity** Useful Friction, p. 104 GENERAL LB **Whiz-Bang Demonstrations** Pull-Ease, Please!* BASIC LB **Whiz-Bang Demonstrations** A Clever Lever* BASIC	OSP **Lesson Plans** (also in print) TR **Bellringer Transparency*** TR P30 Input Force and Distance* TR P31 Machines Change the Size and/or Direction of a Force* SE **Internet Activity,** p. 102 GENERAL CD **Science Tutor**
PACING • 45 min pp. 106–113 **Section 3 Types of Machines** • Identify and give examples of the six types of simple machines. • Analyze the mechanical advantage provided by each simple machine. • Identify the simple machines that make up a compound machine.	TE **Activity** Loads on a First-Class Level, p. 106 GENERAL TE **Activity** Classifying Tools, p. 107 GENERAL TE **Connection Activity** Real World, p. 108 GENERAL TE **Activity** Wheels and Axles, p. 109 BASIC TE **Activity** Gears, p. 109 ADVANCED TE **Activity** Zippers, p. 111 GENERAL TE **Activity** Screws, p. 111 BASIC TE **Connection Activity** Math, p. 111 GENERAL SE **School-to-Home Activity** Everyday Machines, p. 112 GENERAL SE **Skills Practice Lab** Inclined to Move, p. 201 GENERAL SE **Skills Practice Lab** Wheeling and Dealing, p. 202 ADVANCED SE **Inquiry Lab** Building Machines, p. 204 BASIC LB **Long-Term Projects & Research Ideas** To Complicate Things* ADVANCED CRF **Datasheet for LabBook***	OSP **Lesson Plans** (also in print) TR **Bellringer Transparency*** CD **Science Tutor**

PACING • 90 min

CHAPTER REVIEW, ASSESSMENT, AND STANDARDIZED TEST PREPARATION

CRF **Vocabulary Activity*** GENERAL
SE **Chapter Review,** pp. 116–117 GENERAL
CRF **Chapter Review*** ■ GENERAL
CRF **Chapter Tests A*** ■ GENERAL **, B*** ADVANCED **, C*** SPECIAL NEEDS
SE **Standardized Test Preparation,** pp. 118–119 GENERAL
CRF **Standardized Test Preparation*** GENERAL
CRF **Performance-Based Assessment*** GENERAL
OSP **Test Generator, Test Item Listing**

Online and Technology Resources

Visit **go.hrw.com** for access to Holt Online Learning, or enter the keyword **HP7 Home** for a variety of free online resources.

 One-Stop Planner® CD-ROM

This CD-ROM package includes:
• Lab Materials QuickList Software
• Holt Calendar Planner
• Customizable Lesson Plans
• Printable Worksheets

• ExamView® Test Generator
• Interactive Teacher's Edition
• Holt PuzzlePro®
• Holt PowerPoint® Resources

SKILLS DEVELOPMENT RESOURCES	SECTION REVIEW AND ASSESSMENT	CORRELATIONS
SE Pre-Reading Activity, p. 92 GENERAL **OSP** Science Puzzlers, Twisters & Teasers GENERAL		National Science Education Standards SAI 1
CRF Directed Reading A* ■ BASIC, B* SPECIAL NEEDS **IT** Interactive Textbook* Struggling Readers **CRF** Vocabulary and Section Summary* ■ GENERAL **SE** Reading Strategy Reading Organizer, p. 94 GENERAL **TE** Reading Strategy Prediction Guide, p. 95 GENERAL **TE** Support for English Language Learners, p. 95 **TE** Inclusion Strategies, p. 96 **SE** Math Focus More Power to You, p. 98 GENERAL **MS** Math Skills for Science Work and Power* GENERAL	**SE** Reading Checks, pp. 94, 97, 98 GENERAL **TE** Reteaching, p. 98 BASIC **TE** Quiz, p. 98 GENERAL **TE** Alternative Assessment, p. 98 GENERAL **SE** Section Review,* p. 99 ■ GENERAL **CRF** Section Quiz* ■ GENERAL	UCP 3; SAI 1, 2; PS 3a; *Chapter Lab:* SAI 1, 2; PS 3a; ST 2
CRF Directed Reading A* ■ BASIC, B* SPECIAL NEEDS **IT** Interactive Textbook* Struggling Readers **CRF** Vocabulary and Section Summary* ■ GENERAL **SE** Reading Strategy Prediction Guide, p. 100 GENERAL **TE** Reading Strategy Concept Mapping, p. 101 BASIC **SE** Math Practice Finding the Advantage, p. 103 GENERAL **TE** Support for English Language Learners, p. 103 **MS** Math Skills for Science Mechanical Advantage* GENERAL	**SE** Reading Checks, pp. 101, 102, 104 GENERAL **TE** Homework, p. 102 GENERAL **TE** Reteaching, p. 104 BASIC **TE** Quiz, p. 104 GENERAL **TE** Alternative Assessment, p. 104 GENERAL **SE** Section Review,* p. 105 GENERAL **CRF** Section Quiz* ■ GENERAL	UCP 3; SAI 1, 2; ST 2
CRF Directed Reading A* ■ BASIC, B* SPECIAL NEEDS **IT** Interactive Textbook* Struggling Readers **CRF** Vocabulary and Section Summary* ■ GENERAL **SE** Reading Strategy Mnemonics, p. 106 GENERAL **SE** Math Focus Mechanical Advantage of an Inclined Plane, p. 110 GENERAL **TE** Support for English Language Learners, p. 110 **CRF** Reinforcement Worksheet Finding Machines in Everyday Life* BASIC **CRF** Reinforcement Worksheet Mechanical Advantage and Efficiency* BASIC **CRF** Critical Thinking Building Works of Art* ADVANCED	**SE** Reading Checks, pp. 107, 109, 110, 112 GENERAL **TE** Reteaching, p. 112 BASIC **TE** Quiz, p. 112 GENERAL **TE** Alternative Assessment, p. 112 GENERAL **SE** Section Review,* p. 113 ■ GENERAL **CRF** Section Quiz* ■ GENERAL	UCP 3, 5; SAI 1; ST 1, 2; *LabBook:* SAI 1

SCiLINKS.
NSTA
www.scilinks.org
Maintained by the **National Science Teachers Association.** See Chapter Enrichment pages that follow for a complete list of topics.

Current Science®

Check out *Current Science* articles and activities by visiting the HRW Web site at **go.hrw.com**. Just type in the keyword **HP5CS08T.**

Classroom Videos
• **Lab Videos** demonstrate the chapter lab.
• **Brain Food Video Quizzes** help students review the chapter material.

Classroom CD-ROMs
• **Guided Reading Audio CD** (Also in Spanish)
• **Interactive Explorations**
• **Virtual Investigations**
• **Visual Concepts**
• **Science Tutor**

Holt Lab Generator CD-ROM

Search for any lab by topic, standard, difficulty level, or time. Edit any lab to fit your needs, or create your own labs. Use the Lab Materials QuickList software to customize your lab materials list.

Visual Resources

CHAPTER STARTER TRANSPARENCY

Work and Machines CHAPTER STARTER

Would You Believe . . . ?

The Great Pyramid, located in Giza (GEE zuh), Egypt, could be called the largest tombstone ever created. A monument and tomb for the pharaoh King Khufu (KOO foo), it covers an area the size of seven city blocks and rises about 40 stories high. The Great Pyramid is the largest of the three pyramids of Giza. It was built around 2600 BCE and took less than 30 years to complete—a relatively short period of time considering that construction equipment didn't exist 4,000 years ago. So how did the Egyptians do it?

To build the Great Pyramid, the Egyptians cut and moved more than 2 million stone blocks, most averaging 2,000 kg (probably over 40 times your own mass). The blocks were cut from a stone quarry, moved near the pyramid, and then lifted into place. To finish in less than 30 years, the Egyptians would

have had to cut, move, and lift about 200 blocks per day! The Egyptians did not have cranes, bulldozers, or any other heavy-duty machines. What they had were two simple machines–the inclined plane and the lever.

Archaeologists have found the remains of inclined planes, or ramps, made from mud, stone, and wood. The Egyptians pushed or pulled the blocks along these ramps to raise them to the proper height. Using ramps required less force than lifting the blocks straight up. In addition, notches in many blocks indicate that huge levers were used like giant crowbars to lift and move the heavy blocks. The workers pushed down on the lever, and the lever pushed up on a stone block, lifting it into place.

The Egyptians used simple machines to create something truly amazing. In this chapter, you'll learn about work and how machines can help make work easier.

The Great Pyramid was built over 4,000 years ago and remains one of the Seven Wonders of the World.

BELLRINGER TRANSPARENCIES

Work and Machines BELLRINGER TRANSPARENCY

Section: Work and Power

First, in your **science journal**, define what specific kind of work is being done in each activity below. Then, select the activities that require the least amount of work.

- carrying heavy books home
- reading a 300-page novel
- skiing for 1 hour
- lifting a 45 kg mass
- holding a steel beam in place for 3 hours
- jacking up a car

Section: What Is a Machine?

Write a one-paragraph answer in your **science journal** to the following question:

Why do we use machines?

TEACHING TRANSPARENCIES

Work or Not Work? TEACHING TRANSPARENCY P29

Example	Direction of force	Direction of motion	Doing work?
	→	→	Yes
	↑	→	No
	↓	↑	Yes
	↓	→	No

Force Times Distance TEACHING TRANSPARENCY P30

$W = 80 N \times 1 m = 80 J$ — The force needed to lift an object is equal to the gravitational force on the object—in other words, the object's weight.

$W = 160 N \times 1 m = 160 J$ — If you increase the weight, an increased force is needed to lift the object. This increases the amount of work done.

$W = 80 N \times 2 m = 160 J$ — Increasing the distance also increases the amount of work done.

Input Force and Distance

Lifting this box straight up requires an input force equal to the weight of the box. $W = 450 N \times 1 m = 450 J$

Using a ramp to lift the box requires an input force less than the weight of the box, but the input force must be exerted over a greater distance than if you didn't use a ramp. $W = 150 N \times 3 m = 450 J$

TEACHING TRANSPARENCIES

Machines Change the Size and/or Direction of a Force

A simple pulley changes the direction of the input force, but the output force is the same as the input force.

Input force / Output force

A nutcracker increases the force applied and applies it over a shorter distance.

Input force / Output force

When a screwdriver is used as a lever, it increases the force and applies the force over a greater distance than the distance over which the input force is applied.

Input force / Output force

TEACHING TRANSPARENCY P31

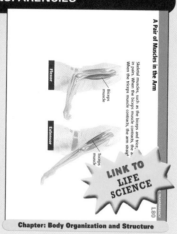

A Pair of Muscles in the Arm

Skeletal muscles, such as the biceps and triceps, work in pairs. When the biceps muscle contracts, the arm bends. When the triceps muscle contracts, the arm straightens.

Flexor — Biceps muscle
Extensor — Triceps muscle

LINK TO LIFE SCIENCE

Chapter: Body Organization and Structure L80

CONCEPT MAPPING TRANSPARENCY

Work and Machines CONCEPT MAPPING TRANSPARENCY

Use the following terms to complete the concept map below: **work input, output force, work, lever, distance, input force, mechanical efficiency, mechanical advantage**

is defined as → force → applied through a → and is made easier by machines, such as a

is done by machines, which have → which is → work output → divided by

which is → divided by

Planning Resources

LESSON PLANS

Lesson Plan SAMPLE

Section: Waves

Pacing

Regular Schedule: with lab(s):2 days / without lab(s):2 days
Block Schedule: with lab(s):1 1/2 days / without lab(s):1 day

Objectives

1. Relate the seven properties of life to a living organism.
2. Describe seven themes that can help you to organize what you learn about biology.
3. Identify the tiny structures that make up all living organisms.
4. Differentiate between reproduction and heredity and between metabolism and homeostasis.

National Science Education Standards Covered

LSInter1: Cells have particular structures that underlie their functions.

LSMat1: Most cell functions involve chemical reactions.

LSBeh1: Cells store and use information to guide their functions.

UCP1: Cell functions are regulated.

SI1: Cells can differentiate and form complete multicellular organisms.

PS1: Species evolve over time.

ESS1: The great diversity of organisms is the result of more than 3.5 billion years of evolution.

ESS2: Natural selection and its evolutionary consequences provide a scientific explanation for the fossil record of ancient life forms as well as for the striking molecular similarities observed among the diverse species of living organisms.

ST1: The millions of different species of plants, animals, and microorganisms that live on Earth today are related by descent from common ancestors.

ST2: The energy for life primarily comes from the sun.

SPSP1: The complexity and organization of organisms accommodates the need for obtaining, transforming, transporting, releasing, and eliminating the matter and energy used to sustain the organism.

SPSP6: As matter and energy flows through different levels of organization of living systems—cells, organs, communities—and between living systems and the physical environment, chemical elements are recombined in different ways.

HNS1: Organisms have behavioral responses to internal and external stimuli.

PARENT LETTER

SAMPLE

Dear Parent,

Your son's or daughter's science class will soon begin exploring the chapter entitled "The World of Physical Science." In this chapter, students will learn about how the scientific method applies to the world of physical science and the role of physical science in the world. By the end of the chapter, students should demonstrate a clear understanding of the chapter's main ideas and be able to discuss the following topics:

1. physical science as the study of energy and matter (Section 1)
2. the role of physical science in the world around them (Section 1)
3. careers that rely on physical science (Section 1)
4. the steps used in the scientific method (Section 2)
5. examples of technology (Section 2)
6. how the scientific method is used to answer questions and solve problems (Section 2)
7. how our knowledge of science changes over time (Section 2)
8. how models represent real objects or systems (Section 3)
9. examples of different ways models are used in science (Section 3)
10. the importance of the International System of Units (Section 4)
11. the appropriate units to use for particular measurements (Section 4)
12. how area and density are derived quantities (Section 4)

Questions to Ask Along the Way

You can help your son or daughter learn about these topics by asking interesting questions such as the following:

- What are some surprising careers that use physical science?
- What is a characteristic of a good hypothesis?
- When is it a good idea to use a model?
- Why do Americans measure things in terms of inches and quarts, feet and meters ?

ALSO IN SPANISH

TEST ITEM LISTING

TEST ITEM LISTING
The World of Science SAMPLE

MULTIPLE CHOICE

1. A limitation of models is that
   a. they are large enough to see.
   b. they do not act exactly like the things that they model.
   c. they are smaller than the things they model.
   d. they model unfamiliar things.
   Answer: B Difficulty: 1 Section: 3 Objective: 2

2. The length 10 m is equal to
   a. 100 cm.
   c. 10,000 mm.
   b. 1,000 cm.
   d. Both (b) and (c)
   Answer: D Difficulty: 1 Section: 3 Objective: 2

3. To be valid, a hypothesis must be
   a. testable.
   c. made into a law.
   b. supported by evidence.
   d. Both (a) and (b)
   Answer: D Difficulty: 1 Section: 2 Objective: 1

4. The statement "Sheila has a stain on her shirt" is an example of a(n)
   a. law.
   c. observation.
   b. hypothesis.
   d. prediction.
   Answer: B Difficulty: 1 Section: 2 Objective: 2

5. A hypothesis is often developed out of
   a. observations.
   c. laws.
   b. experiments.
   d. Both (a) and (b)
   Answer: D Difficulty: 1 Section: 2 Objective: 2

6. How many milliliters are in 3.5 kL?
   a. 3,500. mL
   c. 3,500. 000. mL
   b. 0.0035 mL.
   d. 35,000 mL.
   Answer: C Difficulty: 1 Section: 3 Objective: 2

7. A map of Seattle is an example of a
   a. law.
   c. model.
   b. theory.
   d. unit.
   Answer: B Difficulty: 1 Section: 3 Objective: 2

8. A lab has the safety icons shown below. These icons mean that you should wear
   a. only safety goggles.
   c. safety goggles and a lab apron.
   b. only a lab apron.
   d. safety goggles, a lab apron, and gloves.
   Answer: B Difficulty: 1 Section: 3 Objective: 2

9. The law of conservation of mass says the lot of mass before a chemical change is
   a. more than the total mass after the change.
   b. less than the total mass after the change.
   c. the same as the total mass after the change.
   d. not the same as the total mass after the change.
   Answer: B Difficulty: 1 Section: 3 Objective: 2

10. In which of the following areas might you find a geochemist at work?
    a. studying the chemistry of rocks
    c. studying fishes
    b. studying forestry
    d. studying the atmosphere
    Answer: B Difficulty: 1 Section: 1 Objective: 2

One-Stop Planner® CD-ROM

This CD-ROM includes all of the resources shown here and the following time-saving tools:

- **Lab Materials QuickList Software**
- **Customizable lesson plans**
- **Holt Calendar Planner**
- **The powerful ExamView® Test Generator**

Meeting Individual Needs

DIRECTED READING A

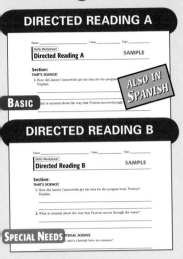

Skills Worksheet
Directed Reading A — SAMPLE

Section:
THAT'S SCIENCE!

1. How did James Czarnowski get his idea for the penguin boat?
Explain.

ALSO IN SPANISH

BASIC

that is unusual about the way that Proteus moves through

DIRECTED READING B

Skills Worksheet
Directed Reading B — SAMPLE

Section:
THAT'S SCIENCE!

1. How did James Czarnowski get his idea for the penguin boat, Proteus?
Explain.

2. What is unusual about the way that Proteus moves through the water?

SPECIAL NEEDS PHYSICAL SCIENCE

a and a cheetah have in common?

VOCABULARY ACTIVITY

Activity
Vocabulary Activity — SAMPLE

Getting the Dirt on the Soil
After you finish reading Chapter: [Unique Title], try this puzzle. Use the clues below to unscramble the vocabulary words. Write your answer in the space provided.

...kdown of rock into ...and smaller pieces
GNETH

... of rock broken beneath not
...
NGETH

9. the chemical breakdown of rocks and minerals into new substances CAMILCHE THEARIGWEN

GENERAL

VOCABULARY AND SECTION SUMMARY

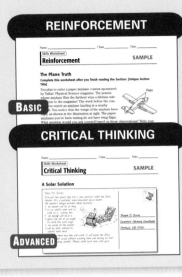

Skills Worksheet
Vocabulary & Notes — SAMPLE

Section:
VOCABULARY

In your own words, write a definition of the following term in the space provided.

1. scientific method

2. technology

ALSO IN SPANISH

GENERAL

REINFORCEMENT

Skills Worksheet
Reinforcement — SAMPLE

The Plane Truth
Complete this worksheet after you finish reading the Section: [Unique Section Title]

You plan to enter a paper airplane contest sponsored by Talkin' Physical Science magazine. The person whose airplane flies the farthest wins a lifetime subscription to the magazine! The week before the contest, you watch an airplane landing at a nearby airport. You notice that the wings of the airplane have flaps, as shown in the illustration at right. The paper airplanes you've been testing do not have wing flaps. What question would you ask yourself based on these observations? Write your

Flaps

BASIC

CRITICAL THINKING

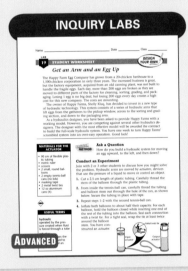

Skills Worksheet
Critical Thinking — SAMPLE

A Solar Solution

Dear Mr. Burns,
...

Joseph D. Burns
...
Portland, OR 97201

ADVANCED

SCILINKS ACTIVITY

Activity
SciLinks Activity — SAMPLE

MARINE ECOSYSTEMS
Go to www.scilinks.com. To find links related to marine ecosystems, type in the keyword HL5490. Then, use the links to answer the questions about marine ecosys-

SciLinks *NSTA*

...percentage of the Earth's surface is covered by water?

GENERAL

SCIENCE PUZZLERS, TWISTERS & TEASERS

CHAPTER **8** **SCIENCE PUZZLERS, TWISTERS & TEASERS**
Work and Machines

Parallel Puzzle
1. What do all the words in the left column have in common that is not shared by any of the words in the right column?

ramp	hammer
screw	faucet
chisel	axle
doorstop	hinge

...zzle
...of this machine are identical. They all have an inner...of 10 cm and an inner shaft circumference of 5 cm. ...is rotated one quarter turn counterclockwise, how...will the clock's hand point?

GENERAL

Labs and Activities

LONG-TERM PROJECTS & RESEARCH IDEAS

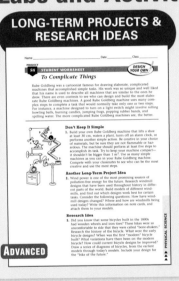

PROJECT
S8 **STUDENT WORKSHEET** — DESIGN YOUR OWN

To Complicate Things

Rube Goldberg was a cartoonist famous for drawing elaborate, complicated machines that accomplished simple tasks. His work was so unique and well liked that his name is used to describe all machines that are similar to the ones he drew. There are even contests to see who can design and build the most elaborate Rube Goldberg machine. A good Rube Goldberg machine uses many complex steps to complete a task that would normally take only one or two steps. For instance, a machine designed to turn on a light switch might involve rolling bowling balls, burning candles, jumping frogs, popping rubber bands, and spilling water. The more complicated Rube Goldberg machines are, the better.

Don't Keep It Simple
1. Build your own Rube Goldberg machine that lifts a shoe at least 30 cm, waters a plant, turns off an alarm clock, or performs another simple action. Be creative in your choice of materials, but be sure they are not flammable or hazardous. The machine should perform at least five steps to accomplish its task. Try to keep your machine compact—it shouldn't be bigger than 1 m³. Use as many simple machines as you can in your Rube Goldberg machine. Compete with your classmates to see who can be the most creative and use the most steps.

Another Long-Term Project Idea
2. Wind power is one of the most promising sources of pollution-free energy for the future. Research windmill designs that have been used throughout history in different parts of the world. Build models of different windmills, and find out which designs work best for certain tasks. Consider the following questions: How have windmill designs changed? Where and how are windmills being used today? Write this information on note cards, and attach them to your models.

Research Idea
3. Did you know that some bicycles built in the 1800s had wooden wheels and iron tires? These bikes were so uncomfortable to ride that they were called "bone-shakers." Research the history of the bicycle. What were the early bicycle designs? When was the first "modern" bicycle built? What variations have there been on the modern bicycle? How could current bicycle designs be improved? Draw a series of diagrams of bicycles, from the earliest models through today's models. Include your design for the "bike of the future."

ADVANCED PHYSICAL SCIENCE

WHIZ-BANG DEMONSTRATIONS

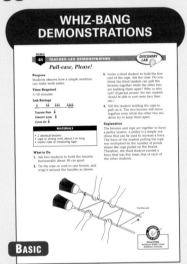

DEMO
48 **TEACHER-LED DEMONSTRATION** — DISCOVERY LAB

Pull-ease, Please!

Purpose
Students observe how a simple machine can make work easier.

Time Required
5–10 minutes

Lab Ratings
TEACHER PREP ▲▲
CONCEPT LEVEL ▲▲
CLEAN UP ▲

MATERIALS
• 2 identical brooms
• rope or string cord, about 1 m long
• metric ruler or measuring tape

What to Do
1. Ask two students to hold the brooms horizontally about 50 cm apart.
2. Tie the rope or cord to one broom, and wrap it around the handles as shown.

3. Invite a third student to hold the free end of the rope. Ask the class: Do you think the third student can pull the brooms together while the other two are holding them apart? Why or why not? (Expected answer: No; two students should be able to exert more force than one.)
4. Tell the student holding the rope to pull on it. The two brooms will move together even while the other two students try to keep them apart.

Explanation
The brooms and rope act together to form a pulley system. A pulley is a simple machine that can be used to increase a force. The force of the student pulling the rope was multiplied by the number of points where the rope pulled on the broom. Therefore, the third student exerted a force that was five times that of each of the other students.

USEFUL TERMS
hydraulic operated by the pressure created when liquid is forced through a...
...the...

BASIC

INQUIRY LABS

LAB
19 **STUDENT WORKSHEET** — DESIGN YOUR OWN

Get an Arm and an Egg Up

The Happy Farm Egg Company has grown from a 20-chicken henhouse to a 1,500-chicken corporation in only three years. The increased business is great, but the factory equipment, acquired from an old canning plant, was not built to handle the fragile eggs. Each day, more than 200 eggs are broken as they are moved to different parts of the factory for cleaning, sorting, grading, and packaging. Losing 1 egg is no big deal, but losing 200 eggs every day creates a high cost for this new company. The costs are mounting.

The owner of Happy Farms, Shelly Klug, has decided to invest in a new type of hydraulic technology. This system consists of a series of hydraulic arms that lift eggs from the gatherers to the pickup window, across to the sorting and grading section, and down to the packaging area.

As a hydraulics designer, you have been asked to provide Happy Farms with a working model. However, you are competing against several other hydraulics designers. The designer with the most effective model will be awarded the contract to build the full-scale hydraulic system. You have one week to turn the Happy Farms' scrambled system into an over-easy operation. Good luck!

MATERIALS FOR THE ACTUATOR
• 90 cm of flexible plastic tubing
• metric ruler
• scissors
• 2 small, round balloons
• 2 empty tennis-ball cans (no lids)
• masking tape
• 2 metal twist ties
• 2 clean aluminum cans (4)

DESIGN YOUR OWN **METHOD**

Ask a Question
How do you build a hydraulic system for moving an egg upward, to the left, and then down?

Conduct an Experiment
Join with 2 or 3 other students to discuss how you might solve the problem. Hydraulic arms are moved by actuators, devices that use the pressure of a liquid to move or control an object.
1. Cut a 2.5 cm length of plastic tubing. Carefully thread the stem of the balloon through the plastic tubing.
2. From inside the tennis-ball can, carefully thread the tubing and balloon stem out through the hole of the can, as shown here. Secure the tubing in place with tape.
3. Repeat steps 1–2 with the second tennis-ball can.
4. Inflate both balloons to about half their capacity. For each balloon, hold the balloon closed while inserting one end of the rest of the tubing into the balloon. Seal each connection with a twist tie. For a tight seal, wrap the tie at least twice around the balloon stem. You have constructed an actuator.

ADVANCED

DATASHEETS FOR QUICK LABS

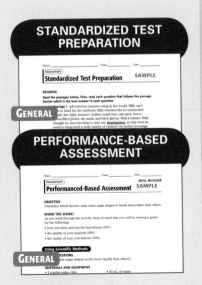

TEACHER RESOURCE PAGE
Quick Lab — DATASHEET FOR QUICK LAB
Reaction to Stress — SAMPLE

Background
The graph below illustrates changes that occur in the membrane potential of a neuron during an action potential. Use the graph to answer the following questions. Refer to Figure 3 as needed.

DATASHEETS FOR CHAPTER LABS

TEACHER RESOURCE PAGE
Skills Worksheet — DATASHEET FOR CHAPTER LAB
Using Scientific Methods — SAMPLE

Teacher's Notes
TIME REQUIRED
One 45-minute class period.

DATASHEETS FOR LABBOOK

TEACHER RESOURCE PAGE
Skills Practice Lab — DATASHEET FOR LABBOOK
Does It All Add Up? — SAMPLE

Teacher's Notes
TIME REQUIRED
One 45-minute class period.

Review and Assessments

SECTION QUIZ

Assessment
Section Quiz — SAMPLE

Section:
In the space provided, write the letter of the description that best matches the term or phrase.

____ 1. building molecules that can be used as an energy source, or breaking down molecules in which energy is stored

____ ...the process by which light energy is converted to chemical energy

____ ...an organism that uses sunlight or inorganic substances to make organic compounds

ALSO IN SPANISH

GENERAL

SECTION REVIEW

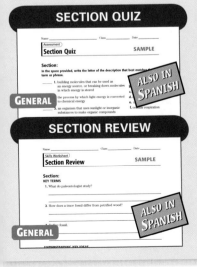

Skills Worksheet
Section Review — SAMPLE

Section:
KEY TERMS
1. What do paleontologists study?

2. How does a trace fossil differ from a petrified wood?

...lithic fossil

ALSO IN SPANISH

GENERAL
...UNDERSTANDING KEY IDEAS

CHAPTER REVIEW

Skills Worksheet
Chapter Review — SAMPLE

USING VOCABULARY
1. Define biome in your own words.

2. Describe the characteristics of a savanna and a desert.

... identify the relationship between trophic and nutritional

ALSO IN SPANISH

GENERAL

CHAPTER TEST A

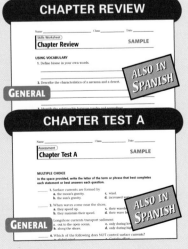

Assessment
Chapter Test A — SAMPLE

MULTIPLE CHOICE
In the space provided, write the letter of the term or phrase that best completes each statement or best answers each question.

____ 1. Surface currents are formed by
a. the moon's gravity.   c. wind.
b. the sun's gravity.   d. increased water density.

____ 2. When waves come near the shore,
a. they speed up.   c. their wavelength increases.
b. they maintain their speed. d. their wave height increases.

____ 3. Longshore currents transport sediment
... out to the open ocean.   c. only during low tide.
... along the shore.   d. only during high tide.

____ 4. Which of the following does NOT control surface currents?

ALSO IN SPANISH

GENERAL

CHAPTER TEST B

Assessment
Chapter Test B — SAMPLE

MULTIPLE CHOICE
In the space provided, write the letter of the term or phrase that best completes each statement or best answers each question.

____ 1. Surface currents are formed by
a. the moon's gravity.   c. wind.
b. the sun's gravity.   d. increased water density.

____ 2. When waves come near the shore,
a. they speed up.   c. their wavelength increases.
b. they maintain their speed. d. their wave height increases.

ADVANCED

CHAPTER TEST C

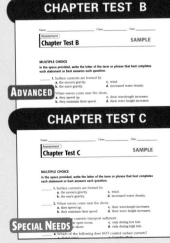

Assessment
Chapter Test C — SAMPLE

MULTIPLE CHOICE
In the space provided, write the letter of the term or phrase that best completes each statement or best answers each question.

____ 1. Surface currents are formed by
a. the moon's gravity.   c. wind.
b. the sun's gravity.   d. increased water density.

____ 2. When waves come near the shore,
a. they speed up.   c. their wavelength increases.
b. they maintain their speed. d. their wave height increases.

... currents transport sediment
... open ocean.   c. only during low tide.
... the shore.   d. only during high tide.

____ 4. Which of the following does NOT control surface currents?

SPECIAL NEEDS

STANDARDIZED TEST PREPARATION

Assessment
Standardized Test Preparation — SAMPLE

READING
Read the passages below. Then, read each question that follows the passage. Decide which is the best answer to each question.

Passage 1 ...adventurous summer camp in the world. Billy can't ...to head for the outdoors. Billy checked the recommended ...ply list: light, summer clothes; sunscreen; rain gear; heavy, ...n-filled jacket; ski mask; and thick gloves. Wait a minute! Billy thought he was traveling to only one **destination**, so why does he need to bring such a wide variety of clothes? On further investigate...

GENERAL

PERFORMANCE-BASED ASSESSMENT

Assessment
Performed-Based Assessment — SKILL BUILDER SAMPLE

OBJECTIVE
Determine which factors cause some sugar shapes to break down faster than others.

KNOW THE SCORE!
As you work through the activity, keep in mind that you will be earning a grade for the following:
• how you form and test the hypotheses (40%)
• the quality of your analysis (40%)
• the clarity of your conclusions (20%)

Using Scientific Methods
...QUESTIONS
...sugar shapes erode more rapidly than others?

MATERIALS AND EQUIPMENT
• 90 mL of water
• 1 regular sugar cube

GENERAL

This Chapter Enrichment provides relevant and interesting information to expand and enhance your presentation of the chapter material.

Section 1

Work and Power

James Prescott Joule (1818–1889)

- James Joule was an English physicist who established that mechanical energy, electrical energy, and thermal energy are basically the same and that one type of energy can be converted into another. This principle is the basis of the first law of thermodynamics, the conservation of energy. It states that the total energy in any closed system remains the same, even when the energy is converted from one type to another.

- Joule developed mathematical equations that described the thermal energy of current in electrical wire and the amount of work needed to produce a unit of thermal energy. The standard unit of work and energy is called the *joule* and was named in Joule's honor.

Converting Energy

- In physics, *energy* is the ability to do work. Energy can exist in different forms, such as thermal, electrical, nuclear, potential, kinetic, and chemical. All forms of energy have to do with motion or position. Energy can be converted from one form to another. For example, electrical energy is usually converted from chemical, nuclear, or mechanical energy.

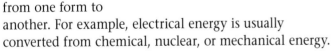

Is That a Fact!

- The term *horsepower* was coined in the late 18th century by Scottish engineer James Watt, who used horses as a measure of power in his experiments. In the English system, 1 horsepower can accomplish 33,000 foot-pounds of work per minute, or allow one to exert the force necessary to lift 33,000 lb by 1 ft in 1 min. This unit was based on the draft horse, a horse adapted for pulling heavy loads.

Section 2

What Is a Machine?

Leonardo da Vinci (1452–1519)

- Leonardo da Vinci was an Italian painter, sculptor, and inventor. The motivating interest behind all of his work was the appearance of everyday things and the way they operated. He studied the flight of birds, the movement of water, the growth of plants, and the anatomy of the human body.

- One of da Vinci's interests was the mechanical advantage that could be obtained with gears. Da Vinci made drawings of complex machines that were centuries ahead of their time. Among his drawings were plans for tanks, a helicopter, and other aircraft. He was especially concerned with the problems of friction and resistance. He described and drew screws, gears, hydraulic jacks, transmission gears, and swiveling devices.

- Da Vinci thought that the basic laws of mechanics operated the same way in all aspects of the world and were the keys to understanding the world and reproducing it through art.

Is That a Fact!

- Many industrial towns in early America were located where water flow could be assured all year. Water and wind were the primary sources of mechanical energy until the end of the 18th century, when steam power was developed. Steam-powered mechanical devices launched the Industrial Revolution.

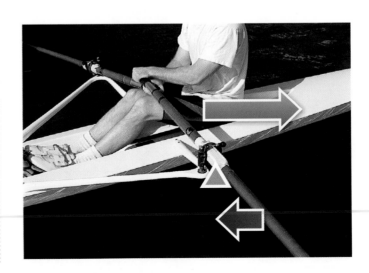

Perpetual Motion

- For centuries, inventors have tried to build a perpetual-motion machine—a device that would run forever once it is set in motion. However, no such machines can work because the laws of thermodynamics would be violated.

- A perpetual-motion machine would have to deliver as much or more energy than is put into it. The first law of thermodynamics states that the total energy of a closed system is constant. The second law states that some energy is always lost as thermal energy from a closed system when energy is used to do work. The practical effect of these two laws is that the output energy from any machine will never be as great as the energy put into it.

- Friction—in which kinetic energy is converted to thermal energy—can be reduced but never eliminated. Although some machines can be made to run very efficiently, they will always need a source of energy to operate, and they will never be able to produce more energy than is put into them.

Section 3

Types of Machines
The Invention of Machines

- The first machines were tools used by prehistoric people to help them hunt and gather food. A wedge shaped out of stone made an excellent cutting tool. Early axes were wedges made of stone. Levers were used in hoes, oars, and slings. Because simple machines multiply force or distance, they provided our early ancestors with a tremendous survival advantage.

The Plow

- The plow was one of the first agricultural machines to be invented, and it is still one of the most important. Evidence shows that plows first appeared more than 6,000 years ago. The first plow was not much more than a digging stick drawn by a person or an animal. As primitive as it was, the plow allowed people to dig deeper to turn over and loosen the soil. This simple machine magnified the effort of a single person enough to produce food for many people.

Is That a Fact!

- Tiny machines are being built with gears and levers so small they can be seen only under a powerful microscope. Scientists are learning how to make even tinier machines out of molecules. Tiny gears have been shaped out of strands of DNA molecules, and hydrogen molecules may one day control microscopic computers.

SciLinks is maintained by the National Science Teachers Association to provide you and your students with interesting, up-to-date links that will enrich your classroom presentation of the chapter.

Visit www.scilinks.org and enter the SciLinks code for more information about the topic listed.

Topic: Work and Power
SciLinks code: HSM1675

Topic: Simple Machines
SciLinks code: HSM1395

Topic: Mechanical Efficiency
SciLinks code: HSM0929

Topic: Compound Machines
SciLinks code: HSM0331

Overview

This chapter describes the relationship between energy and work, the way machines do work, and the different types of simple and compound machines.

Assessing Prior Knowledge

Students should be familiar with the following topics:

• matter

• forces

• motion

Identifying Misconceptions

As students learn the concepts in this chapter, they will encounter the scientific usage of the word *work*. Students will need to learn the meaning of *work* in terms of force applied over a distance instead of in terms of effort expended. Students may also have to overcome the common usage of the word *machine*, which connotes a large and complicated apparatus, such as a car engine. Students may be slow to consider a simple device, such as a lever, to be a machine.

4

Work and Machines

The Big Idea Work is the transfer of energy to an object, and power is the rate at which work is done. Machines are devices that help make work easier.

About the PHOTO

"One, two, stroke!" shouts the coach as the team races to the finish line. This paddling team is competing in Hong Kong's annual Dragon Boat Races. The Dragon Boat Festival is a 2,000-year-old Chinese tradition that commemorates Qu Yuan, a national hero. The paddlers that you see here are using the paddles to move the boat forward. Even though they are celebrating by racing their dragon boat, in scientific terms, this team is doing work.

PRE-READING ACTIVITY

FOLDNOTES **Booklet** Before you read the chapter, create the FoldNote entitled "Booklet" described in the **Study Skills** section of the Appendix. Label each page of the booklet with a main idea from the chapter. As you read the chapter, write what you learn about each main idea on the appropriate page of the booklet.

Standards Correlations

National Science Education Standards

The following codes indicate the National Science Education Standards that correlate to this chapter. The full text of the standards is at the front of the book.

Chapter Opener
SAI 1

Section 1 Work and Power
UCP 3; SAI 1, 2; PS 3a

Section 2 What Is a Machine?
UCP 3; SAI 1, 2; ST 2

Section 3 Types of Machines
UCP 3, 5; SAI 1; ST 1, 2; *LabBook:* SAI 1

Chapter Lab A Powerful Workout
SAI 1, 2; PS 3a; ST 2

Chapter Review
SAI 1; PS 3a; ST 2

Science in Action
SAI 1, 2

STARTUP ACTIVITY
MATERIALS
FOR EACH GROUP
• books (2)
• pencil eraser, large
• ruler, wooden
• table

Safety Caution: The rulers should be fairly stiff and sturdy. Use lightweight books if necessary. If the books are not too heavy and the activity is done carefully, the rulers should not get broken.

Teacher's Notes: The word *lever* comes from the Latin word *levare,* meaning "to lift." The lever was one of the first simple machines to be developed. It is thought that tree limbs may have been used by early humans as pry bars to move heavy rocks.

Answers

1. Students should find that lifting the books with the ruler was easier because less effort (force) was required.

2. The direction of the force applied by students' fingers on the books was up, and the direction of the force applied on the ruler was down. Using the ruler changed the direction of the force.

STARTUP ACTIVITY

C'mon, Lever a Little!

In this activity, you will use a simple machine, a lever, to make your task a little easier.

Procedure

1. Stack **two books,** one on top of the other, on a **table.**

2. Slide your index finger underneath the edge of the bottom book. Using only the force of your finger, try to lift one side of the books 2 or 3 cm off the table. Is it hard to do so? Write your observations.

3. Slide the end of a **wooden ruler** underneath the edge of the bottom book. Then, slip a **large pencil eraser** or similar object under the ruler.

4. Again, using only your index finger, push down on the edge of the ruler and try to lift the books. Record your observations. **Caution:** Push down slowly to keep the ruler and eraser from flipping.

Analysis

1. Which was easier: lifting the books with your finger or lifting the books with the ruler? Explain your answer.

2. In what way did the direction of the force that your finger applied on the books differ from the direction of the force that your finger applied on the ruler?

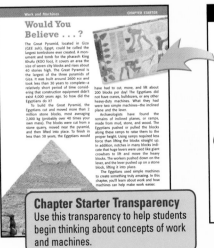

Would You Believe . . . ?

The Great Pyramid, located in Giza (GEE zuh), Egypt, could be called the largest tombstone ever created. A monument and tomb for the pharaoh King Khufu (KOO too), it covers an area the size of seven city blocks and rises about 40 stories high. The Great Pyramid is the largest of the three pyramids of Giza. It was built around 2600 BCE and took less than 30 years to complete—a relatively short period of time considering that construction equipment didn't exist 4,000 years ago. So how did the Egyptians do it?

To build the Great Pyramid, the Egyptians cut and moved more than 2 million stone blocks, most averaging 2,000 kg (probably over 40 times your own mass). The blocks were cut from a stone quarry, moved near the pyramid, and then lifted into place. To finish in less than 30 years, the Egyptians would

have had to cut, move, and lift about 200 blocks per day! The Egyptians did not have cranes, bulldozers, or any other heavy-duty machines. What they had were two simple machines—the inclined plane and the lever.

Archaeologists have found the remains of inclined planes, or ramps, made from mud, stone, and wood. The Egyptians pushed or pulled the blocks along these ramps to raise them to the proper height. Using ramps required less force than lifting the blocks straight up. In addition, notches in many blocks indicate that huge levers were used like giant crowbars to lift and move the heavy blocks. The workers pushed down on the lever, and the lever pushed up on a stone block, lifting it into place.

The Egyptians used simple machines to create something truly amazing. In this chapter, you'll learn about work and how machines can help make work easier.

Chapter Starter Transparency
Use this transparency to help students begin thinking about concepts of work and machines.

Technology

 **Transparencies**
• Chapter Starter Transparency

READING
SKILLS

 Student Edition on CD-ROM

Guided Reading Audio CD
• English or Spanish

Classroom Videos
• Brain Food Video Quiz

Workbooks

Science Puzzlers, Twisters & Teasers
• Work and Machines GENERAL

Focus

Overview

This section introduces the scientific definitions of *work* and *power* and explains how to calculate work and power.

Bellringer

Write the following task for students on the board:

Select the activities below that require the least amount of work.

• carrying heavy books home

• reading a 300-page novel

• skiing for 1 h

• lifting a 45 kg mass

• holding a steel beam in place for 3 h

• jacking up a car

Remind students to explain what work is being done in each of their selected activities.

Motivate

ACTiViTY ———————— GENERAL

Work in Sports Have students, in groups of three or four, select a sport and discuss the different ways work is done in that sport. Have them estimate how much work is done in an average game. Kinesthetic

---

Work and Power

Your science teacher has just given you tonight's homework assignment. You have to read an entire chapter by tomorrow. That sounds like a lot of work!

Actually, in the scientific sense, you won't be doing much work at all! How can that be? In science, **work** is done when a force causes an object to move in the direction of the force. In the example above, you may have to put a lot of mental effort into doing your homework, but you won't be using force to move anything. So, in the scientific sense, you will not be doing work—except the work to turn the pages of your book!

What Is Work?

The student in **Figure 1** is having a lot of fun, isn't she? But she is doing work, even though she is having fun. She is doing work because she is applying a force to the bowling ball and making the ball move through a distance. However, she is doing work on the ball only as long as she is touching it. The ball will keep moving away from her after she releases it. But she will no longer be doing work on the ball because she will no longer be applying a force to it.

What You Will Learn

● Determine when work is being done on an object.

● Calculate the amount of work done on an object.

● Explain the difference between work and power.

Vocabulary

work	power
joule	watt

READING STRATEGY

Reading Organizer As you read this section, make a table comparing work and power.

Figure 1
You might be surprised to find out that bowling is work!

Transfer of Energy

One way you can tell that the bowler in **Figure 1** has done work on the bowling ball is that the ball now has *kinetic energy*. This means that the ball is now moving. The bowler has transferred energy to the ball.

Differences Between Force and Work

Applying a force doesn't always result in work being done. Suppose that you help push a stalled car. You push and push, but the car doesn't budge. The pushing may have made you tired. But you haven't done any work on the car, because the car hasn't moved.

You do work on the car as soon as the car moves. Whenever you apply a force to an object and the object moves in the direction of the force, you have done work on the object.

Reading Check Is work done every time a force is applied to an object? Explain. (*See the Appendix for answers to Reading Checks.*)

CHAPTER RESOURCES

Chapter Resource File

• Lesson Plan
• Directed Reading A **BASIC**
• Directed Reading B **SPECIAL NEEDS**

Technology

Transparencies
• Bellringer
• P29 Work or Not Work?
• *LINK TO LIFE SCIENCE* L80 A Pair of Muscles in the Arm

Workbooks

Interactive Textbook Struggling Readers

Answer to Reading Check

No, work is done on an object only if force makes the object move in a direction that is parallel to the force.

Force and Motion in the Same Direction

Suppose you are in the airport and late for a flight. You have to run through the airport carrying a heavy suitcase. Because you are making the suitcase move, you are doing work on it, right? Wrong! For work to be done on an object, the object must move in the *same direction* as the force. You are applying a force to hold the suitcase up, but the suitcase is moving forward. So, no work is done on the suitcase. But work *is* done on the suitcase when you lift it off the ground.

Work is done on an object if two things happen: (1) the object moves as a force is applied and (2) the direction of the object's motion is the same as the direction of the force. The pictures and arrows in **Figure 2** will help you understand when work is being done on an object.

work the transfer of energy to an object by using a force that causes the object to move in the direction of the force

Figure 2	Work or Not Work?		
Example	**Direction of force**	**Direction of motion**	**Doing work?**
			Yes
			No
			Yes
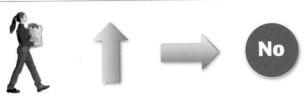			No

CONNECTION TO Biology

WRITING SKILL **Work in the Human Body**

You may not be doing any work on a suitcase if you are just holding it in your hands, but your body will still get tired from the effort because you are doing work on the muscles inside your body. Your muscles can contract thousands of times in just a few seconds while you try to keep the suitcase from falling. What other situations can you think of that might involve work being done somewhere inside your body? Describe these situations in your **science journal.**

MISCONCEPTION ALERT

Work and Force The text states that the girl does work on the bowling ball only when she is touching it. The ball continues to move when she lets go of it, but she's no longer applying a force to it. Disregarding friction, once the ball is moving, no additional force is needed to keep it moving at constant speed because of Newton's first law of motion.

READING STRATEGY — GENERAL

Prediction Guide Before students read this section, ask them whether they agree with the following statements:

1. Any time a force is applied to an object, work is being done. (false)

2. Power, work, and force are the same. (false)

3. More power means doing work faster. (true)

LS Logical

SUPPORT FOR

English Language Learners

Work and the Direction of Force Students will better understand when work is being performed if they create their own examples. After they have read the text and chart on these pages, review the examples in the chart as a class. Ask volunteers to point out where work is being done and why. Then, have each student create a similar chart with four of their own examples from their everyday lives, including sports and games. They should draw each example, specify direction of force and motion with arrows, and indicate whether or not work is being done. Emphasize to students that they should not just copy the information from the chart in the text. When charts are completed, ask students to exchange charts and look for any misconceptions about work. Discuss these in class.

LS Visual/Interpersonal

On a piece of paper write the word "Force" with a thick arrow drawn underneath and make 4 copies. On another piece of paper write "Motion" with a thick arrow drawn underneath and make 4 copies. Write a large "Yes" on a third piece of paper and a large "No" on a fourth piece of paper and make 4 copies of each.

Divide the class into 4 teams. Give each team one Force arrow, one Motion arrow, a Yes, and a No. Assign one of the following tasks. Ask each team to determine whether their task is work. Have each team demonstrate their assigned task, use the arrows to show the direction of the force and the motion, and Yes or No to state whether work is done.

Shut the door. (Both arrows to the right; Yes.) Carry a book. (Force arrow up, motion arrow sideways; No.) Push a rolling chair. (Both arrows to the right; Yes.) Lift a book. (Both arrows up; Yes.)

LS Interpersonal

English Language Learners

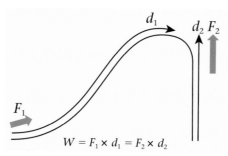

$$W = F_1 \times d_1 = F_2 \times d_2$$

Figure 3 *For each path, the same work is done to move the car to the top of the hill, although distance and force along the two paths differ.*

How Much Work?

Would you do more work on a car by pushing it up a long road to reach the top of a hill or by using a cable to raise the car up the side of a cliff to the top of the same hill? You would certainly need a different amount of force. Common use of the word *work* may make it seem that there would be a difference in the amount of work done in the two cases as well.

Same Work, Different Forces

You may be surprised to learn that the same amount of work is being done to push the car up a road as to raise it up the cliff. Look at **Figure 3.** A certain amount of energy is needed to move the car from the bottom to the top of the hill. Because the car ends up at the same place either way, the work done on the car is the same. However, pushing the car along the road up a hill seems easier than lifting it straight up. Why?

The reason is that work depends on distance as well as force. Consider a mountain climber who reaches the top of a mountain by climbing straight up a cliff, as in **Figure 4.** She must use enough force to overcome her entire weight. But the distance she travels up the cliff is shorter than the distance traveled by hikers who reach the top of the same mountain by walking up a slope. Either way, the same amount of work is done. But the hikers going up a slope don't need to use as much force as if they were going straight up the side of the cliff. This shows how you can use less force to do the same amount of work.

Figure 4 *Climbers going to the top of a mountain do the same amount of work whether they hike up a slope or go straight up a cliff.*

ACTIVITY — GENERAL

Work Done on a Spring Scale Obtain a meter stick, string, a spring scale, and various objects to lift. Organize students into pairs. Have each pair attach each object in turn to the spring scale and slowly lift or pull the object and then record how much force was used. Next, have them measure the distance that the object moved and record the distance in meters. Have them calculate how much work was done.

LS Kinesthetic

alculating Work

he amount of work (W) done in moving an object, such as he barbell in **Figure 5,** can be calculated by multiplying the orce (F) applied to the object by the distance (d) through which he force is applied, as shown in the following equation:

$$W = F \times d$$

Force is expressed in newtons, and the meter is the basic SI nit for length or distance. Therefore, the unit used to express vork is the newton-meter (N × m), which is more simply called he **joule.** Because work is the transfer of energy to an object, he joule (J) is also the unit used to measure energy.

joule the unit used to express energy; equivalent to the amount of work done by a force of 1 N acting through a distance of 1 m in the direction of the force (symbol, J)

Reading Check How is work calculated?

Figure 5 Force Times Distance

80 N

160 N

80 N

W = 80 N × 1 m = 80 J
The force needed to lift an object is equal to the gravitational force on the object—in other words, the object's weight.

W = 160 N × 1 m = 160 J
If you increase the weight, an increased force is needed to lift the object. This increases the amount of work done.

W = 80 N × 2 m = 160 J
Increasing the distance also increases the amount of work done.

Get to Work!

1. Use a **loop of string** to attach a **spring scale** to a **weight.**

2. Slowly pull the weight across a **table** by dragging the spring scale. Record the amount of force that you exerted on the weight.

3. Use a **metric ruler** to measure the distance that you pulled the weight.

4. Now, use the spring scale to slowly pull the weight up a **ramp.** Pull the weight the same distance that you pulled it across the table.

5. Calculate the work you did on the weight for both trials.

6. How were the amounts of work and force affected by the way you pulled the weight? What other ways of pulling the weight could you test?

MATERIALS

FOR EACH STUDENT
• ramp
• ruler, metric
• scale, spring
• string, loop
• table
• weight

Teacher's Note: Be sure that students pull the weight with a constant speed. They should also keep the spring scale parallel to the tabletop or ramp when pulling.

Answer

6. Sample answer: More force was needed to pull the weight across the ramp than to pull it across the table. Therefore, more work was done when pulling the weight across the ramp. Other ways of pulling the weight might include using a much steeper ramp or pulling the weight straight up a vertical surface.

Answer to Reading Check

Work is calculated as force times distance.

CHAPTER RESOURCES

Technology

Transparencies
• P30 Force Times Distance

Workbooks

Math Skills for Science
• Work and Power GENERAL

Reteaching — BASIC

Work and Power After students read the section on work and power, discuss with students the use of the words *work* and *power* in everyday language. Identify usages that do not match the scientific definition of *work*, and discuss why the two usages are different. **English Language Learners**

LS Verbal

Quiz — GENERAL

1. What are the two things that must happen for work to be done? (A force must be exerted on an object, and the object must move in the direction of the force.)

2. You use 75 N of force to push a box 3 m across the floor. How much work has been done? (225 J)

3. What is the power of a small motor that can do 4,500 J of work in 25 s? (180 W)

Alternative Assessment — GENERAL

Concept Mapping Have students create a concept map using the words *work, force, distance, power,* and *time* in a way that matches their scientific definitions. **LS Visual**

---

power the rate at which work is done or energy is transformed

watt the unit used to express power; equivalent to joules per second (symbol, W)

Figure 6 *No matter how fast you can sand by hand, an electric sander can do the same amount of work faster. Therefore, the electric sander has more power.*

MATH FOCUS

More Power to You A stage manager at a play raises the curtain by doing 5,976 J of work on the curtain in 12 s. What is the power output of the stage manager?

Step 1: Write the equation for power.

$$P = \frac{W}{t}$$

Step 2: Replace *W* and *t* with work and time.

$$P = \frac{5,976\,J}{12\,s} = 498\ W$$

Now It's Your Turn

1. If it takes you 10 s to do 150 J of work on a box to move it up a ramp, what is your power output?

2. A light bulb is on for 12 s, and during that time it uses 1,200 J of electrical energy. What is the wattage (power) of the light bulb?

Power: How Fast Work Is Done

Like the term *work,* the term *power* is used a lot in everyday language but has a very specific meaning in science. **Power** the rate at which energy is transferred.

Calculating Power

To calculate power (*P*), you divide the amount of work done (*W*) by the time (*t*) it takes to do that work, as shown in the following equation:

$$P = \frac{W}{t}$$

The unit used to express power is joules per second (J/s) also called the **watt.** One watt (W) is equal to 1 J/s. So if you do 50 J of work in 5 s, your power is 10 J/s, or 10 W.

Power measures how fast work happens, or how quickly energy is transferred. When more work is done in a given amount of time, the power output is greater. Power output is also greater when the time it takes to do a certain amount of work is decreased, as shown in **Figure 6.**

✓ Reading Check How is power calculated?

SCIENCE HUMOR

Q: What is the unit of power?

A: Watt.

Q: I said, What is the unit of power?

A: Watt!

Q: I SAID . . .

Answer to Reading Check

Power is calculated as work done (in joules) divided by the time (in seconds) in which the work was done.

Answers to Math Focus

1. 150 J ÷ 10 s = 15 W
2. 1,200 J ÷ 12 s = 100 W

Increasing Power

It may take you longer to sand a wooden shelf by hand than by using an electric sander, but the amount of energy needed is the same either way. Only the power output is lower when you sand the shelf by hand (although your hand may get more tired). You could also dry your hair with a fan, but it would take a long time! A hair dryer is more powerful. It can give off energy more quickly than a fan does, so your hair dries faster.

Car engines are usually rated with a certain power output. The more powerful the engine is, the more quickly the engine can move a car. And for a given speed, a more powerful engine can move a heavier car than a less powerful engine can.

CONNECTION TO Language Arts

WRITING SKILL **Horsepower** The unit of power most commonly used to rate car engines is the *horsepower* (hp). Look up the word *horsepower* in a dictionary. How many watts is equal to 1 hp? Do you think all horses output exactly 1 hp? Why or why not? Write your answers in your **science journal.**

SECTION Review

Summary

- In scientific terms, *work* is done when a force causes an object to move in the direction of the force.
- Work is calculated as force times distance. The unit of work is the newton-meter, or joule.
- *Power* is a measure of how fast work is done.
- Power is calculated as work divided by time. The unit of power is the joule per second, or watt.

Using Key Terms

For each pair of terms, explain how the meanings of the terms differ.

1. *work* and *joule*

2. *power* and *watt*

Understanding Key Ideas

3. How is work calculated?
   a. force times distance
   b. force divided by distance
   c. power times distance
   d. power divided by distance

4. What is the difference between work and power?

Math Skills

5. Using a force of 10 N, you push a shopping cart 10 m. How much work did you do?

6. If you did 100 J of work in 5 s, what was your power output?

Critical Thinking

7. **Analyzing Processes** Work is done on a ball when a pitcher throws it. Is the pitcher still doing work on the ball as it flies through the air? Explain.

8. **Applying Concepts** You lift a chair that weighs 50 N to a height of 0.5 m and carry it 10 m across the room. How much work do you do on the chair?

Interpreting Graphics

9. What idea about work and force does the following diagram describe? Explain your answer.

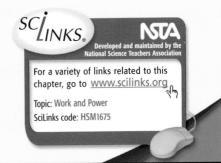

$$W = F_1 \times d_1 = F_2 \times d_2$$

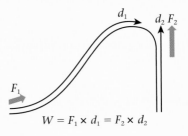

SCiLINKS **NSTA** Developed and maintained by the National Science Teachers Association

For a variety of links related to this chapter, go to www.scilinks.org

Topic: Work and Power
SciLinks code: HSM1675

SECTION 2

Focus

Overview

This section explains how machines make work easier. It also explains how to calculate and compare the mechanical advantage of machines and the mechanical efficiency of machines.

Bellringer

Pose the following question to your students, and have them write a one-paragraph answer in their **science journal:** "Why do we use machines?"

Motivate

Discussion ———— GENERAL

Examples of Machines Show students a selection of pictures of familiar objects that represent simple machines either alone or in combination. Discuss with students how each of the objects can be used to make work easier. Later, when simple machines are introduced, you can have students identify the simple machines in each picture.
 Visual

What You Will Learn

- Explain how a machine makes work easier.
- Describe and give examples of the force-distance trade-off that occurs when a machine is used.
- Calculate mechanical advantage.
- Explain why machines are not 100% efficient.

Vocabulary

machine
work input
work output
mechanical advantage
mechanical efficiency

READING STRATEGY

Prediction Guide Before reading this section, write the title of each heading in this section. Next, under each heading, write what you think you will learn.

What Is a Machine?

You are in the car with your mom on the way to a party when suddenly—KABLOOM hisssss—a tire blows out. "Now I'm going to be late!" you think as your mom pulls over to the side of the road.

You watch as she opens the trunk and gets out a jack and a tire iron. Using the tire iron, she pries the hubcap off and begins to unscrew the lug nuts from the wheel. She then puts the jack under the car and turns the jack's handle several times until the flat tire no longer touches the ground. After exchanging the flat tire with the spare, she lowers the jack and puts the lug nuts and hubcap back on the wheel.

"Wow!" you think, "That wasn't as hard as I thought it would be." As your mom drops you off at the party, you think how lucky it was that she had the right equipment to change the tire.

Machines: Making Work Easier

Now, imagine changing a tire without the jack and the tire iron. Would it have been easy? No, you would have needed several people just to hold up the car! Sometimes, you need the help of machines to do work. A **machine** is a device that makes work easier by changing the size or direction of a force.

When you think of machines, you might think of things such as cars, big construction equipment, or even computers. But not all machines are complicated. In fact, you use many simple machines in your everyday life. **Figure 1** shows some examples of machines.

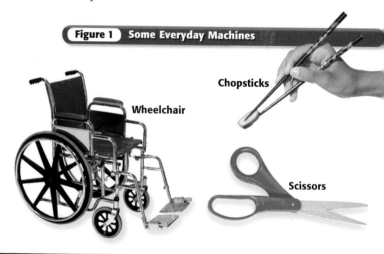

Figure 1   Some Everyday Machines

Chopsticks
Wheelchair
Scissors

CHAPTER RESOURCES

Chapter Resource File

- Lesson Plan
- Directed Reading A **BASIC**
- Directed Reading B **SPECIAL NEEDS**

Technology

Transparencies
- Bellringer

Workbooks

Interactive Textbook **Struggling Readers**

CONNECTION ACTIVITY
Home Economics— GENERAL

Kitchen Utensils as Machines Show students some common kitchen utensils, such as knives, forks, can and bottle openers, nutcrackers, and manual eggbeaters. Allow students to examine the utensils and discuss their uses. Then, have students speculate how each machine makes work easier.
 Visual

Work In, Work Out

Suppose that you need to get the lid off a can of paint. What do you do? One way to pry the lid off is to use a common machine known as a *lever*. **Figure 2** shows a screwdriver being used as a lever. You place the tip of the screwdriver under the edge of the lid and then push down on the screwdriver's handle. The tip of the screwdriver lifts the lid as you push down. In other words, you do work on the screwdriver, and the screwdriver does work on the lid.

Work is done when a force is applied through a distance. Look again at **Figure 2.** The work that you do on a machine is called **work input.** You apply a force, called the *input force,* to the machine through a distance. The work done by the machine on an object is called **work output.** The machine applies a force, called the *output force,* through a distance.

How Machines Help

You might think that machines help you because they increase the amount of work done. But that's not true. If you multiplied the forces by the distances through which the forces are applied in **Figure 2** (remember that $W = F \times d$), you would find that the screwdriver does not do more work on the lid than you do on the screwdriver. Work output can never be greater than work input. Machines allow force to be applied over a greater distance, which means that less force will be needed for the same amount of work.

> ✔ **Reading Check** How do machines make work easier? (*See the Appendix for answers to Reading Checks.*)

machine a device that helps do work by either overcoming a force or changing the direction of the applied force

work input the work done on a machine; the product of the input force and the distance through which the force is exerted

work output the work done by a machine; the product of the output force and the distance through which the force is exerted

Output force

Input force

Figure 2 *When you use a machine, you do work on the machine, and the machine does work on something else.*

Answer to Reading Check

Machines make work easier by allowing force to be applied over a greater distance.

📖 READING STRATEGY — BASIC

Concept Mapping Have students begin constructing a concept map of this section and continue it as they progress through the section. They should illustrate at least half the bubbles with their own drawings or photographs from magazines. The illustrations should elaborate on or relate to the ideas included in the map. **LS** Visual

Discussion — GENERAL

Benefits and Drawbacks of Machines Encourage a student debate about the benefits and drawbacks of machines since the Industrial Revolution. Students should understand that although machines have many benefits, machines may bring problems, such as pollution and workplace injuries. **LS** Interpersonal

Using Science Fiction — ADVANCED

Have students read the story "Clean Up Your Room!" by Laura Anne Gilman in the *Holt Anthology of Science Fiction.* As you discuss the story, ask students to compare the positive and negative aspects of technology in our lives. **LS** Verbal

Machines as Solutions to Problems Have students think of a problem that has no apparent solution. The problem may also be something that students think may become a problem in the future. Challenge them to invent a machine that solves that problem. Have them describe it as carefully as possible and illustrate it with their own artwork. **LS** Logical

CONNECTION ACTIVITY
Math   GENERAL

Graphing Force and Distance
A certain task takes 480 J of work. Remind students that many combinations of $F \times d$ result in 480 J of work (480 N $\times$ 1 m or 64 N $\times$ 7.5 m). Help students find combinations of forces and distances whose products are 480 J. Have them use these number pairs to plot and connect points on a graph (with F on the x-axis and d on the y-axis). Discuss what the graphs show about the relationship between force and distance. (F and d are inversely related.) Students can start with any two of the quantities, calculate the third, and then make the graph. **LS** Visual

INTERNET ACTIVITY
For another activity related to this chapter, go to **go.hrw.com** and type in the keyword **HP5WRKW.**

Same Work, Different Force

Machines make work easier by changing the size or direction (or both) of the input force. When a screwdriver is used as a lever to open a paint can, both the size and direction of the input force change. Remember that using a machine does not change the amount of work you will do. As **Figure 3** shows, the same amount of work is done with or without the ramp. The ramp decreases the size of the input force needed to lift the box but increases the distance over which the force is exerted. So, the machine allows a smaller force to be applied over a longer distance.

The Force-Distance Trade-Off

When a machine changes the size of the force, the distance through which the force is exerted must also change. Force or distance can increase, but both cannot increase. When one increases, the other must decrease.

Figure 4 shows how machines change force and distance. Whenever a machine changes the size of a force, the machine also changes the distance through which the force is applied. **Figure 4** also shows that some machines change only the direction of the force, not the size of the force or the distance through which the force is exerted.

Reading Check What are the two things that a machine can change about how work is done?

Figure 3 | **Input Force and Distance**

Lifting this box straight up requires an input force equal to the weight of the box.

$$W = 450 \text{ N} \times 1 \text{ m} = 450 \text{ J}$$

Using a ramp to lift the box requires an input force less than the weight of the box, but the input force must be exerted over a greater distance than if you didn't use a ramp.

$$W = 150 \text{ N} \times 3 \text{ m} = 450 \text{ J}$$

Homework ————— GENERAL

Everyday Use of Machines Have students keep a "machine diary" for a week. Each day, they should describe the machines they used or came into contact with over the course of the day. Have them expand their ideas of what a machine is by examining ordinary actions such as writing or playing and deciding whether a machine is involved. **LS** Intrapersonal

Answer to Reading Check
Machines can change the force or the distance through which force is applied.

Figure 4 Machines Change the Size and/or Direction of a Force

Input force

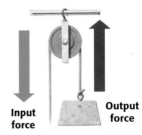
Output force

A nutcracker *increases* the force but applies it over a *shorter* distance.

A hammer *decreases* the force, but applies it over a *greater* distance.

Output force

Input force

A simple pulley changes the *direction* of the input force, but the size of the output force is the same as the input force.

Input force

Output force

When a screw-driver is used as a lever, it *increases* the force and *decreases* the distance over which the force is applied.

Output force

Input force

Mechanical Advantage

Some machines make work easier than others do because they can increase force more than other machines can. A machine's **mechanical advantage** is the number of times the machine multiplies force. In other words, the mechanical advantage compares the input force with the output force.

Calculating Mechanical Advantage

You can find mechanical advantage by using the following equation:

$$\text{mechanical advantage (MA)} = \frac{\text{output force}}{\text{input force}}$$

For example, imagine that you had to push a 500 N weight up a ramp and only needed to push with 50 N of force the entire time. The mechanical advantage of the ramp would be calculated as follows:

$$MA = \frac{500\ \text{N}}{50\ \text{N}} = 10$$

A machine that has a mechanical advantage that is greater than 1 can help move or lift heavy objects because the output force is greater than the input force. A machine that has a mechanical advantage that is less than 1 will reduce the output force but can increase the distance an object moves. **Figure 4** shows an example of such a machine—a hammer.

mechanical advantage a number that tells how many times a machine multiplies force

Finding the Advantage

A grocer uses a handcart to lift a heavy stack of canned food. Suppose that he applies an input force of 40 N to the handcart. The cart applies an output force of 320 N to the stack of canned food. What is the mechanical advantage of the handcart?

SUPPORT FOR

English Language Learners

Machines and Force Visual aids may help students understand the different effects machines can have on force. Provide pairs of students pictures of several types of machines, such as those used in construction or industry. Draw a two-circle Venn diagram on the board, and label the circles *size* and *direction*. Have one student from each pair copy the diagram onto a sheet of paper. Ask students to analyze whether each machine changes the size or the direction (or both) of a force, and tape the picture in the correct place on the diagram. Remind students that machines affecting both size and direction of forces should be placed in the circles' overlap. When students have finished, ask them to show their diagrams to the class and briefly explain their reasons for placements. **LS** Visual/Logical

CONNECTION ACTiViTY
History——————— GENERAL

Prehistoric Machines Have students research prehistoric uses of machines, especially the earliest occurrences of machines that change the size or direction of a force in the same ways that the examples in **Figure 4** do. **LS** Logical

Answers to Math Practice
$MA = 320\ \text{N} \div 40\ \text{N} = 8$

CONNECTION ACTiViTY
Life Science——————— GENERAL

Animals Using Tools Humans aren't the only animals that use tools. Chimpanzees fashion specialized twigs to snare termites from inside their mounds, and some otters use carefully selected rocks to crack open shellfish. The use of tools is considered a distinct evolutionary advantage. Have students find information about such tool use and make some creative presentations to the class. **LS** Verbal

CHAPTER RESOURCES

Technology

Transparencies
- P30 Input Force and Distance
- P31 Machines Change the Size and/or Direction of a Force

Workbooks

Math Skills for Science
- Mechanical Advantage GENERAL

Section 2 • What Is a Machine? **103**

Close

Reteaching — **BASIC**

Design of Machines For each of the examples of machines in **Figure 4** on the previous page, have students design a different machine that would accomplish the same job. The machine can be as simple or as elaborate as desired. Does the new machine change force in the same way as the original? **LS** Visual

Quiz — **GENERAL**

1. How does a machine make work easier? (by changing the size or direction (or both) of a force)

2. What two things do you need to know in order to calculate mechanical efficiency? (work input and work output)

3. If the mechanical advantage of a machine is 5, how does the output force compare with the input force? (The output force is 5 times greater than the input force.)

Alternative Assessment — **GENERAL**

Rube Goldberg Machines Show students one of Rube Goldberg's cartoons. Ask them to decipher what is happening in the cartoon. Focus students' attention on the action in each step and the results of the action. Challenge students to design and draw their own machine that uses multiple steps to perform a simple task. **LS** Logical

mechanical efficiency a quantity, usually expressed as a percentage, that measures the ratio of work output to work input; it can be calculated by dividing work output by work input

Useful Friction

Friction is always present when two objects touch or rub together, and friction usually slows down moving parts in a machine and heats them up. In some cases, parts in a machine are designed to increase friction. While at home, observe three situations in which friction is useful. Describe them in your **science journal.**

ACTIVITY

Mechanical Efficiency

The work output of a machine can never be greater than the work input. In fact, the work output of a machine is always less than the work input. Why? Some of the work done by the machine is used to overcome the friction created by the use of the machine. But keep in mind that no work is lost. The work output plus the work done to overcome friction is equal to the work input.

The less work a machine has to do to overcome friction, the more efficient the machine is. **Mechanical efficiency** (muh KAN i kuhl e FISH uhn see) is a comparison of a machine's work output with the work input.

Calculating Efficiency

A machine's mechanical efficiency is calculated using the following equation:

$$\text{mechanical efficiency} = \frac{\text{work output}}{\text{work input}} \times 100$$

The 100 in this equation means that mechanical efficiency is expressed as a percentage. Mechanical efficiency tells you what percentage of the work input gets converted into work output.

Figure 5 shows a machine that is used to drill holes in metal. Some of the work input is used to overcome the friction between the metal and the drill. This energy cannot be used to do work on the steel block. Instead, it heats up the steel and the machine itself.

✓ **Reading Check** How is mechanical efficiency calculated?

Figure 5 *In this machine, some of the work input is converted into sound and heat energy.*

Answer to Reading Check
mechanical efficiency = (work output ÷ work input) × 100

Perfect Efficiency?

An *ideal machine* would be a machine that had 100% mechanical efficiency. An ideal machine's useful work output would equal the work done on the machine. Ideal machines are impossible to build, because every machine has moving parts. Moving parts always use some of the work input to overcome friction. But new technologies help increase efficiency so that more energy is available to do useful work. The train in **Figure 6** is floating on magnets, so there is almost no friction between the train and the tracks. Other machines use lubricants, such as oil or grease, to lower the friction between their moving parts, which makes the machines more efficient.

Figure 6 *There is very little friction between this magnetic levitation train and its tracks, so it is highly efficient.*

SECTION Review

Summary

- A machine makes work easier by changing the size or direction (or both) of a force.
- A machine can increase force or distance, but not both.
- Mechanical advantage tells how many times a machine multiplies force.
- Mechanical efficiency is a comparison of a machine's work output with work input.
- Machines are not 100% efficient because some of the work done is used to overcome friction.

Using Key Terms

For each pair of terms, explain how the meanings of the terms differ.

1. *work input* and *work output*

2. *mechanical advantage* and *mechanical efficiency*

Understanding Key Ideas

3. Which of the following is the correct way to calculate mechanical advantage?

   a. input force ÷ output force

   b. output force ÷ input force

   c. work input ÷ work output

   d. work output ÷ work input

4. Explain how using a ramp makes work easier.

5. Give a specific example of a machine, and describe how its mechanical efficiency might be calculated.

6. Why can't a machine be 100% efficient?

Math Skills

7. Suppose that you exert 60 N on a machine and the machine exerts 300 N on another object. What is the machine's mechanical advantage?

8. What is the mechanical efficiency of a machine whose work input is 100 J and work output is 30 J?

Critical Thinking

9. **Making Inferences** For a machine with a mechanical advantage of 3, how does the distance through which the output force is exerted differ from the distance through which the input force is exerted?

10. **Analyzing Processes** Describe the effect that friction has on a machine's mechanical efficiency. How do lubricants increase a machine's mechanical efficiency?

For a variety of links related to this chapter, go to www.scilinks.org

Topic: Mechanical Efficiency
SciLinks code: HSM0929

Developed and maintained by the National Science Teachers Association

CHAPTER RESOURCES

Chapter Resource File

- Section Quiz GENERAL
- Section Review GENERAL
- Vocabulary and Section Summary GENERAL

Focus

Overview

This section describes the six simple machines and explains how to determine the mechanical advantage of each. Students learn about compound machines and combinations of simple machines they commonly encounter, and they learn how combining simple machines affects efficiency.

Bellringer

Pose the following question to students: What type of machine can be found on at least half the students in this room right now? (zipper)

Motivate

 ——————— GENERAL

Loads on a First-Class Lever
Organize the class into small groups. Have each group use a string to hang a meterstick from a ring. The meterstick should be balanced until it hangs level. Then, ask the groups to tie five large metal washers tied together to the meterstick at the 2 cm mark. Challenge them to find a way to again balance the meterstick without adding any weights to the opposite end. Discuss the students' solutions to the problem. **Kinesthetic**

Types of Machines

Imagine that it's a hot summer day. You have a whole ice-col watermelon in front of you. It would taste cool and delicious if only you had a machine that could cut it!

The machine you need is a knife. But how is a knife a machine A knife is actually a very sharp wedge, which is one of th six simple machines. The six simple machines are the leve the inclined plane, the wedge, the screw, the pulley, and th wheel and axle. All machines are made from one or more c these simple machines.

Levers

Have you ever used the claw end of a hammer to remove nail from a piece of wood? If so, you were using the ham mer as a lever. A **lever** is a simple machine that has a ba that pivots at a fixed point, called a *fulcrum*. Levers are use to apply a force to a load. There are three classes of levers which are based on the placements of the fulcrum, the load and the input force.

First-Class Levers

With a first-class lever, the fulcrum is between the input force and the load, as shown in **Figure 1.** First-class levers alway change the direction of the input force. And depending o the location of the fulcrum, first-class levers can be used t increase force or to increase distance.

What You Will Learn
- Identify and give examples of the six types of simple machines.
- Analyze the mechanical advantage provided by each simple machine.
- Identify the simple machines that make up a compound machine.

Vocabulary

lever	wedge
pulley	screw
wheel and axle	compound machine
inclined plane	

READING STRATEGY

Mnemonics As you read this section, create a mnemonic device to help you remember the different types of levers.

Figure 1 **Examples of First-Class Levers**

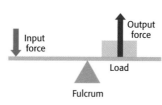

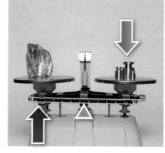

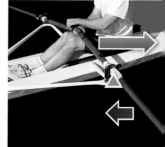

When the fulcrum is closer to the load than to the input force, the lever has a **mechanical advantage of greater than 1.** The output force is increased because it is exerted over a shorter distance.

When the fulcrum is exactly in the middle, the lever has a **mechanical advantage of 1.** The output force is not increased because the input force's distance is not increased.

When the fulcrum is closer to the input force than to the load, the lever has a **mechanical advantage of less than 1.** Although the output force is less than the input force, distance increases.

CHAPTER RESOURCES

Chapter Resource File

- **Lesson Plan**
- **Directed Reading A** BASIC
- **Directed Reading B** SPECIAL NEEDS

Technology

Transparencies
- Bellringer

Workbooks

Interactive Textbook Struggling Readers

Figure 2 Examples of Second-Class Levers

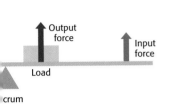

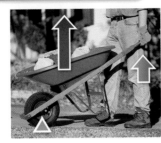

Output force

Input force

Load

crum

a **second-class lever,** the output rce, or load, is between the input rce and the fulcrum.

Using a second-class lever results in a **mechanical advantage of greater than 1.** The closer the load is to the fulcrum, the more the force is increased and the greater the mechanical advantage is.

econd-Class Levers

he load of a second-class lever is between the fulcrum and e input force, as shown in **Figure 2.** Second-class levers do ot change the direction of the input force. But they allow ou to apply less force than the force exerted by the load. ecause the output force is greater than the input force, you ust exert the input force over a greater distance.

hird-Class Levers

he input force in a third-class lever is between the fulcrum id the load, as shown in **Figure 3.** Third-class levers do not ange the direction of the input force. In addition, they do ot increase the input force. Therefore, the output force is ways less than the input force.

lever a simple machine that consists of a bar that pivots at a fixed point called a *fulcrum*

Reading Check How do the three types of levers differ from e another? (*See the Appendix for answers to Reading Checks.*)

Figure 3 Examples of Third-Class Levers

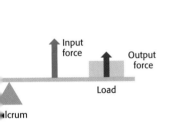

Input force

Output force

Load

lcrum

a **third-class lever,** the input rce is between the fulcrum and e load.

Using a third-class lever results in a **mechanical advantage of less than 1** because force is decreased. But third-class levers increase the distance through which the output force is exerted.

BRAIN FOOD

Levers Besides being used in bottle openers and nail pullers, levers are used in devices such as fishing rods, cranes, typewriters, pianos, parking meters, and scales.

Is That a Fact!

The human body uses simple machines. Muscles and bones form first-class and third-class levers. When you look up, the skull pivots on the neck vertebrae, forming a first-class lever. When you kick a soccer ball, the contracting muscle pulls your leg upward, acting as a third-class lever.

Figure 4 The mechanical advantage of a pulley is equal to the number of rope segments that support the load. Each of these supporting rope segments applies a force equal to the input force to do the work of lifting the load. For this reason, the movable pulley has two input force arrows. The combined distance through which those input forces are exerted is the input distance, which is twice the distance that the load is actually lifted. **LS** Visual

Guided Practice — GENERAL

Simple Machines Collage Collect some old magazines. After students have read the section on simple machines, have them look through the magazines for pictures of different types of simple machines. Have students make a collage that classifies the pictures according to the type of simple machine they represent. **LS** Visual

pulley a simple machine that consists of a wheel over which a rope, chain, or wire passes

Pulleys

When you open window blinds by pulling on a cord, you're using a pulley. A **pulley** is a simple machine that has a grooved wheel that holds a rope or a cable. A load is attached to one end of the rope, and an input force is applied to the other end. Types of pulleys are shown in **Figure 4.**

Fixed Pulleys

A fixed pulley is attached to something that does not move. By using a fixed pulley, you can pull down on the rope to lift the load up. The pulley changes the direction of the force. Elevators make use of fixed pulleys.

Movable Pulleys

Unlike fixed pulleys, movable pulleys are attached to the object being moved. A movable pulley does not change a force's direction. Movable pulleys do increase force, but they also increase the distance over which the input force must be exerted.

Block and Tackles

When a fixed pulley and a movable pulley are used together, the pulley system is called a *block and tackle*. The mechanical advantage of a block and tackle depends on the number of rope segments.

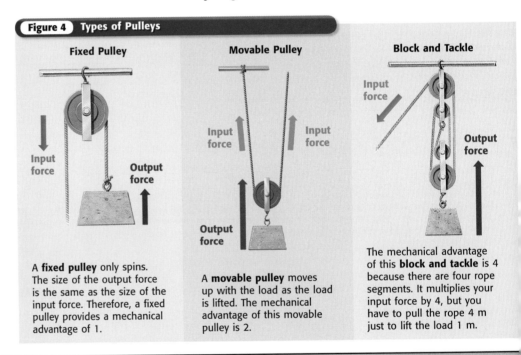

Figure 4 Types of Pulleys

Fixed Pulley
Input force
Output force

A **fixed pulley** only spins. The size of the output force is the same as the size of the input force. Therefore, a fixed pulley provides a mechanical advantage of 1.

Movable Pulley
Input force   Input force
Output force

A **movable pulley** moves up with the load as the load is lifted. The mechanical advantage of this movable pulley is 2.

Block and Tackle
Input force
Output force

The mechanical advantage of this **block and tackle** is 4 because there are four rope segments. It multiplies your input force by 4, but you have to pull the rope 4 m just to lift the load 1 m.

CONNECTION ACTIVITY
Real World — GENERAL

Machines in Your School Take students to visit the custodian's area in the school building. Have the custodian demonstrate the uses of different machines, and discuss how machines make the necessary tasks of maintaining the school building easier. **LS** Interpersonal

Figure 5 How a Wheel and Axle Works

Wheel

Input force

Axle

Output force

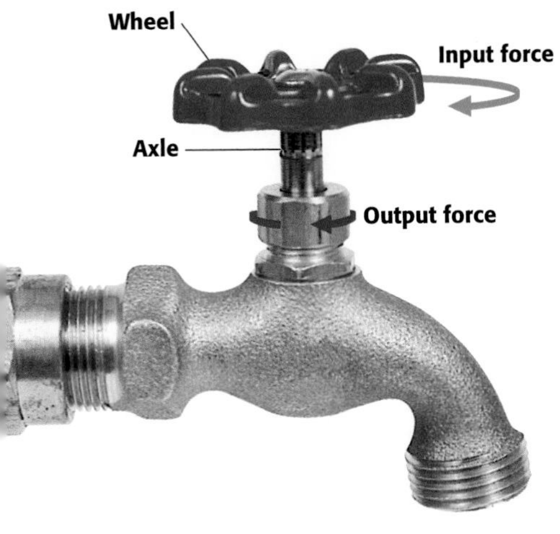

a When a small input force is applied to the wheel, the wheel rotates through a circular distance.

b As the wheel turns, so does the axle. But because the axle is smaller than the wheel, it rotates through a smaller distance, which makes the output force larger than the input force

Wheel and Axle

Did you know that a faucet is a machine? The faucet shown in Figure 5 is an example of a **wheel and axle,** a simple machine consisting of two circular objects of different sizes. Doorknobs, wrenches, and steering wheels all use a wheel and axle. **Figure 5** shows how a wheel and axle works.

wheel and axle a simple machine consisting of two circular objects of different sizes; the wheel is the larger of the two circular objects

Mechanical Advantage of a Wheel and Axle

The mechanical advantage of a wheel and axle can be found by dividing the *radius* (the distance from the center to the edge) of the wheel by the radius of the axle, as shown in Figure 6. Turning the wheel results in a mechanical advantage of greater than 1 because the radius of the wheel is larger than the radius of the axle.

Reading Check How is the mechanical advantage of a wheel and axle calculated?

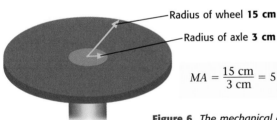

Radius of wheel **15 cm**

Radius of axle **3 cm**

$$MA = \frac{15 \text{ cm}}{3 \text{ cm}} = 5$$

Figure 6 *The mechanical advantage of a wheel and axle is the radius of the wheel divided by the radius of the axle.*

Teach, continued

Using the Figure — GENERAL

Inclined Planes Use **Figure 7** to explain how you can determine mechanical advantage of an inclined plane by using distances. Explain the process as follows:

work input = work output

F (input) × d (input) = F (output) × d (output)

This equation can be rearranged into ratios to show

$$\frac{F\ (input)}{F\ (output)} = \frac{d\ (output)}{d\ (input)}$$

The force ratio can be used to determine mechanical advantage. Because the distance ratio is equivalent to the force ratio, the distance ratio can also be used to determine mechanical advantage. **LS** Visual

Answer to Reading Check

A slanted surface that makes the raising of loads easier, such as a ramp.

Answers to Math Focus

1. $MA = 9\ m \div 1.5\ m = 6$
2. $MA = 120\ m \div 20\ m = 6$
3. $MA = 2\ m \div 8\ m = 0.25$

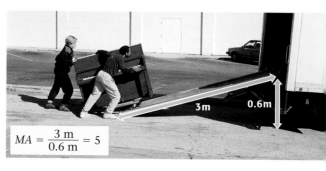

Figure 7 The work you do on the piano to roll it up the ramp is the same as the work you would do to lift it straight up. An inclined plane simply allows you to apply a smaller force over a greater distance.

$$MA = \frac{3\ m}{0.6\ m} = 5$$

inclined plane a simple machine that is a straight, slanted surface, which facilitates the raising of loads; a ramp

Inclined Planes

Do you remember the story about how the Egyptians built the Great Pyramid? One of the machines they used was the **inclined plane.** An *inclined plane* is a simple machine that is a straight, slanted surface. A ramp is an inclined plane.

Using an inclined plane to load a piano into a truck, as **Figure 7** shows, is easier than lifting the piano into the truck. Rolling the piano along an inclined plane requires a smaller input force than is needed to lift the piano into the truck. The same work is done on the piano, just over a longer distance.

✓ **Reading Check** What is an inclined plane?

Mechanical Advantage of Inclined Planes

The greater the ratio of an inclined plane's length to its height is, the greater the mechanical advantage is. The mechanical advantage (*MA*) of an inclined plane can be calculated by dividing the *length* of the inclined plane by the *height* to which the load is lifted. The inclined plane in **Figure 7** has a mechanical advantage of 3 m/0.6 m = 5.

Mechanical Advantage of an Inclined Plane A heavy box is pushed up a ramp that has an incline of 4.8 m long and 1.2 m high. What is the mechanical advantage of the ramp?

Step 1: Write the equation for the mechanical advantage of an inclined plane.

$$MA = \frac{l}{h}$$

Step 2: Replace *l* and *h* with length and height.

$$MA = \frac{4.8\ m}{1.2\ m} = 4$$

Now It's Your Turn

1. A wheelchair ramp is 9 m long and 1.5 m high. What is the mechanical advantage of the ramp?
2. As a pyramid is built, a stone block is dragged up a ramp that is 120 m long and 20 m high. What is the mechanical advantage of the ramp?
3. If an inclined plane were 2 m long and 8 m high, what would be its mechanical advantage?

SUPPORT FOR

English Language Learners

Types of Machines Students will need additional help processing all the information presented in this section. As they read, ask them to fill in a table listing each type of machine and summarizing its advantages in their own words. Encourage students to sketch the machine and write the mechanical advantage equation to help them remember it. Allow them to use dictionaries if needed for comprehension, but remind them the information in the table should relate to the uses of words in the textbook. When students have finished reading and their tables are complete, call on students to assist you in narrating a brief demonstration of each type of machine, followed by an open discussion of its mechanical advantage. Encourage full participation. **LS** Verbal/Visual

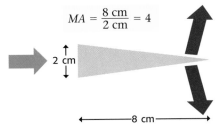

$$MA = \frac{8 \text{ cm}}{2 \text{ cm}} = 4$$

2 cm

8 cm

Figure 8 *A knife is a common example of a wedge, a simple machine consisting of two inclined planes back to back.*

Wedges

Imagine trying to cut a melon in half with a spoon. It wouldn't be easy, would it? A knife is much more useful for cutting because it is a **wedge.** A *wedge* is a pair of inclined planes that move. A wedge applies an output force that is greater than your input force, but you apply the input force over a greater distance. For example, a knife is a common wedge that can easily cut into a melon and push apart its two halves, as shown in **Figure 8.** Other useful wedges include doorstops, plows, ax heads, and chisels.

Mechanical Advantage of Wedges

The longer and thinner the wedge is, the greater its mechanical advantage is. That's why axes and knives cut better when you sharpen them—you are making the wedge thinner. Therefore, less input force is required. The mechanical advantage of a wedge can be found by dividing the length of the wedge by its greatest thickness, as shown in **Figure 8.**

Screws

A **screw** is an inclined plane that is wrapped in a spiral around a cylinder, as you can see in **Figure 9.** When a screw is turned, a small force is applied over the long distance along the inclined plane of the screw. Meanwhile, the screw applies a large force through the short distance it is pushed. Screws are used most commonly as fasteners.

Mechanical Advantage of Screws

If you could unwind the inclined plane of a screw, you would see that the plane is very long and has a gentle slope. Recall that the longer an inclined plane is compared with its height, the greater its mechanical advantage. Similarly, the longer the spiral on a screw is and the closer together the threads are, the greater the screw's mechanical advantage is. A jar lid is a screw that has a large mechanical advantage.

wedge a simple machine that is made up of two inclined planes and that moves; often used for cutting

screw a simple machine that consists of an inclined plane wrapped around a cylinder

Figure 9 *If you could unwind a screw, you would see that it is actually a very long inclined plane.*

Close

Reteaching ——— BASIC

Simple Versus Compound Machines Review the types of simple machines and the ways in which each changes size or direction of force. Then, ask students for examples of compound machines and the simple machines that compose them.
LS Logical

Quiz ——————— GENERAL

1. Why are simple machines so useful? (They make work easier.)

2. Identify types of simple machines you might find on a playground. Describe how each of them modifies work. (Sample answer: seesaw: lever changes direction of input force; merry-go-round: wheel and axle makes the input force on the axle cause the wheel to move in a circle)

3. How does reducing friction increase the mechanical efficiency of a compound machine? (Less work input is used to overcome friction, so work output is higher, and mechanical efficiency is higher.)

Alternative Assessment ——— GENERAL

Machines in a Story Have each student write a story that incorporates six simple or compound machines. The machines must operate in some way appropriate to the story line. Suggest that students illustrate their stories. **LS** Verbal

compound machine a machine made of more than one simple machine

SCHOOL to HOME

Everyday Machines
With an adult, think of five simple or compound machines that you encounter each day. List them in your **science journal,** and indicate what type of machine each is. Include at least one compound machine and one machine that is part of your body.

ACTIVITY

Compound Machines

You are surrounded by machines. You even have machines in your body! But most of the machines in your world are **compound machines,** machines that are made of two or more simple machines. You have already seen one example of a compound machine: a block and tackle. A block and tackle consists of two or more pulleys.

Figure 10 shows a common example of a compound machine. A can opener may seem simple, but it is actually three machines combined. It consists of a second-class lever, a wheel and axle, and a wedge. When you squeeze the handle, you are making use of a second-class lever. The blade of the can opener acts as a wedge as it cuts into the can's top. The knob that you turn to open the can is a wheel and axle.

Mechanical Efficiency of Compound Machines

The mechanical efficiency of most compound machines is low. The efficiency is low because compound machines have more moving parts than simple machines do, thus there is more friction to overcome. Compound machines, such as automobiles and airplanes, can involve many simple machines. It is very important to reduce friction as much as possible, because too much friction can damage the simple machines that make up the compound machine. Friction can be lowered by using lubrication and other techniques.

✓ Reading Check What special disadvantage do compound machines have?

Wheel and axle

Wedge

Second class lever

Figure 10 *A can opener is a compound machine. The handle is a second-class lever, the knob is a wheel and axle, and a wedge is used to open the can.*

Answer to Reading Check
They have more moving parts than simple machines do, so compound machines tend to be less efficient than simple machines are.

SECTION
Review

Summary

- In a first-class lever, the fulcrum is between the force and the load. In a second-class lever, the load is between the force and the fulcrum. In a third-class lever, the force is between the fulcrum and the load.

- The mechanical advantage of an inclined plane is length divided by height. Wedges and screws are types of inclined planes.

- A wedge is a type of inclined plane. Its mechanical advantage is its length divided by its greatest thickness.

- The mechanical advantage of a wheel and axle is the radius of the wheel divided by the radius of the axle.

- Types of pulleys include fixed pulleys, movable pulleys, and block and tackles.

- Compound machines consist of two or more simple machines.

- Compound machines have low mechanical efficiencies because they have more moving parts and therefore more friction to overcome.

Using Key Terms

1. In your own words, write a definition for the term *lever*.

2. Use the following terms in the same sentence: *inclined plane*, *wedge*, and *screw*.

Understanding Key Ideas

3. Which class of lever always has a mechanical advantage of greater than 1?
   a. first-class
   b. second-class
   c. third-class
   d. None of the above

4. Give an example of each of the following simple machines: first-class lever, second-class lever, third-class lever, inclined plane, wedge, and screw.

Math Skills

5. A ramp is 0.5 m high and has a slope that is 4 m long. What is its mechanical advantage?

6. The radius of the wheel of a wheel and axle is 4 times the radius of the axle. What is the mechanical advantage of the wheel and axle?

Critical Thinking

7. **Applying Concepts** A third-class lever has a mechanical advantage of less than 1. Explain why it is useful for some tasks.

8. **Making Inferences** Which compound machine would you expect to have the lowest mechanical efficiency: a can opener or a pair of scissors? Explain your answer.

Interpreting Graphics

9. Indicate two simple machines being used in the picture below.

For a variety of links related to this chapter, go to www.scilinks.org
Topic: Simple Machines;
       Compound Machines
SciLinks code: HSM1395; HSM0331

Answers to Section Review

1. Sample answer: A lever is a simple machine consisting of a bar that pivots at a fulcrum, acting to lift a load.

2. Sample answer: Wedges and screws are two special types of inclined planes.

3. b

4. Sample answer: first-class lever: seesaw; second-class lever: bottle opener; third-class lever: hammer; inclined plane: ramp; wedge: doorstop; screw: jar lid

5. $MA = 4 \text{ m} \div 0.5 \text{ m} = 8$

6. $MA = 4 \div 1 = 4$

7. A third-class lever increases the distance through which force is output.

8. Sample answer: a can opener; It is a compound machine that consists of three simple machines, whereas a pair of scissors is a compound machine that consists of two simple machines. The fewer the number of simple machines that make up a compound, the greater the mechanical efficiency of the compound machine. A compound machine consisting of few simple machines has fewer moving parts.

9. The door on its hinge is a lever (second-class); the knob is a wheel and axle.

A Powerful Workout

Teacher's Notes

Time Required

One or two 45-minute class periods

Lab Ratings

EASY ——————→ HARD

Teacher Prep 🧪
Student Set-Up 🧪
Concept Level 🧪🧪
Clean Up 🧪

MATERIALS

The materials listed for this lab are for the entire class or for smaller groups. Students in wheelchairs can use a ramp instead of a flight of stairs.

Safety Caution

Students who have asthma or any other respiratory problems should not perform this lab. Any student who becomes winded should sit down and take deep breaths. Caution students that this is not a race to see who can get the fastest time.

Answer

2. Sample answer: Climbing up a flight of stairs takes less than 100 W of power. This amount of energy doesn't seem to be as much energy as a light bulb gives off.

Lab Notes

To help students calculate averages, set up a class data table on the board. The table should have four columns: "Student"; "Power S" (for power for slow walk); "Power Q" (for power for quick walk); and "Average" (each student's average power). An individual's average power is one-half of the sum of the power for a slow walk and the power for a quick walk. The class average power is all the individual averages together divided by the number of students in the class.

OBJECTIVES

Calculate the work and power used to climb a flight of stairs.

Compare your work and power with that of a 100 W light bulb.

MATERIALS

- flight of stairs
- ruler, metric
- stopwatch

Using Scientific Methods

Skills Practice Lab

A Powerful Workout

Does the amount of work that you do depend on how fast you do it? No! But the amount of time in which you do work does affect your power—the rate of work done. In this lab, you'll calculate your work and power for climbing a flight of stairs at different speeds. Then you'll compare your power with that of an ordinary household object—a 100 W light bulb.

Ask a Question

1. How does your power in climbing a flight of stairs compare with the power of a 100 W light bulb?

Form a Hypothesis

2. Write a hypothesis that answers the question in step 1. Explain your reasoning.

Data Collection Table				
Height of step (cm)	Number of steps	Height of stairs (m)	Time for slow walk (s)	Time for quick walk (s)
		DO NOT WRITE IN BOOK		

Test the Hypothesis

3. Copy the Data Collection Table onto a separate sheet of paper.

4. Use a metric ruler to measure the height of one stair step. Record the measurement in your Data Collection Table. Be sure to include units for all measurements.

5. Count the number of stairs, including the top step, and record this number in your Data Collection Table.

6. Calculate the height of the climb by multiplying the number of steps by the height of one step. Record your answer in meters. (You will need to convert your answer from centimeters to meters.)

7. Use a stopwatch to measure how many seconds it takes you to walk slowly up a flight of stairs. Record your measurement in your Data Collection Table.

CHAPTER RESOURCES

Chapter Resource File

- Datasheet for Chapter Lab
- Lab Notes and Answers

Technology

 Classroom Videos
- Lab Video

- Inclined to Move
- Wheeling and Dealing
- Building Machines

8 Now measure how many seconds it takes you to walk quickly up a flight of stairs. Be careful not to overexert yourself. This is not a race to see who can get the fastest time!

Analyze the Results

1 **Constructing Tables** Copy the Calculations Table below onto a separate sheet of paper.

Calculations Table

Weight (N)	Work (J)	Power for slow walk (W)	Power for quick walk (W)
	DO NOT WRITE IN BOOK		

2 **Examining Data** Determine your weight in newtons, and record it in your Calculations Table. Your weight in newtons is your weight in pounds (lb) multiplied by 4.45 N/lb.

3 **Examining Data** Calculate and record your work done in climbing the stairs by using the following equation:

$$work = force \times distance$$

(Hint: If you are having trouble determining the force exerted, remember that force is measured in newtons.)

4 **Examining Data** Calculate and record your power output by using the following equation:

$$power = \frac{work}{time}$$

The unit for power is the watt (1 watt = 1 joule/second).

Draw Conclusions

5 **Evaluating Methods** In step 3 of "Analyze the Results," you were asked to calculate your work done in climbing the stairs. Why weren't you asked to calculate your work for each trial (slow walk and quick walk)?

6 **Drawing Conclusions** Look at your hypothesis. Was your hypothesis correct? Now that you have measured your power, write a statement that describes how your power compares with that of a 100 W light bulb.

7 **Applying Conclusions** The work done to move one electron in a light bulb is very small. Write down two reasons why the power used is large. (Hint: How many electrons are in the filament of a light bulb? How did you use more power in trial 2?)

Communicating Your Data

Your teacher will provide a class data table on the board. Add your average power to the table. Then calculate the average power from the class data. How many students would it take to create power equal to the power of a 100 W bulb?

Analyze the Results

2. Sample answer: 100 lb × 4.45 N/lb = 445 N.

3. Sample answer: 445 N × 4 m = 1,780 J.

4. Sample answer: 1,780 J ÷ 10 s = 178 W; 1,780 J ÷ 5 s = 356 W

Draw Conclusions

5. The work is the same no matter how long it takes.

6. Sample answer: The power output in both the slow and quick walks was greater than the power of a 100 W light bulb. The original hypothesis was not correct.

7. The power of a light bulb is large because there is a huge number of electrons moving in the filament and the electrons are moving back and forth very quickly.

Communicating Your Data

Sample answer: The average power for the class was 250 W, so it would take two and a half 100 W bulbs to equal the power of one student.

CHAPTER RESOURCES

Workbooks

📙 **Whiz-Bang Demonstrations**
• Pull-Ease, Please! **BASIC**
• A Clever Lever **BASIC**

📙 **Inquiry Labs**
• Get an Arm and an Egg Up **ADVANCED**

📙 **Long-Term Projects & Research Ideas**
• To Complicate Things **ADVANCED**

Holt Lab Generator CD-ROM

Search for any lab by topic, standard, difficulty level, or time. Edit any lab to fit your needs, or create your own labs. Use the Lab Materials QuickList software to customize your lab materials list.

CLASSROOM TESTED & APPROVED

Terry Rakes
Elmwood Junior High
Rogers, Arkansas

Assignment Guide

Section	Questions
1	1, 4–5, 8–9, 11,
2	7, 12, 15–16, 18, 20, 22
3	2–3, 6, 10, 13, 17, 19, 21, 23–24

ANSWERS

Using Key Terms

1. Sample answer: Work is a measure of the energy required to exert force over a distance. Power is a measure of the rate at which work is done.

2. Sample answer: A lever is a simple machine that consists of a bar that pivots on a fulcrum. An inclined plane is a simple machine that consists of a straight, slanted surface.

3. Sample answer: A wheel and axle is a simple machine that consists of two attached circular objects of different sizes. A pulley is a simple machine consisting of a grooved wheel that holds a rope or a cable.

Understanding Key Ideas

4. c
5. a
6. b
7. d
8. d
9. c
10. first-class levers and wedges

USING KEY TERMS

For each pair of terms, explain how the meanings of the terms differ.

1. *work* and *power*
2. *lever* and *inclined plane*
3. *wheel and axle* and *pulley*

UNDERSTANDING KEY IDEAS

Multiple Choice

4. Work is being done when
   a. you apply a force to an object.
   b. an object is moving after you applied a force to it.
   c. you exert a force that moves an object in the direction of the force.
   d. you do something that is difficult.

5. What is the unit for work?
   a. joule
   b. joule per second
   c. newton
   d. watt

6. Which of the following is a simple machine?
   a. a bicycle
   b. a jar lid
   c. a pair of scissors
   d. a can opener

7. A machine can increase
   a. distance by decreasing force.
   b. force by decreasing distance.
   c. neither distance nor force.
   d. Either (a) or (b)

8. What is power?
   a. the strength of someone or something
   b. the force that is used
   c. the work that is done
   d. the rate at which work is done

9. What is the unit for power?
   a. newton
   b. kilogram
   c. watt
   d. joule

Short Answer

10. Identify the two simple machines that make up a pair of scissors.

11. Explain why you do work on a bag of groceries when you pick it up but not when you carry it.

12. Why is the work output of a machine always less than the work input?

13. What does the mechanical advantage of a first-class lever depend upon? Describe how it can be changed.

Math Skills

14. You and a friend together apply a force of 1,000 N to a car, which makes the car roll 10 m in 1 min and 40 s.
    a. How much work did you and your friend do together?
    b. What was the power output?

15. A lever allows a 35 N load to be lifted with a force of 7 N. What is the mechanical advantage of the lever?

11. Sample answer: When you pick up a bag of groceries, the bag moves in the direction of the force. While you are holding the bag and walking, your forward motion is perpendicular to the upward force you are using to carry the bag, so you are not doing work on the bag.

12. Friction involved in the operation of the machine's moving parts causes some of the input energy to be lost as heat.

13. Sample answer: The mechanical advantage of a first-class lever depends upon the placement of the fulcrum. If the fulcrum is closer to the load than to the input force, the lever has a mechanical advantage of greater than 1. If the fulcrum is exactly in the middle of the load and the input force, the mechanical advantage of the lever is 1. If the fulcrum is closer to the input force than to the load, the lever has a mechanical advantage of less than 1.

14. a. $W = 1,000 \text{ N} \times 10 \text{ m} = 10,000 \text{ J}$
    b. $P = 10,000 \text{ J} \div 100 \text{ s} = 100 \text{ W}$

15. $MA = 35 \text{ N} \div 7 \text{ N} = 5$

CRITICAL THINKING

6 Concept Mapping Use the following terms to create a concept map: *work, force, distance, machine,* and *mechanical advantage.*

7 Analyzing Ideas Explain why levers usually have a greater mechanical efficiency than other simple machines do.

8 Making Inferences The amount of work done on a machine is 300 J, and the machine does 50 J of work. What can you say about the amount of friction that the machine has while operating?

19 Applying Concepts The winding road shown below is a series of inclined planes. Describe how a winding road makes it easier for vehicles to travel up a hill.

20 Predicting Consequences Why wouldn't you want to reduce the friction involved in using a winding road?

21 Making Comparisons How does the way that a wedge's mechanical advantage is determined differ from the way that a screw's mechanical advantage is determined?

22 Identifying Relationships If the mechanical advantage of a certain machine is greater than 1, what does that tell you about the relationship between the input force and distance and output force and distance?

INTERPRETING GRAPHICS

For each of the images below, identify the class of lever used and calculate the mechanical advantage of the lever.

23

Fulcrum

Input force 40 N

Output force 120 N

24

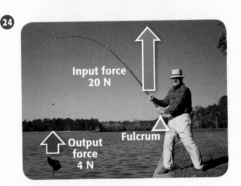

Input force 20 N

Output force 4 N

Fulcrum

Critical Thinking

16. An answer to this exercise can be found at the end of this book.

17. Levers don't have a lot of moving parts, so they don't generate as much friction as other machines do.

18. Sample answer: The work output of the machine is much lower than the work input. Presumably, the machine operates with a lot of friction.

19. It allows the work needed to climb up the hill to be spread out over a long distance, thereby requiring less force.

20. Sample answer: This is a case in which friction is useful. It increases the traction of the cars' tires on the road and keeps them from slipping as they make turns. Reducing the friction on the winding road would make the road more dangerous to drive on.

21. A wedge's mechanical advantage is its length divided by greatest width. A screw's mechanical advantage is determined by comparing its spiral thread length with its vertical length.

22. The input force will be less than the output force, and the input distance will be greater than the output distance.

Interpreting Graphics

23. second-class lever; $MA = 120\ N \div 40\ N = 3$

24. third-class lever; $MA = 4\ N \div 20\ N = 0.2$

CHAPTER RESOURCES

Chapter Resource File

- Chapter Review **GENERAL**
- Chapter Test A **GENERAL**
- Chapter Test B **ADVANCED**
- Chapter Test C **SPECIAL NEEDS**
- Vocabulary Activity **GENERAL**

Workbooks

Study Guide
- Study Guide is also available in Spanish.

Teacher's Note

To provide practice under more realistic testing conditions, give students 20 minutes to answer all of the questions in this Standardized Test Preparation.

MISCONCEPTION ALERT

Answers to the standardized test preparation can help you identify student misconceptions and misunderstandings.

READING

Passage 1

1. D
2. F

TEST DOCTOR

Question 1: The information stated in answers A, B, and C is true, but those answers do not encompass the main idea of the passage as answer D does.

READING

Read each of the passages below. Then, answer the questions that follow each passage.

Passage 1 The Great Pyramid, located in Giza, Egypt, covers an area the size of 7 city blocks and rises about 40 stories high. The Great Pyramid was built around 2600 BCE and took less than 30 years to complete. During this time, the Egyptians cut and moved more than 2 million stone blocks, most of which average 2,000 kg. The workers did not have cranes, bulldozers, or any other heavy-duty machines. What they did have were two simple machines—the inclined plane and the lever. Archeologists have found the remains of inclined planes, or ramps, made from mud, stone, and wood. The Egyptians pushed or pulled the blocks along ramps to raise the blocks to the proper height. Notches in many blocks indicate that huge levers were used as giant crowbars to lift and move the heavy blocks.

1. What is the main idea of the passage?
   A Archeologists have found the remains of inclined planes near the pyramids.
   B The Great Pyramid at Giza was built in less than 30 years.
   C The Egyptians cut and moved more than 2 million stone blocks.
   D The Egyptians used simple machines to build the Great Pyramid at Giza.

2. Which of the following is a fact stated in the passage?
   F The Great Pyramid was made using more than 2 million stone blocks.
   G Each of the stone blocks used to build the Great Pyramid was exactly 2,000 kg.
   H Ancient Egyptians used cranes to build the Great Pyramid.
   I The Great Pyramid at Giza has a mass of about 2 million kg.

Passage 2 While riding a bicycle, you have probably experienced vibrations when the wheels of the bicycle hit bumps in the road. The force of the vibrations travels up through the frame to the rider. Slight vibrations can cause discomfort. Large ones can cause you to lose control of the bike and crash. Early bicycle designs made no attempt to dampen the shock of vibrations. Later designs used air-filled rubber tires and softer seats with springs to absorb some of the vibrations. Today's bike designs provide a safer, more comfortable ride. Various new materials—titanium, for example—absorb shock better than traditional steel and aluminum do. More important, designers are putting a variety of shock absorbers—devices that absorb energy—into bike designs.

1. In the passage, what does the term *shock* mean?
   A a medical emergency that can be caused by blood loss
   B a dry material used in early bicycles
   C a feeling of being stunned and surprised
   D a jolt or impact

2. Which of the following is a fact stated in the passage?
   F You have experienced vibrations while bicycle riding.
   G Slight vibrations can cause severe discomfort.
   H Titanium absorbs shock better than aluminum does.
   I Today's bike designs provide a more fashionable ride.

Passage 2

1. D
2. H

TEST DOCTOR

Question 1: A and C may be true alternative definitions of the word *shock,* but D states the meaning of the word given in the passage. This question tests students' ability to read for meaning in context.

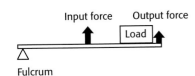
se the diagram below to answer the ques-
ons that follow.

Input force   Output force

Load

Fulcrum

How does this lever make work easier?

A by changing the direction of the force

B by increasing both force and distance

C by increasing force and decreasing distance

D by decreasing force and increasing distance

What would the mechanical advantage of this
lever be?

F less than 1

G 1

H greater than 1

I There is not enough information to
determine the answer.

What type of lever is the lever in the diagram?

A a first-class lever

B a second-class lever

C a third-class lever

D There is not enough information to
determine the answer.

Which of the following items is the same type
of lever as the lever in the diagram?

F a seesaw

G a wheelbarrow

H a bottle opener

I an arm lifting a barbell

MATH

Read each question below, and choose the
best answer.

1. For a special musical number during a school
choir concert, 6 students stood in the first row,
10 students stood in the second row, and 14
students stood in the third row. If the pattern
continued, how many students stood in the
fifth row?

A 18

B 22

C 26

D 30

2. Michael baked some bread for his friends. He
put 2½ cups of flour in each loaf. He used a
total of 12½ cups of flour. How many loaves
did he make?

F 2 loaves

G 4 loaves

H 5 loaves

I 15 loaves

3. A force of 15 N is exerted over a distance of
6 m. How much work was done? (Use the
equation $W = F \times d$.)

A 21 J

B 21 N

C 90 J

D 90 N

4. If 350 J of work was done in 50 s, what was the
power output? (Use the equation $P = W/t$.)

F 7 W

G 70 W

H 1,750 W

I 17,500 W

Standardized Test Preparation

INTERPRETING GRAPHICS

1. D

2. F

3. C

4. I

 TEST DOCTOR

Question 1: The difference in sizes
between the input force and output
force arrows in the diagram indicates
that the output force is smaller than
the input force. This information alone
is enough to point to answer D. You
can tell by the directions of the arrows
that the direction of the force is not
changed.

MATH

1. B

2. H

3. C

4. F

 **TEST DOCTOR**

Question 3: The unit of work and
energy is joules, so B and D can be
ruled out. A would be selected by a
student mistakenly adding force and
distance instead of multiplying them.

CHAPTER RESOURCES

Chapter Resource File

• Standardized Test Preparation **GENERAL**

State Resources

For specific resources for your state,
visit **go.hrw.com** and type in the
keyword **HSMSTR**.

Science, Technology, and Society

Background

The kinetic sculpture pictured was built by Alexander Calder, who is best known for inventing the mobile. He died at the age of 78, after creating 16,000 works of art.

Weird Science

Background

Advances in microtechnology have allowed scientists to achieve impressive results in many fields. For example, medical researchers are working on special pills equipped with sensors, tiny pumps, and drug reservoirs.

Other technological advances include microscopic filters and air turbines for controlling the temperature of microchip arrays. One team of scientists has created a molecular "on-off switch" that could be used to store information in computers.

Science in Action

Science, Technology, and Society

Kinetic Sculpture

The collection of tubes, tracks, balls, and blocks of wood shown in the photo is an audio-kinetic sculpture. A conveyor belt lifts the balls to a point high on the track, and the balls wind their way down as they are pulled by the force of gravity and pushed by various other forces. They twist through spirals, drop straight down tubes, and sometimes go up and around loops as if on a roller coaster. All this is made possible by the artist's applications of principles of kinetic energy, the energy of motion.

Math ACTIVITY

A conveyor belt on a kinetic sculpture lifts a ball to a point 0.8 m high. It exerts 0.05 N of force as it does so. How much work does the conveyor belt do on the ball?

Weird Science

Nanomachines

The technology of making things smaller and smaller keeps growing and growing. Powerful computers can now be held in the palm of your hand. But what can motors that are smaller than grains of pepper do? How can gnat-sized robots that can swim through the bloodstream be used? One possible field in which very small machines, *nanomachines,* can be used is in medicine.

Some scientists are looking into the possibility of creating cell-sized machines called *nanobots.* These tiny robots may have many uses in medicine if they can be injected into a person's bloodstream.

Language Arts ACTIVITY

WRITING SKILL Write a short story in which nanobots are used to save someone's life. Describe the machines the nanobots use in destroying deadly bacteria, clearing blood clots, or delivering medicine.

Answer to Math Activity
$W = 0.05 \text{ N} \times 0.8 \text{ m} = 0.04 \text{ J}$

Answer to Language Arts Activity
Encourage creativity and scientific accuracy by providing students with a body atlas or similar reference work. Suggest the idea of specialized nanobots who can travel through only certain systems of the body (such as the circulatory, endocrine, or nervous system). What common problems might occur in that environment, and what could they do to help? For example, a nanobot inside a lung would see bronchial tubes, alveoli, and capillaries. The nanobot could break down contaminants in the air sacs, help fight off infections, or remove fluids in patients who have pneumonia.

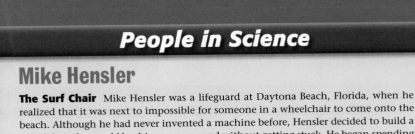

People in Science

Mike Hensler

The Surf Chair Mike Hensler was a lifeguard at Daytona Beach, Florida, when he realized that it was next to impossible for someone in a wheelchair to come onto the beach. Although he had never invented a machine before, Hensler decided to build a wheelchair that could be driven across sand without getting stuck. He began spending many evenings in his driveway with a pile of lawn-chair parts, designing the chair by trial and error.

The result of Hensler's efforts looks very different from a conventional wheelchair. With huge rubber wheels and a thick frame of white PVC pipe, the Surf Chair not only moves easily over sandy terrain but also is weather resistant and easy to clean. The newest models of the Surf Chair come with optional attachments, such as a variety of umbrellas, detachable armrests and footrests, and even places to attach fishing rods.

Social Studies ACTiViTY

List some simple and compound machines that are used as access devices for people who are disabled. Research how these machines came to be in common use.

go.hrw.com
To learn more about these Science in Action topics, visit go.hrw.com and type in the keyword HP5WRKF.

Current Science
Check out Current Science® articles related to this chapter by visiting go.hrw.com. Just type in the keyword HP5CS08.

People in Science

Background

In designing the Surf Chair, Hensler purposely avoided materials that would make the chair look cumbersome or clinical. Because the beach is a place to relax and have fun, Hensler designed his chair to blend easily into such an environment. This fun and practical wheelchair is now available at many public beaches. Daytona Beach, for example, provides free use of the Surf Chair for people who need wheelchairs.

Teaching Strategy · GENERAL

Have students design a device to help people at home who are mobility impaired. You might want to give them a specific goal, such as designing a device to retrieve something from the refrigerator.

Answer to Social Studies Activity
Wheelchairs consist of two wheels and axles. Wheelchair access ramps are inclined planes. Elevators (used instead of stairs by people who use wheelchairs) usually involve pulleys.

Energy and Energy Resources
Chapter Planning Guide

Compression guide:
To shorten instruction because of time limitations, omit Section 4.

OBJECTIVES	LABS, DEMONSTRATIONS, AND ACTIVITIES	TECHNOLOGY RESOURCES
PACING • 90 min pp. 122–131 **Chapter Opener**	SE **Start-up Activity,** p. 123 (GENERAL)	OSP **Parent Letter** ■ CD **Student Edition on CD-ROM** CD **Guided Reading Audio CD** ■ TR **Chapter Starter Transparency*** VID **Brain Food Video Quiz**
Section 1 What Is Energy? • Explain the relationship between energy and work. • Compare kinetic and potential energy. • Describe the different forms of energy.	TE **Demonstration** Forms of Energy, p. 124 (GENERAL) TE **Demonstration** All Wound Up!, p. 125 (GENERAL) TE **Activity** El Niño, p. 128 (ADVANCED) SE **Quick Lab** Hear That Energy!, p. 129 (GENERAL) CRF **Datasheet for Quick Lab*** LB **Whiz-Bang Demonstrations** Wrong-Way Roller?* (BASIC) LB **Calculator-Based Labs** Power of the Sun* (ADVANCED)	OSP **Lesson Plans** (also in print) TR **Bellringer Transparency*** TR **P32 Energy and Work*** TR **P33 Thermal Energy in Water*** CRF **SciLinks Activity*** (GENERAL) SE **Internet Activity,** p. 128 (GENERAL) CD **Science Tutor**
PACING • 90 min pp. 132–137 **Section 2 Energy Conversions** • Describe an energy conversion. • Give examples of energy conversions for the different forms of energy. • Explain how energy conversions make energy useful. • Explain the role of machines in energy conversions.	TE **Connection Activity** Environmental Science, p. 134 (GENERAL) SE **Skills Practice Lab** Finding Energy, p. 148 (GENERAL) CRF **Datasheet for Chapter Lab*** SE **Skills Practice Lab** Energy of a Pendulum, p. 205 (GENERAL) CRF **Datasheet for LabBook*** LB **Whiz-Bang Demonstrations** Pendulum Peril* (BASIC)	OSP **Lesson Plans** (also in print) TR **Bellringer Transparency*** TR **P34 Potential Energy and Kinetic Energy*** TR **P35 From Light Energy to Chemical Energy*** TR **LINK TO LIFE SCIENCE** L46 Photosynthesis*** TR **P36 Energy Conversions in a Bicycle*** VID **Lab Videos for Physical Science** CD **Science Tutor**
PACING • 45 min pp. 138–141 **Section 3 Conservation of Energy** • Explain how energy is conserved within a closed system. • Explain the law of conservation of energy. • Give examples of how thermal energy is always a result of energy conversion. • Explain why perpetual motion is impossible.	TE **Demonstration** Where Does the Energy Go?, p. 138 (GENERAL) TE **Activity** Chemical Energy to Thermal Energy, p. 139 (GENERAL) SE **School-to-Home Activity** Energy Conversions, p. 140 (GENERAL) LB **Labs You Can Eat** Power-Packed Peanuts* (BASIC)	OSP **Lesson Plans** (also in print) TR **Bellringer Transparency*** TR **P37 Energy Conversions in a Roller Coaster*** CD **Science Tutor**
PACING • 45 min pp. 142–147 **Section 4 Energy Resources** • Name several energy resources. • Explain how the sun is the source of most energy on Earth. • Evaluate the advantages and disadvantages of using various energy resources.	TE **Activity** Sources of Energy, p. 142 (GENERAL) TE **Connection Activity** Math, p. 143 (GENERAL) TE **Connection Activity** History, p. 143 (GENERAL) TE **Activity** The Ozone Layer, p. 145 (ADVANCED) LB **Labs You Can Eat** Now You're Cooking!* (BASIC) LB **Long-Term Projects & Research Ideas** Great Balls of Fire* (ADVANCED) SE **Science in Action** Math, Social Studies, and Language Arts Activities, pp. 154–155 (GENERAL) LB **Calculator-Based Labs** Solar Homes* (ADVANCED)	OSP **Lesson Plans** (also in print) TR **Bellringer Transparency*** TR **P38 Formation of Fossil Fuels*** TR **LINK TO EARTH SCIENCE** E11 Porous Rocks as Reservoirs for Fossil Fuels*** CD **Interactive Explorations** CD-ROM The Generation Gap (GENERAL) CD **Science Tutor**

PACING • 90 min

CHAPTER REVIEW, ASSESSMENT, AND STANDARDIZED TEST PREPARATION

CRF **Vocabulary Activity*** (GENERAL)
SE **Chapter Review,** pp. 150–151 (GENERAL)
CRF **Chapter Review*** ■ (GENERAL)
CRF **Chapter Tests A*** ■ (GENERAL), **B*** (ADVANCED), **C*** (SPECIAL NEEDS)
SE **Standardized Test Preparation,** pp. 152–153 (GENERAL)
CRF **Standardized Test Preparation*** (GENERAL)
CRF **Performance-Based Assessment*** (GENERAL)
OSP **Test Generator, Test Item Listing**

Online and Technology Resources

 Holt Online Learning

Visit **go.hrw.com** for access to Holt Online Learning, or enter the keyword **HP7 Home** for a variety of free online resources.

 One-Stop Planner® CD-ROM

This CD-ROM package includes:
• Lab Materials QuickList Software
• Holt Calendar Planner
• Customizable Lesson Plans
• Printable Worksheets
• ExamView® Test Generator
• Interactive Teacher's Edition
• Holt PuzzlePro®
• Holt PowerPoint® Resources

SKILLS DEVELOPMENT RESOURCES	SECTION REVIEW AND ASSESSMENT	CORRELATIONS
SE **Pre-Reading Activity,** p. 122 GENERAL OSP **Science Puzzlers, Twisters & Teasers** GENERAL		National Science Education Standards PS 3a; SAI 1, 2
CRF **Directed Reading A*** ■ BASIC, **B*** SPECIAL NEEDS IT **Interactive Textbook*** Struggling Readers CRF **Vocabulary and Section Summary*** ■ GENERAL SE **Reading Strategy** Discussion, p. 124 GENERAL SE **Math Focus** Kinetic Energy, p. 125 GENERAL SE **Math Focus** Gravitational Potential Energy, p. 126 GENERAL TE **Support for English Language Learners,** p. 129	SE **Reading Checks,** pp. 124, 127, 129, 130 GENERAL TE **Reteaching,** p. 130 BASIC TE **Quiz,** p. 130 GENERAL TE **Alternative Assessment,** p. 130 GENERAL SE **Section Review,*** p. 131 GENERAL CRF **Section Quiz*** ■ GENERAL	SAI 1; PS 3a, 3e, 3f
CRF **Directed Reading A*** ■ BASIC, **B*** SPECIAL NEEDS IT **Interactive Textbook*** Struggling Readers CRF **Vocabulary and Section Summary*** ■ GENERAL SE **Reading Strategy** Brainstorming, p. 132 GENERAL TE **Support for English Language Learners,** p. 135 MS **Math Skills for Science** A Bicycle Trip* GENERAL CRF **Reinforcement Worksheet** See What I Saw; Energetic Cooking* BASIC	SE **Reading Checks,** pp. 133, 134, 136 GENERAL TE **Reteaching,** p. 136 BASIC TE **Quiz,** p. 136 GENERAL TE **Alternative Assessment,** p. 136 GENERAL SE **Section Review,*** p. 137 ■ GENERAL CRF **Section Quiz*** ■ GENERAL	UCP 3; PS 3a, 3d, 3f; *Chapter Lab:* UCP 2; SAI 1, 2; PS 3a; *LabBook:* SAI 1, 2; PS 3a
CRF **Directed Reading A*** ■ BASIC, **B*** SPECIAL NEEDS IT **Interactive Textbook*** Struggling Readers CRF **Vocabulary and Section Summary*** ■ GENERAL SE **Reading Strategy** Paired Summarizing, p. 138 GENERAL TE **Support for English Language Learners,** p. 139	SE **Reading Checks,** pp. 139, 140 GENERAL TE **Reteaching,** p. 140 BASIC TE **Quiz,** p. 140 GENERAL TE **Alternative Assessment,** p. 140 GENERAL SE **Section Review,*** p. 141 ■ GENERAL CRF **Section Quiz*** ■ GENERAL	UCP 1, 3; ST 2; PS 3a
CRF **Directed Reading A*** ■ BASIC, **B*** SPECIAL NEEDS IT **Interactive Textbook*** Struggling Readers CRF **Vocabulary and Section Summary*** ■ GENERAL SE **Reading Strategy** Reading Organizer, p. 142 GENERAL TE **Inclusion Strategies,** p. 144 TE **Support for English Language Learners,** p. 145 CRF **Critical Thinking** The Armchair Enviro-Challenge* ADVANCED	SE **Reading Checks,** pp. 142, 144, 146 GENERAL TE **Reteaching,** p. 146 BASIC TE **Quiz,** p. 146 GENERAL TE **Alternative Assessment,** p. 146 GENERAL SE **Section Review,*** p. 147 ■ GENERAL CRF **Section Quiz*** ■ GENERAL	SPSP 2; PS 3a, 3e, 3f

SCI LINKS NSTA
www.scilinks.org
Maintained by the **National Science Teachers Association.** See Chapter Enrichment pages that follow for a complete list of topics.

Current Science®
Check out *Current Science* articles and activities by visiting the HRW Web site at **go.hrw.com.** Just type in the keyword **HP5CS09T.**

 **Classroom Videos**
• **Lab Videos** demonstrate the chapter lab.
• **Brain Food Video Quizzes** help students review the chapter material.

 **Classroom CD-ROMs**
• **Guided Reading Audio CD** (Also in Spanish)
• **Interactive Explorations**
• **Virtual Investigations**
• **Visual Concepts**
• **Science Tutor**

 **Holt Lab Generator CD-ROM**
Search for any lab by topic, standard, difficulty level, or time. Edit any lab to fit your needs, or create your own labs. Use the Lab Materials QuickList software to customize your lab materials list.

Visual Resources

CHAPTER STARTER TRANSPARENCY

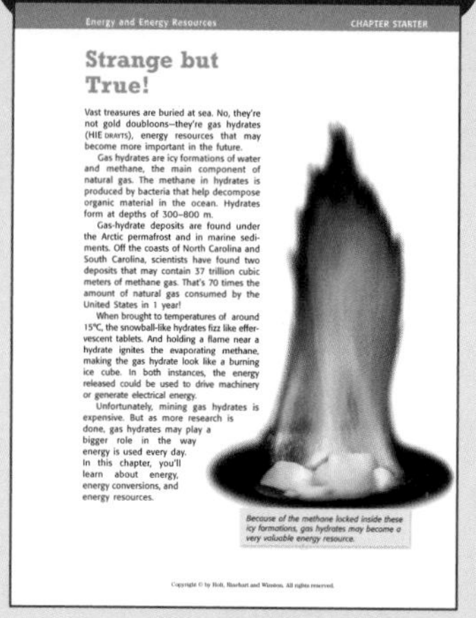

Energy and Energy Resources — CHAPTER STARTER

Strange but True!

Vast treasures are buried at sea. No, they're not gold doubloons—they're gas hydrates (HIE·drayts), energy resources that may become more important in the future.

Gas hydrates are icy formations of water and methane, the main component of natural gas. The methane in hydrates is produced by bacteria that help decompose organic material in the ocean. Hydrates form at depths of 300–800 m.

Gas-hydrate deposits are found under the Arctic permafrost and in marine sediments. Off the coasts of North Carolina and South Carolina, scientists have found two deposits that may contain 37 trillion cubic meters of methane gas. That's 70 times the amount of natural gas consumed by the United States in 1 year!

When brought to temperatures of around 15°C, the snowball-like hydrates fizz like effervescent tablets. And holding a flame near a hydrate ignites the evaporating methane, making the gas hydrate look like a burning ice cube. In both instances, the energy released could be used to drive machinery or generate electrical energy.

Unfortunately, mining gas hydrates is expensive. But as more research is done, gas hydrates may play a bigger role in the way energy is used every day. In this chapter, you'll learn about energy, energy conversions, and energy resources.

Because of the methane locked inside these icy formations, gas hydrates may become a very valuable energy resource.

BELLRINGER TRANSPARENCIES

Energy and Energy Resources — BELLRINGER TRANSPARENCY

Section: What Is Energy?
Finish the following phrase:
"Energy is the ability to ____."

Write your completed phrase in your **science journal.** We often use the words *energy* and *power* synonymously, but they have specific meanings. What is the distinction between energy and power?

Section: Energy Conversions
What do the following objects have in common: a plant, a Bunsen burner, a pendulum. Can you think of three more objects that have the same common link?

Record your guesses in your **science journal.**

TEACHING TRANSPARENCIES

Energy and Energy Resources — TEACHING TRANSPARENCY

Energy and Work

The tennis player does work and transfers energy to the rocket. With this energy, the rocket can then do work on the ball.

Energy and Energy Resources — TEACHING TRANSPARENCY

Potential Energy and Kinetic Energy

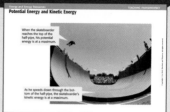

When the skateboarder reaches the top of the half-pipe, his potential energy is at a maximum.

As he speeds down through the bottom of the half-pipe, the skateboarder's kinetic energy is at a maximum.

Energy and Energy Resources — TEACHING TRANSPARENCY

From Light Energy to Chemical Energy

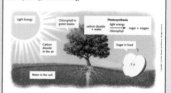

TEACHING TRANSPARENCIES

Energy and Energy Resources — TEACHING TRANSPARENCY

Energy Conversions in a Bicycle

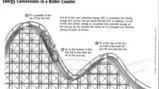

For your bike to start and keep moving, energy must be transferred and converted.

Energy and Energy Resources — TEACHING TRANSPARENCY

Energy Conversions in a Roller Coaster

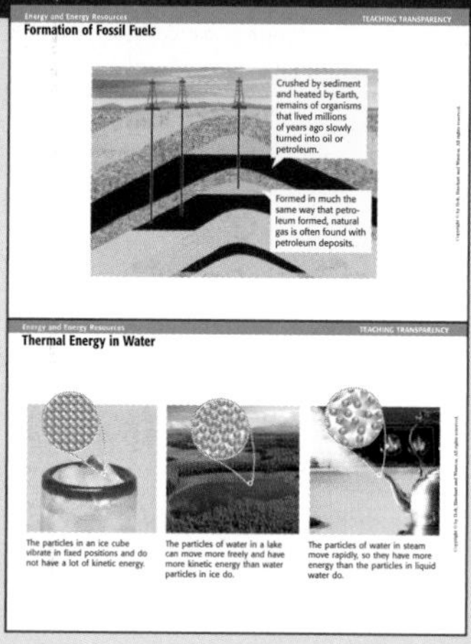

Energy and Energy Resources — TEACHING TRANSPARENCY

Formation of Fossil Fuels

Crushed by sediment and heated by Earth, remains of organisms that lived millions of years ago slowly turned into oil or petroleum.

Formed in much the same way that petroleum formed, natural gas is often found with petroleum deposits.

Energy and Energy Resources — TEACHING TRANSPARENCY

Thermal Energy in Water

The particles in an ice cube vibrate in fixed positions and do not have a lot of kinetic energy.

The particles of water in a lake can move more freely and have more kinetic energy than water particles in ice do.

The particles of water in steam move rapidly, so they have more energy than the particles in liquid water do.

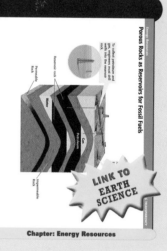

Porous Rocks as Reservoirs for Fossil Fuels

LINK TO EARTH SCIENCE

Chapter: Energy Resources

CONCEPT MAPPING TRANSPARENCY

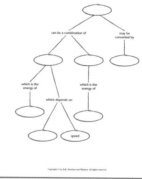

Energy and Energy Resources — CONCEPT MAPPING TRANSPARENCY

Use the following terms to complete the concept map below:
potential energy, position, mechanical energy, motion, kinetic energy, mass, machines

Planning Resources

LESSON PLANS

Lesson Plan   SAMPLE

Section: Waves

Pacing
Regular Schedule: with lab(s):2 days   without lab(s):1 days
Block Schedule: with lab(s): 1 1/2 days without lab(s):1 day

Objectives
1. Relate the seven properties of life to a living organism.
2. Describe seven themes that can help you to organize what you learn about biology.
3. Identify the tiny structures that make up all living organisms.
4. Differentiate between reproduction and heredity and between metabolism and homeostasis.

National Science Education Standards Covered
LS1Inten:Cells have particular structures that underlie their functions.
LS1Mat1: Most cell functions involve chemical reactions.
LS1Beh1:Cells store and use information to guide their functions.
UCP1:Cell functions are regulated.
SI1: Cells can differentiate and form complete multicellular organisms.
PS1: Species evolve over time.
ESS1: The great diversity of organisms is the result of more than 3.5 billion years of evolution.
ESS2: Natural selection and its evolutionary consequences provide a scientific explanation for the history of life on Earth as well as for the striking molecular similarities observed among the diverse species of living organisms.
ST1: The millions of different species of plants, animals, and microorganisms that live on Earth today are related by descent from common ancestors.
ST2: The energy for life primarily comes from the sun.
SPSP1: The complexity and organization of organisms accommodates the need for obtaining, transforming, transporting, releasing, and eliminating the matter and energy used to sustain the organism.
SPSP6: As matter and energy flows through different levels of organization of living systems—cells, organs, communities—and between living systems and the physical environment are recombined in different ways.
HNS1: Organisms have behavioral responses to internal changes and external stimuli.

PARENT LETTER

SAMPLE

Dear Parent,

Your son's or daughter's science class will soon begin exploring the chapter entitled "The World of Physical Science." In this chapter, students will learn about how the scientific method applies to the world of physical science and the role of physical science in the world. By the end of the chapter, students should demonstrate a clear understanding of the chapter's main ideas and be able to discuss the following topics:

1. physical science as the study of energy and matter (Section 1)
2. the role of physical science in the world around them (Section 1)
3. careers that rely on physical science (Section 1)
4. the steps used in the scientific method (Section 2)
5. examples of technology (Section 2)
6. how the scientific method is used to answer questions and solve problems (Section 2)
7. how our knowledge of science changes over time (Section 2)
8. how models represent real objects or systems (Section 3)
9. examples of different ways models are used in science (Section 3)
10. the importance of the International System of Units (Section 4)
11. the appropriate units to use for particular measurements (Section 4)
12. how area and density are derived quantities (Section 4)

Questions to Ask Along the Way
You can help your son or daughter learn about these topics by asking interesting questions such as the following:

• What are some surprising careers that use physical science?
• What is a characteristic of a good hypothesis?
• When is it a good idea to use a model?
• Why do Americans measure things in terms of inches and yards and meters ?

ALSO IN SPANISH

TEST ITEM LISTING

TEST ITEM LISTING
The World of Science   SAMPLE

MULTIPLE CHOICE

1. A limitation of models is that
   a. they are large enough to see.
   b. they do not act exactly like the things that they model.
   c. they are smaller than the things that they model.
   d. they model unfamiliar things.
   Answer: B   Difficulty: 1   Section: 3   Objective: 2

2. The length 10 m is equal to
   a. 100 cm.   c. 10,000 mm.
   b. 1,000 cm.   d. Both (a) and (c)
   Answer: B   Difficulty: 1   Section: 3   Objective: 2

3. To be valid, a hypothesis must be
   a. testable.   c. made into a law.
   b. supported by evidence. d. Both (a) and (b)
   Answer: D   Difficulty: 1   Section: 3   Objective: 2 1

4. The statement "Sheila has a stain on her shirt" is an example of a(n)
   a. law.   c. observation.
   b. hypothesis.   d. prediction.
   Answer: C   Difficulty: 1   Section: 2   Objective: 2

5. A hypothesis is often developed out of
   a. observations.   c. laws.
   b. experiments.   d. Both (a) and (b)
   Answer: D   Difficulty: 1   Section: 2   Objective: 2

6. How many milliliters are in 3.5 kL?
   a. 3,500 mL   c. 3,500, 000 mL
   b. 0.0035 mL.   d. 35,000 mL.
   Answer: C   Difficulty: 1   Section: 3   Objective: 2

7. A map of Seattle is an example of a
   a. law.   c. model.
   b. theory.   d. unit.
   Answer: C   Difficulty: 1   Section: 3   Objective: 2

8. A lab has the safety icons shown below. These icons mean that you should wear
   a. only safety goggles.   c. safety goggles and a lab apron.
   b. only a lab apron.   d. safety goggles, a lab apron, and gloves.
   Answer: B   Difficulty: 1   Section: 3   Objective: 2

9. The law of conservation of mass says that the total mass
   a. more than the total mass after the change.
   b. less than the total mass after the change.
   c. the same as the total mass after the change.
   d. not the same as the total mass after the change.
   Answer: B   Difficulty: 1   Section: 3   Objective: 2

10. In which of the following areas might your son or daughter learn to work as a geochemist at work?
    a. studying the chemistry of rocks   c. studying fishes
    b. studying forestry   d. studying the atmosphere
    Answer: B   Difficulty: 1   Section: 3   Objective: 2

One-Stop Planner® CD-ROM

This CD-ROM includes all of the resources shown here and the following time-saving tools:

• *Lab Materials QuickList Software*
• *Customizable lesson plans*
• *Holt Calendar Planner*
• *The powerful ExamView® Test Generator*

Meeting Individual Needs

DIRECTED READING A

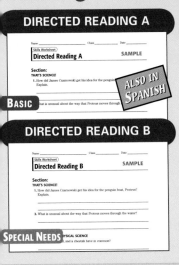

Name _____ Class _____ Date _____

Skills Worksheet
Directed Reading A   SAMPLE

Section:
THAT'S SCIENCE!

1. How did James Czarnowski get his idea for the penguin
Explain.

BASIC

ALSO IN SPANISH

DIRECTED READING B

Name _____ Class _____ Date _____

Skills Worksheet
Directed Reading B   SAMPLE

Section:
THAT'S SCIENCE!

1. How did James Czarnowski get his idea for the penguin boat, Proteus?
Explain.

2. What is unusual about the way that Proteus moves through the water?

SPECIAL NEEDS   PHYSICAL SCIENCE
and, and a cheetah have in common?

VOCABULARY ACTIVITY

Name _____ Class _____ Date _____

Activity
Vocabulary Activity   SAMPLE

Getting the Dirt on the Soil

After you finish reading Chapter: [Unique Title], try this puzzle! Use the clues below to unscramble the vocabulary words. Write your answer in the space provided.

GENERAL

...kdown of rock into
...and smaller pieces:
...GNETH

9. the chemical breakdown of rocks and minerals into new substances: CAMILCHE THEARGWEN

1. ...type of rock laire beneath soil

VOCABULARY AND SECTION SUMMARY

Name _____ Class _____ Date _____

Skills Worksheet
Vocabulary & Notes   SAMPLE

Section:
VOCABULARY
In your own words, write a definition of the following term in the space provided.

1. scientific method

2. technology

GENERAL   *ALSO IN SPANISH*

REINFORCEMENT

Name _____ Class _____ Date _____

Skills Worksheet
Reinforcement   SAMPLE

The Plane Truth

Complete this worksheet after you finish reading the Section: [Unique Section Title]

You plan to enter a paper airplane contest sponsored by Talkin' Physical Science magazine. The person whose airplane flies the farthest wins a lifetime subscription to the magazine! The week before the contest you watch an airplane landing at a nearby airport. You notice that the wings of the airplane have flaps, as shown in the illustration at right. The paper airplanes you've been testing do not have wing flaps. What question would you ask yourself based on these observations? Write your

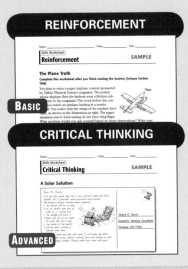

BASIC

CRITICAL THINKING

Name _____ Class _____ Date _____

Skills Worksheet
Critical Thinking   SAMPLE

A Solar Solution

ADVANCED

SCILINKS ACTIVITY

Name _____ Class _____ Date _____

Activity
SciLinks Activity   SAMPLE

MARINE ECOSYSTEMS
Go to www.scilinks.com. To find links related to marine ecosystems, type in the keyword HL5490. Then, use the links to answer the questions about marine ecosystems.

GENERAL

...percentage of the Earth's surface is covered by water?

SCIENCE PUZZLERS, TWISTERS & TEASERS

Name _____ Date _____ Class _____

CHAPTER
9 SCIENCE PUZZLERS, TWISTERS & TEASERS
Energy and Energy Resources

When They Were in the 8th Grade (Tall Tales)

1. When they were in the 8th grade, some famous scientists and inventors had some strange ideas about various types of energy. From the clues, identify the types of energy and write them in the blanks.

a. Sir Isaac Newton wanted to invent an air conditioner for birds. He constructed a wind tunnel and pointed it at the apple tree where his favorite birds perched themselves. As a result, the _____ energy of the apples was converted into _____ energy and they fell on Newton's head. And now we have a theory of gravity.

b. _____ Oppenheimer wanted to make water lighter so that his _____ would weigh less when he went hiking. He decided to do this by splitting the hydrogen atom (of which there are two per each water molecule) in half. The result was a large explosion

GENERAL

Labs and Activities

LONG-TERM PROJECTS & RESEARCH IDEAS

Name _____ Date _____ Class _____

PROJECT
59 STUDENT WORKSHEET   DESIGN YOUR OWN
Great Balls of Fire

While sitting on her front porch during a thunderstorm in 1985, a Massachusetts woman saw a "white ball of fire" rolling up her street. It was sparking and crackling and sending out small fingers of lightning to the cars and telephone poles it passed. The ball, about a meter in diameter, split into three pieces, then into six, then joined back to three, and then back to its original size before disappearing. The power in the neighborhood went out for 2.1 hours.

Seem strange? Most people have witnessed lightning bolts in thunderstorms, but few have ever seen ball lightning. Although rare, it has been noted by individuals all the way back to the ancient Greeks. Ball lightning has been reported to enter airplanes and even to "chase" a flight attendant around the cabin! The nature of ball lightning is not well understood, ranking it among the more interesting scientific mysteries of the day.

INTERNET KEYWORD
ball lightning

A Striking Idea
1. Using the library and the Internet, find out more about ball lightning. How often is it reported? What are some theories to explain it? Are there any myths about ball lightning? Write a report in the form of a scientific magazine article. If possible, include quotes from firsthand reports of its sightings.

Another Research Idea
2. Where will the energy your children use come from? Though we rely on fossil fuels for the majority of our energy today, their limited supply and environmental impact force us to keep seeking new ways to generate energy. What are the most promising alternative energy sources being explored today? Choose one technology and create a Web page or report about it. Include its advantages and disadvantages, its potential for large-scale use, and a brief history of its development.

Long-Term Project Idea
3. Is your refrigerator taking money from you? Is your dishwasher sapping precious energy? Some appliances use more energy than others to do the same amount of work. Visit an appliance store, choose one type of appliance, and record the information shown on the yellow Energy Guide tag (the estimated cost of using that appliance for one year) for each model of that appliance. Make a chart listing several appliances in one category from highest to lowest Energy Guide rating. What features might lower the Energy Guide rating for the appliance you chose? Prepare a report with your findings.

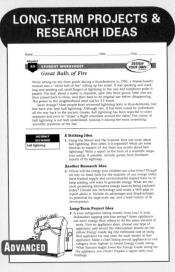

ADVANCED

WHIZ-BANG DEMONSTRATIONS

DEMO
50 TEACHER-LED DEMONSTRATION   DISCOVERY LAB
Pendulum Peril

Purpose
Students observe the movement of a water-balloon pendulum to understand conversions between potential and kinetic energy.

Time Required
10–15 minutes

Lab Ratings

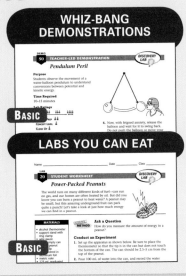

4. Now, with feigned anxiety, release the balloon and wait for it to swing back. Do not push the balloon or move your

Ask a Question

BASIC

LABS YOU CAN EAT

Name _____ Date _____ Class _____

LAB
20 STUDENT WORKSHEET   DISCOVERY LAB
Power-Packed Peanuts

The world runs on many different kinds of fuel—cars run on gas, and our homes are often heated by oil. But did you know you can burn a peanut to heat water? A peanut may be small, but this amazing underground fruit can pack quite a punch! Let's take a look at just how much energy we can find in a peanut.

MATERIALS
• alcohol thermometer
• support stand with ring clamp
• wire gauze
• empty can
• peanut
...

PROCESS METHOD   **Ask a Question**
How do you measure the amount of energy in a peanut?

Conduct an Experiment
1. Set up the apparatus as shown below. Be sure to place the thermometer so that the tip is in the can but does not touch the bottom of the can. The can should be 2.5–5 cm from the top of the peanut.
2. Pour 100 mL of water into the can, and record the water

BASIC

LABS YOU CAN EAT

Name _____ Date _____ Class _____

LAB
21 STUDENT WORKSHEET   DESIGN YOUR OWN
Now You're Cooking!

Have you ever walked barefoot across a black surface on a hot summer day? Ouch! The black surface gets much hotter than the air around you because the surface is an effective absorber of the sun's rays, or solar energy. The pavement absorbs solar energy and stores it as heat. Solar energy can be used to cook other things besides your feet. In this project, you will be part of a competition that will compare to build the best solar energy cooker for cooking a hot dog. The winning cooker will be the first to cook a hot dog. The planning construction of the cooker is up to you, so put your best ideas to work!

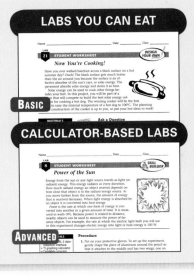

BASIC

CALCULATOR-BASED LABS

Name _____ Date _____ Class _____

LAB
8 STUDENT WORKSHEET   SKILL BUILDER
Power of the Sun

Energy from the sun or any light source travels as light (or radiant) energy. This energy radiates in every direction. How much radiant energy an object receives depends on how close that object is to the radiant energy source. As you move farther from the source, the amount of energy that is received decreases. When light energy is absorbed by an object it is converted into heat energy.

Power is the rate at which one form of energy is converted into another in a given amount of time. It is measured in watts (W). Because power is related to distance, nearby objects can be used to measure the power of faraway objects. For example, the rate at which the electric light bulb you will use in this experiment changes electric energy into light or heat energy is 100 W.

MATERIALS   ...3, 2 data-
...interface
• TI graphing calculator
• DataMate program

Procedure
1. Put on your protective gloves. To set up the experiment, gently shape the piece of aluminum around the pencil so that it attaches to the middle and has two wings, one on

ADVANCED

DATASHEETS FOR QUICK LABS

TEACHER RESOURCE PAGE

Quick Lab   DATASHEET FOR QUICK LAB
Reaction to Stress   SAMPLE

Background
The graph below illustrates changes that occur in the membrane potential of a neuron during an action potential. Use the graph to answer the following questions. Refer to Figure 3 as needed.

DATASHEETS FOR CHAPTER LABS

TEACHER RESOURCE PAGE

Skills Practice Lab   DATASHEET FOR CHAPTER LAB
Using Scientific Methods   SAMPLE

Teacher's Notes
TIME REQUIRED
One 45-minute class period.

DATASHEETS FOR LABBOOK

TEACHER RESOURCE PAGE

Skills Practice Lab   DATASHEET FOR LABBOOK LAB
Does It All Add Up?   SAMPLE

Teacher's Notes
TIME REQUIRED
One 45-minute class period.

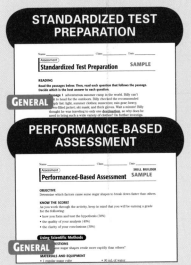

Review and Assessments

SECTION QUIZ

Name _____ Class _____ Date _____

Assessment
Section Quiz   SAMPLE

Section:

In the space provided, write the letter of the description that best matches the term or phrase.

___ 1. building molecules that can be used as an energy source, or breaking down molecules in which energy is stored

___ 2. the process by which light energy is converted to chemical energy

___ 3. an organism that uses sunlight or inorganic substances to make organic compounds

GENERAL   *ALSO IN SPANISH*

SECTION REVIEW

Name _____ Class _____ Date _____

Skills Worksheet
Section Review   SAMPLE

Section:
KEY TERMS
1. What do paleontologist study?

2. How does a trace fossil differ from petrified wood?

...fossil

GENERAL   *ALSO IN SPANISH*

UNDERSTANDING KEY IDEAS

CHAPTER REVIEW

Name _____ Class _____ Date _____

Skills Worksheet
Chapter Review   SAMPLE

USING VOCABULARY
1. Define biome in your own words.

2. Describe the characteristics of a savanna and a desert.

GENERAL   *ALSO IN SPANISH*

3. Identify the relationship between tundra and permafrost

CHAPTER TEST A

Name _____ Class _____ Date _____

Assessment
Chapter Test A   SAMPLE

MULTIPLE CHOICE
In the space provided, write the letter of the term or phrase that best completes each statement or best answers each question.

___ 1. Surface currents are formed by
   a. the moon's gravity.   c. wind.
   b. the sun's gravity.   d. increased water density.

___ 2. When waves come near the shore,
   a. they speed up.   c. their wavelength increases.
   b. they maintain their speed. d. their wave height increases.

Longhore currents transport sediment
   a. out to the open ocean.   c. only during low tide.
   b. along the shore.   d. only during high tide.

4. Which of the following does NOT control surface currents?

GENERAL   *ALSO IN SPANISH*

CHAPTER TEST B

Name _____ Class _____ Date _____

Assessment
Chapter Test B   SAMPLE

MULTIPLE CHOICE
In the space provided, write the letter of the term or phrase that best completes each statement or best answers each question.

___ 1. Surface currents are formed by
   a. the moon's gravity.   c. wind.
   b. the sun's gravity.   d. increased water density.

___ 2. When waves come near the shore,
   a. they speed up.   c. their wavelength increases.
   b. they maintain their speed. d. their wave height increases.

ADVANCED

CHAPTER TEST C

Name _____ Class _____ Date _____

Assessment
Chapter Test C   SAMPLE

MULTIPLE CHOICE
In the space provided, write the letter of the term or phrase that best completes each statement or best answers each question.

___ 1. Surface currents are formed by
   a. the moon's gravity.   c. wind.
   b. the sun's gravity.   d. increased water density.

___ 2. When waves come near the shore,
   a. they speed up.   c. their wavelength increases.
   b. they maintain their speed. d. their wave height increases.

...currents transport sediment
   ...to the open ocean.   c. only during low tide.
   ...shore.   d. only during high tide.

4. Which of the following does NOT control surface currents?

SPECIAL NEEDS

STANDARDIZED TEST PREPARATION

Name _____ Class _____ Date _____

Assessment
Standardized Test Preparation   SAMPLE

READING
Read the passages below. Then, read each question that follows the passage. Decide which is the best answer to each question.

Passage 1 adventurous summer camp in the world. Billy can't wait to head for the outdoors. Billy checked the recommended supply list: light, summer clothes; sunscreen; rain gear; heavy, down-filled jacket; ski mask; and thick gloves. Wait a minute! Billy thought he was traveling to only one destination, so why does he need to bring such a wide variety of clothes? On further investiga-

GENERAL

PERFORMANCE-BASED ASSESSMENT

Name _____ Class _____ Date _____

Assessment
Performance-Based Assessment   SKILL BUILDER   SAMPLE

OBJECTIVE
Determine which factors cause sugar shapes to break down faster than others.

KNOW THE SCORE!
As you work through the activity, keep in mind that you will be earning a grade for the following:
• how you form and test the hypothesis (30%)
• the quality of your analysis (40%)
• the clarity of your conclusions (30%)

Using Scientific Methods
...QUESTIONS
MATERIALS AND EQUIPMENT
• 1 regular sugar cube   • 80 mL of water

GENERAL

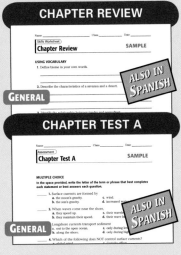
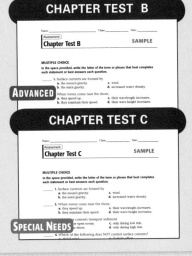

This Chapter Enrichment provides relevant and interesting information to expand and enhance your presentation of the chapter material.

Section 1

What Is Energy?

Energy

- Energy is the ability to do work. Work occurs when a force causes an object to move in the direction of the force. Both energy and work are expressed in units called *joules* (J), named for James Prescott Joule. One joule is the amount of work done when a force of 1 N acts through a distance of 1 m ($1 J = 1 N \times 1 m$).

James Prescott Joule

- The English scientist James Prescott Joule (1818–1889) was the son of a wealthy brewery owner. Joule used his financial resources to conduct research in a variety of areas. Joule worked to improve the efficiency of electric motors so that they could be used to replace steam engines. His research was some of the first to show the connection between thermal energy and other forms of energy.

Is That a Fact!

- The countries of North America consume about 30% of the total world energy output. The countries of the former Soviet Union consume about 11% to 15%.

Section 2

Energy Conversions

Kinetic and Potential Energy

- The conversion of potential energy to kinetic energy (and vice versa) is classically demonstrated by a bouncing ball.

- A moving object has kinetic energy. The amount of kinetic energy is proportional to the mass of the object and the square of the speed of the object.

Gravitational Potential Energy

- An object that has been lifted from its position on Earth's surface has gravitational potential energy. If you drop the object and nothing is in its way, the gravitational potential energy will immediately begin to change into kinetic energy as the object accelerates toward Earth.

Light Energy to Chemical Energy

- Plants use photosynthesis to make molecules that have high chemical energy, such as sugars, from water and carbon dioxide, which have low chemical energy. To increase the amount of chemical energy, light energy is converted to chemical energy, and ATP is formed. In a separate series of reactions, plants convert sugars to starches.

- When you eat plants, your digestive system transforms the high-energy sugars and starches into smaller, lower-energy molecules. The chemical energy in the sugars and starches fuels your body functions and movements and provides the thermal energy that keeps your body temperature constant.

Chemical Energy to Electrical Energy

- Batteries consist of cells. A cell converts chemical energy into electrical energy. A cell has two electrodes and an electrolyte. Between the electrodes are positive and negative ions. In positively charged ions, there are fewer electrons than protons, and in negatively charged ions, there are more electrons than protons. When a circuit is completed, the electrodes react with the electrolyte. In this reaction, electrons leave one of the electrodes and build up on the other. Work is done in separating the charges, and that work is stored in the battery as electrical potential energy.

- Whenever the electrodes of the battery are connected with a wire, work is done on the electrons in the wire as charges flow from the negative electrode of the battery to the positive electrode.

Section 3

Conservation of Energy

The Law of Conservation of Energy

- In the presence of friction, mechanical energy (*KE* + *PE*) is not conserved. But mechanical energy does not take into account the other objects and conversions within a closed system. Total energy is always conserved even if mechanical energy is not.

Is That a Fact!

- ◆ The British Patent Office does not accept applications for perpetual motion machines. Such machines would violate the laws of physics and are therefore considered impossible.

- ◆ The United States Patent Office accepts about 100 applications for perpetual motion machines every year.

Section 4

Energy Resources

Fossil Fuels

- Fossil fuels take hundreds of thousands—or even millions—of years to form.

- Coal is formed from plant material that is compressed in swamps.
- Petroleum and natural gas form from the remains of dead organisms.

Energy Alternatives

- Energy sources can be found in nature in a variety of forms. Wind energy, tidal energy, hydroelectric energy, and solar energy are alternatives to the nonrenewable fossil fuels used today.

- Although the sun is technically a limited energy source, it still has approximately 5 billion years left in its life span. In the time frame of human experience, the sun is considered a limitless source of energy.

SCiLINKS.

NSTA
Developed and maintained by the
National Science Teachers Association

SciLinks is maintained by the National Science Teachers Association to provide you and your students with interesting, up-to-date links that will enrich your classroom presentation of the chapter.

Visit www.scilinks.org and enter the SciLinks code for more information about the topic listed.

Topic: What Is Energy?
SciLinks code: HSM1660

Topic: Forms of Energy
SciLinks code: HSM0612

Topic: Energy Conversions
SciLinks code: HSM0511

Topic: Law of Conservation of Energy
SciLinks code: HSM0856

Topic: Energy Resources
SciLinks code: HSM0515

Overview

Tell students that this chapter will help them recognize energy in its different forms, learn how energy is measured, and learn how energy can be converted from one form to another.

Assessing Prior Knowledge

Students should be familiar with the following topics:

• matter

• motion

• forces

Identifying Misconceptions

Students may believe either that energy is associated only with inanimate objects or only with humans or that energy is a fluid, ingredient, or fuel. Many students believe that energy transformations involve only one form of energy at a time. Transformations such as the transformation from motion to heat are especially hard to visualize. The idea of energy conservation is counter-intuitive to many students. Students often interpret "Energy is neither created nor destroyed" to mean that energy is stored up in a system and often is released in its original form. Teaching energy (heat) dissipation ideas and energy conservation at the same time may help alleviate confusion.

5

Energy and Energy Resources

The Big Idea Energy can be changed from one form into another form, but energy cannot be created or destroyed.

About the PHOTO

Imagine that you're a driver in this race. Your car needs a lot of energy to finish. So, it probably needs a lot of gasoline, right? No, it just needs a lot of sunshine! This car runs on solar energy. Solar energy is one of the many forms of energy. Energy is needed to drive a car, turn on a light bulb, play sports, and walk to school. Energy is always being changed into different forms for different uses.

PRE-READING ACTIVITY

FOLDNOTES **Layered Book** Before you read the chapter, create the FoldNote entitled "Layered Book" described in the **Study Skills** section of the Appendix. Label the tabs of the layered book with "Types of energy," "Energy conversions," "Conservation of energy," and "Energy resources." As you read the chapter, write information you learn about each category under the appropriate tab.

Standards Correlations

National Science Education Standards

The following codes indicate the National Science Education Standards that correlate to this chapter. The full text of the standards is at the front of the book.

Chapter Opener
SAI 1, 2; PS 3a

Section 1 What Is Energy?
SAI 1; PS 3a, 3e, 3f

Section 2 Energy Conversions
UCP 3; PS 3a, 3d, 3f; *LabBook:* SAI 1, 2; PS 3a

Section 3 Conservation of Energy
UCP 1, 3; ST 2; PS 3a

Section 4 Energy Resources
SPSP 2; PS 3a, 3e, 3f

Chapter Lab
UCP 2; SAI 1; PS 3a

Chapter Review
SAI 1; PS 3a

Science in Action
SAI 2; ST2; SPSP 5; HNS 1; PS 3a

START-UP ACTIVITY
MATERIALS
FOR EACH GROUP
• mass, 100 g hooked
• string, 50 cm long

Safety Caution: Remind students to review all safety cautions and icons before beginning this activity. Goggles must be worn for this activity.

Answers

1. Accept all reasonable responses. Sample answer: The pendulum has energy because it moves.

2. Accept all reasonable responses. Sample answer: Gravity causes the pendulum to move.

3. Accept all reasonable responses. Sample answer: The pendulum has energy. It is storing the energy that I used to move it. That energy is released when I let go of the pendulum.

START-UP ACTIVITY

Energy Swings!

In this activity, you'll observe a moving pendulum to learn about energy.

Procedure

1. Make a pendulum by tying a **50 cm long string** around the hook of a **100 g hooked mass.**

2. Hold the string with one hand. Pull the mass slightly to the side, and let go of the mass without pushing it. Watch it swing at least 10 times.

3. Record your observations. Note how fast and how high the pendulum swings.

4. Repeat step 2, but pull the mass farther to the side.

5. Record your observations. Note how fast and how high the pendulum swings.

Analysis

1. Does the pendulum have energy? Explain your answer.

2. What causes the pendulum to move?

3. Do you think the pendulum had energy before you let go of the mass? Explain your answer.

Chapter Starter Transparency
Use this transparency to help students begin thinking about energy and energy resources.

CHAPTER RESOURCES

Technology

Transparencies
• Chapter Starter Transparency

READING
SKILLS

Student Edition on CD-ROM

Guided Reading Audio CD
• English or Spanish

Classroom Videos
• Brain Food Video Quiz

Workbooks

Science Puzzlers, Twisters & Teasers
• Energy and Energy Resources GENERAL

SECTION
1

Focus

Overview

This section introduces the concept of energy. Students will learn how kinetic and potential energy differ and how these forms of energy relate to mechanical energy. This section also discusses and compares different forms of energy.

 Bellringer

Write the following on the board: "Energy is the ability to _____." Ask students to think about this sentence and to write in their **science journal** how they think it should be completed. Lead a brief discussion to introduce the concept of energy as the ability to do work.

Motivate

Demonstration — GENERAL

Forms of Energy At the beginning of class, strike a match and let it burn for a few moments. Wind up a windup toy, and let it run. Turn off the lights in the classroom, and turn on a flashlight. Knock a tennis ball off a table so that the ball bounces onto the floor. Ask students to explain how energy was involved in each event. Lead students to conclude that there are many forms of energy.

 Visual

What You Will Learn

- Explain the relationship between energy and work.
- Compare kinetic and potential energy.
- Describe the different forms of energy.

Vocabulary

energy
kinetic energy
potential energy
mechanical energy

READING STRATEGY

Discussion Read this section silently. Write down questions that you have about this section. Discuss your questions in a small group.

energy the capacity to do work

Figure 1 *The tennis player does work and transfers energy to the racket. With this energy, the racket can then do work on the ball.*

What Is Energy?

It's match point. The crowd is silent. The tennis player tosse[s] the ball into the air and then slams it with her racket. The ba[ll] flies toward her opponent, who swings her racket at the ball THWOOSH!! The ball goes into the net, causing it to shake. Game set, and match!!

The tennis player needs energy to slam the ball with he[r] racket. The ball also must have energy in order to cause th[e] net to shake. Energy is around you all of the time. But what exactly, is energy?

Energy and Work: Working Together

In science, **energy** is the ability to do work. Work is done when a force causes an object to move in the direction of the force[.] How do energy and work help you play tennis? The tenni[s] player in **Figure 1** does work on her racket by exerting a force on it. The racket does work on the ball, and the ball does work on the net. When one object does work on another, energy is transferred from the first object to the second object. Thi[s] energy allows the second object to do work. So, work is a transfer of energy. Like work, energy is expressed in units o[f] joules (J).

Reading Check What is energy? (*See the Appendix for answers to Reading Checks.*)

CHAPTER RESOURCES

Chapter Resource File

- Lesson Plan
- Directed Reading A BASIC
- Directed Reading B SPECIAL NEEDS

Technology

Transparencies
- Bellringer
- P32 Energy and Work

Workbooks

Interactive Textbook Struggling Readers

Answer to Reading Check
Energy is the ability to do work.

Kinetic Energy

In tennis, energy is transferred from the racket to the ball. As it flies over the net, the ball has kinetic (ki NET ik) energy. **Kinetic energy** is the energy of motion. All moving objects have kinetic energy. Like all forms of energy, kinetic energy can be used to do work. For example, kinetic energy allows a hammer to do work on a nail, as shown in **Figure 2**.

Kinetic Energy Depends on Mass and Speed

An object's kinetic energy can be found by the following equation:

$$kinetic\ energy = \frac{mv^2}{2}$$

The *m* stands for the object's mass in kilograms. The *v* stands for the object's speed. The faster something is moving, the more kinetic energy it has. Also, the greater the mass of a moving object, the greater its kinetic energy is.

A large car has more kinetic energy than a car that has less mass and that is moving at the same speed does. But as you can see from the equation, speed is squared. So speed has a greater effect on kinetic energy than mass does. For this reason, car crashes are much more dangerous at higher speeds than at lower speeds. A moving car has *4 times* the kinetic energy of the same car going half the speed! This is because it's going twice the speed of the slower car, and 2 squared is 4.

kinetic energy the energy of an object that is due to the object's motion

Figure 2 *When you swing a hammer, you give it kinetic energy, which does work on the nail.*

MATH FOCUS

Kinetic Energy What is the kinetic energy of a car that has a mass of 1,200 kg and is moving at a speed of 20 m/s?

Step 1: Write the equation for kinetic energy.

$$KE = \frac{mv^2}{2}$$

Step 2: Replace *m* and *v* with the measurements given, and solve.

$$KE = \frac{1,200\ kg \times (20\ m/s)^2}{2}$$

$$KE = \frac{1,200\ kg \times 400\ m^2/s^2}{2}$$

$$KE = \frac{480,000\ kg\bullet m^2/s^2}{2}$$

$$KE = 240,000\ kg\bullet m^2/s^2 = 240,000\ J$$

Now It's Your Turn

1. What is the kinetic energy of a car that has a mass of 2,400 kg and is moving at 20 m/s? How does this kinetic energy compare to the kinetic energy of the car in the example given at left?
2. What is the kinetic energy of a 4,000 kg elephant that is running at 2 m/s? at 4 m/s? How do the two kinetic energies compare with one another?
3. What is the kinetic energy of a 2,000 kg bus that is moving at 30 m/s?
4. What is the kinetic energy of a 3,000 kg bus that is moving at 20 m/s?

Is That a Fact!

One joule is approximately the amount of energy required to lift an apple 1 m. In sports, some activities require considerably more energy. The average serve of a tennis ball requires 75 J of kinetic energy, a single fastball pitch requires 120 J, and a forward pass in football requires 150 J.

Potential and Kinetic Energy in a Pendulum

Use a pendulum to show the difference between potential energy and kinetic energy. As you pull the pendulum to the side, explain that you are giving it potential energy. Write the term *potential energy* on the board. Draw a picture of the pendulum's position next to the term. Allow the pendulum to swing down, and write the term *kinetic energy* on the board. Discuss with students the difference between kinetic energy and potential energy. **LS** Visual

Figure 3 *The stored potential energy of the bow and string allows them to do work on the arrow when the string is released.*

Potential Energy

Not all energy has to do with motion. **Potential energy** is th energy an object has because of its position. For example, th stretched bow shown in **Figure 3** has potential energy. The bo has energy because work has been done to change its shap The energy of that work is turned into potential energy.

Gravitational Potential Energy

When you lift an object, you do work on it. You use a forc that is against the force of gravity. When you do this, yo transfer energy to the object and give the object *gravitation potential energy.* Books on a shelf have gravitational potenti energy. So does your backpack after you lift it on to your bac The amount of gravitational potential energy that an obje has depends on its weight and its height.

Calculating Gravitational Potential Energy

You can find gravitational potential energy by using th following equation:

$$gravitational\ potential\ energy = weight \times height$$

Because weight is expressed in newtons and height in meter gravitational potential energy is expressed in newton-mete (N•m), or joules (J).

Recall that *work = force × distance.* Weight is the amoun of force that you must use on an object to lift it, and heigh is a distance. So, gravitational potential energy is equal t the amount of work done on the object to lift it to a certai height. Or, you can think of gravitational potential energy a being equal to the work that would be done by the object i it were dropped from that height.

Gravitational Potential Energy What is the gravitational potential energy of a book with a weight of 13 N at a height of 1.5 m off the ground?

Step 1: Write the equation for gravitational potential energy (GPE).

$GPE = weight \times height$

Step 2: Replace the weight and height with the measurements given in the problem, and solve.

$GPE = 13\ N \times 1.5\ m$

$GPE = 19.5\ N•m = 19.5\ J$

Now It's Your Turn

1. What is the gravitational potential energy of a cat that weighs 40 N standing on a table that is 0.8 m above the ground?
2. What is the gravitational potential energy of a diver who weighs 500 N standing on a platform that is 10 m off the ground?
3. What is the gravitational potential energy of a diver who weighs 600 N standing on a platform that is 8 m off the ground?

Cultural Awareness GENERAL

Origins of Bungee Jumping Bungee jumping began as a ritual called *land diving* that was practiced by the people of Pentecost Island in the Pacific archipelago of Vanuatu. Every year, a tower that is about 25 m tall is built. Men with vines attached to their ankles dive from platforms on the tower. Members of the Dangerous Sport Club at Oxford University, England, held the first bungee jump off a bridge in 1979.

Answers to Math Focus

1. $GPE = 40\ N \times 0.8\ m = 32\ J$
2. $GPE = 500\ N \times 10\ m = 5,000\ J$
3. $GPE = 600\ N \times 8\ m = 4,800\ J$

Height Above What?

When you want to find out an object's gravitational potential energy, the "ground" that you measure the object's height from depends on where it is. For example, what if you want to measure the gravitational potential energy of an egg sitting on the kitchen counter? In this case, you would measure the egg's height from the floor. But if you were holding the egg over a balcony several stories from the ground, you would measure the egg's height from the ground! You can see that gravitational potential energy depends on your point of view. So, the height you use in calculating gravitational potential energy is a measure of how far an object has to fall.

Mechanical Energy

How would you describe the energy of the juggler's pins in **Figure 4**? To describe their total energy, you would state their mechanical energy. **Mechanical energy** is the total energy of motion and position of an object. Both potential energy and kinetic energy are kinds of mechanical energy. Mechanical energy can be all potential energy, all kinetic energy, or some of each. You can use the following equation to find mechanical energy:

mechanical energy = potential energy + kinetic energy

✓ Reading Check What two kinds of energy can make up the mechanical energy of an object?

Mechanical Energy in a Juggler's Pin

The mechanical energy of an object remains the same unless it transfers some of its energy to another object. But even if the mechanical energy of an object stays the same, the potential energy or kinetic energy it has can increase or decrease.

Look at **Figure 4**. While the juggler is moving the pin with his hand, he is doing work on the pin to give it kinetic energy. But as soon as the pin leaves his hand, the pin's kinetic energy starts changing into potential energy. How can you tell that the kinetic energy is decreasing? The pin slows down as it moves upwards. Eventually, all of the pin's kinetic energy turns into potential energy, and it stops moving upward.

As the pin starts to fall back down again, its potential energy starts changing back into kinetic energy. More and more of its potential energy turns into kinetic energy. You can tell because the pin speeds up as it falls towards the ground.

potential energy the energy that an object has because of the position, shape, or condition of the object

mechanical energy the amount of work an object can do because of the object's kinetic and potential energies

Figure 4 *As a pin is juggled, its mechanical energy is the sum of its potential energy and its kinetic energy at any point.*

BRAIN FOOD

Potential Energy in a Music Box Before a music box will play music, it must be wound up. When you wind a music box, you do work on the spring inside. The energy required to do this work gets stored as potential energy. The music box then has the ability to do the work of playing music. An example of a similar device is a windup watch.

ACTIVITY — ADVANCED

El Niño The thermal energy of Earth's oceans has a profound effect on climate and weather. An example of this effect is the phenomenon known as El Niño and its counterpart, La Niña. Have students research El Niño and La Niña and write a report or create a poster that describes how thermal energy is responsible for them. **LS** Logical

Using the Figure — GENERAL

Thermal Energy Use **Figure 5** to help students understand that the thermal energy of a substance is related to the substance's temperature as well as to its state. Point out the difference in the appearance of the particles of ocean water and the particles of steam. Explain that at 100°C, equal masses of liquid water and steam have different amounts of thermal energy. The reason is that work must be done to force particles of liquid water apart when water changes to steam. The energy used to do this work is stored by the particles of steam as potential energy. As a result, the steam has more thermal energy than the liquid water does. **LS** Visual

INTERNET ACTIVITY

For another activity related to this chapter, go to **go.hrw.com** and type in the keyword **HP5ENGW.**

Figure 5 Thermal Energy in Water

The particles in an ice cube vibrate in fixed positions and do not have a lot of kinetic energy.

The particles of water in a lake can move more freely and have more kinetic energy than water particles in ice do.

The particles of water in steam move rapidly, so they have more energy than the particles in liquid water do.

Other Forms of Energy

Energy can come in a number of forms besides mechanical energy. These forms of energy include thermal, chemical, electrical, sound, light, and nuclear energy. As you read the next few pages, you will learn what these different forms of energy have to do with kinetic and potential energy.

Thermal Energy

All matter is made of particles that are always in random motion. Because the particles are in motion, they have kinetic energy. *Thermal energy* is all of the kinetic energy due to random motion of the particles that make up an object.

As you can see in **Figure 5,** particles move faster at higher temperatures than at lower temperatures. The faster the particles move, the greater their kinetic energy and the greater the object's thermal energy. Thermal energy also depends on the number of particles. Water in the form of steam has a higher temperature than water in a lake does. But the lake has more thermal energy because the lake has more water particles.

Chemical Energy

Where does the energy in food come from? Food is made of chemical compounds. When compounds such as sugar form, work is done to join the different atoms together. *Chemical energy* is the energy of a compound that changes as its atoms are rearranged. Chemical energy is a form of potential energy because it depends on the position and arrangement of the atoms in a compound.

MISCONCEPTION ALERT

Heat Versus Thermal Energy Students may confuse heat with thermal energy. Energy is transferred from higher-temperature objects to lower-temperature objects. Heat is this energy as it is being transferred. After the energy is transferred, it is thermal energy.

CHAPTER RESOURCES

Technology

 Transparencies
• P33 Thermal Energy in Water

Hear That Energy!

1. Make a simple drum by covering the open end of an **empty coffee can** with **wax paper**. Secure the wax paper with a **rubber band**.
2. Using the eraser end of a **pencil**, tap lightly on the wax paper. Describe how the paper responds. What do you hear?
3. Repeat step 2, but tap the paper a bit harder. Compare your results with those of step 2.
4. Cover half of the wax paper with one hand. Now, tap the paper. What happened? How can you describe sound energy as a form of mechanical energy?

Electrical Energy

The electrical outlets in your home allow you to use electrical energy. *Electrical energy* is the energy of moving electrons. Electrons are the negatively charged particles of atoms.

Suppose you plug an electrical device, such as the amplifier shown in **Figure 6**, into an outlet and turn it on. The electrons in the wires will transfer energy to different parts inside the amplifier. The electrical energy of moving electrons is used to do work that makes the sound that you hear from the amplifier.

The electrical energy used in your home comes from power plants. Huge generators turn magnets inside loops of wire. The changing position of a magnet makes electrical energy run through the wire. This electrical energy can be thought of as potential energy that is used when you plug in an electrical appliance and use it.

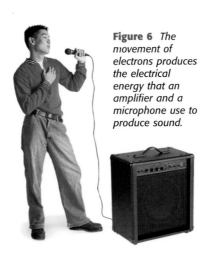

Figure 6 *The movement of electrons produces the electrical energy that an amplifier and a microphone use to produce sound.*

Sound Energy

Figure 7 shows how a vibrating object transmits energy through the air around it. Sound energy is caused by an object's vibrations. When you stretch a guitar string, the string stores potential energy. When you let the string go, this potential energy is turned into kinetic energy, which makes the string vibrate. The string also transmits some of this kinetic energy to the air around it. The air particles also vibrate, and transmit this energy to your ear. When the sound energy reaches your ear, you hear the sound of the guitar.

Reading Check What does sound energy consist of?

Figure 7 *As the guitar strings vibrate, they cause particles in the air to vibrate. These vibrations transmit sound energy.*

Answer to Reading Check
Sound energy consists of vibrations carried through the air.

CONNECTION to History —— GENERAL

Electrical Energy in the Home
Today, we take electrical energy for granted. It is always there at the flick of a switch. However, as late as 1930, only 1 out of 10 rural homes in the United States had electric service. Running lines many miles out to homes in the countryside was costly, and many power companies did not spend the money to do so. In 1935 and 1936, the Rural Electrification Administration (REA) was established to provide electrical energy to rural homes and farms. The REA made loans to nonprofit cooperatives to build electric systems in rural areas. Because of the REA, more than 99% of rural homes and farms in the United States now have electric service.

MATERIALS

FOR EACH STUDENT
• coffee can, empty
• pencil with an eraser
• rubber band
• wax paper

Answers
2. Sample answer: a sound something like a drum
3. Sample answer: The sound was louder when I tapped harder. The paper has a larger vibration when it is hit harder. This larger vibration causes the air particles near the paper to vibrate more. More energy is transmitted by the air particles, so the sound is louder.
4. Sample answer: The paper was not able to vibrate as much when it was held still, so the sound was more muffled. Sound energy is a form of mechanical energy because vibration involves a change of position and changes in back-and-forth motion.

Figure 8 *The energy used to cook food in a microwave is a form of light energy.*

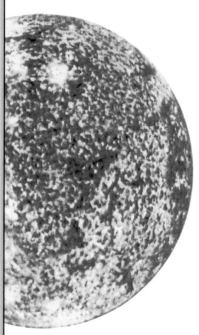

Figure 9 *Without the nuclear energy from the sun, life on Earth would not be possible.*

Light Energy

Light allows you to see, but did you know that not all light can be seen? **Figure 8** shows a type of light that we use but can't see. *Light energy* is produced by the vibrations of electrically charged particles. Like sound vibrations, light vibrations cause energy to be transmitted. But the vibrations that transmit light energy don't need to be carried through matter. In fact, light energy can move through a vacuum (an area where there is no matter).

Nuclear Energy

There is a form of energy that comes from a tiny amount of matter. It is used to generate electrical energy, and it gives the sun its energy. It is *nuclear* (NOO klee uhr) *energy*, the energy that comes from changes in the nucleus (NOO klee uhs) of an atom.

Atoms store a lot of potential energy because of the positions of the particles in the nucleus of the atoms. When two or more small nuclei (NOO klee ie) join together, or when the nucleus of a large atom splits apart, energy is given off.

The energy given off by the sun comes from nuclear energy. In the sun, shown in **Figure 9,** hydrogen nuclei join together to make a larger helium nucleus. This reaction, known as *fusion,* gives off a huge amount of energy. The sun's light and heat come from these reactions.

When a nucleus of a heavy element such as uranium is split apart, the potential energy in the nucleus is given off. This kind of nuclear energy is called *fission*. Fission is used to generate electrical energy at nuclear power plants.

Reading Check Where does nuclear energy come from?

Nuclear Fusion Hydrogen nuclei can join together to form a helium nucleus only at temperatures close to 100,000,000°C! For this reason, duplicating this reaction on Earth is not practical.

Summary

- Energy is the ability to do work, and work equals the transfer of energy. Energy and work are expressed in units of joules (J).
- Kinetic energy is energy of motion and depends on speed and mass.
- Potential energy is energy of position. Gravitational potential energy depends on weight and height.

- Mechanical energy is the sum of kinetic energy and potential energy.
- Thermal energy and sound energy can be considered forms of kinetic energy.
- Chemical energy, electrical energy, and nuclear energy can be considered forms of potential energy.

Using Key Terms

1. In your own words, write a definition for the term *energy*.

2. Use the following terms in the same sentence: *kinetic energy, potential energy,* and *mechanical energy*.

Understanding Key Ideas

3. What determines an object's thermal energy?
   a. the motion of its particles
   b. its size
   c. its potential energy
   d. its mechanical energy

4. How are energy and work related?

5. What two factors determine gravitational potential energy?

6. Describe why chemical energy is a form of potential energy.

Critical Thinking

7. **Identifying Relationships** When you hit a nail into a board by using a hammer, the head of the nail gets warm. In terms of kinetic and thermal energy, describe why you think the nail head gets warm.

8. **Applying Concepts** Explain why a high-speed collision may cause more damage to vehicles than a low-speed collision does.

Interpreting Graphics

9. Which part of mechanical energy does the girl in the picture below have the most of?

SCILINKS®
NSTA
Developed and maintained by the
National Science Teachers Association

For a variety of links related to this chapter, go to www.scilinks.org

Topic: What Is Energy? ; Forms of Energy
SciLinks code: HSM1660; HSM0612

CHAPTER RESOURCES

Chapter Resource File

- **Section Quiz** GENERAL
- **Section Review** GENERAL
- **Vocabulary and Section Summary** GENERAL
- **SciLinks Activity** GENERAL
- **Datasheet for Quick Lab**

Answers to Section Review

1. Sample answer: Energy is the ability to do work.

2. Sample answer: Mechanical energy can consist of kinetic energy, potential energy, or both.

3. a

4. Energy is the ability to do work.

5. weight and height

6. It depends on the position of atoms in a molecule.

7. Kinetic energy is used to nail the hammer into the board, and that energy becomes thermal energy.

8. A vehicle moving at high speed has a lot more kinetic energy than a vehicle moving at low speed does, so the high-speed vehicle is able to cause more damage in a collision.

9. potential energy

Focus

Overview

This lesson discusses energy conversions. Students will be given examples of ways that energy is converted from one form to another. This section also explains the role of machines in energy conversions.

 **Bellringer**

Display a plant, a Bunsen burner or small propane camping stove, and a pendulum. Ask students what they think these objects have in common. (All are capable of converting energy from one form to another.)

Motivate

Discussion ———— GENERAL

Kinetic and Potential Energy

Have a windup alarm clock set up for students to see. Display a label next to the clock that reads "Potential energy." The clock should be wound and set to go off when students are seated and attentive. When the clock alarm sounds, turn the label around so that it reads "Kinetic energy." Ask students to try to define *kinetic energy* and *potential energy* based on the demonstration. You may need to describe how the alarm clock works. Lead a discussion that addresses energy conversions. **LS** Logical

---

What You Will Learn

- Describe an energy conversion.
- Give examples of energy conversions for the different forms of energy.
- Explain how energy conversions make energy useful.
- Explain the role of machines in energy conversions.

Vocabulary

energy conversion

READING STRATEGY

Brainstorming The key idea of this section is energy conversion. Brainstorm words and phrases related to energy conversion.

energy conversion a change from one form of energy to another

---

Energy Conversions

Imagine you're finishing a clay mug in art class. You turn around, and your elbow knocks the mug off the table. Luckily you catch the mug before it hits the ground.

The mug has gravitational potential energy while it is on the table. As the mug falls, its potential energy changes into kinetic energy. This change is an example of an energy conversion. An **energy conversion** is a change from one form of energy to another. Any form of energy can change into any other form of energy. Often, one form of energy changes into more than one other form.

Kinetic Energy and Potential Energy

Look at **Figure 1.** At the instant this picture was taken, the skateboarder on the left side of the picture was hardly moving. How did he get up so high in the air? As you might guess, he was moving at a high speed on his way up the half-pipe. So, he had a lot of kinetic energy. What happened to that energy? His kinetic energy changed into potential energy. Imagine that the picture below is a freeze-frame of a video. What happens once the video starts running again? The skateboarder's potential energy will become kinetic energy once again as he speeds down the side of the half-pipe.

Figure 1 Potential Energy and Kinetic Energy

When the skateboarder reaches the top of the half-pipe, his potential energy is at a maximum.

As he speeds down through the bottom of the half-pipe, the skateboarder's kinetic energy is at a maximum.

CHAPTER RESOURCES

Chapter Resource File

- Lesson Plan
- Directed Reading A BASIC
- Directed Reading B SPECIAL NEEDS

Technology

 Transparencies
- Bellringer
- P34 Potential Energy and Kinetic Energy

Workbooks

 Interactive Textbook Struggling Readers

Elastic Potential Energy

A rubber band can be used to show another example of an energy conversion. Did you know that energy can be stored in a rubber band? Look at **Figure 2.** The wound-up rubber band in the toy airplane has a kind of potential energy called *elastic potential energy.* When the rubber band is let go, the stored energy becomes kinetic energy, spins the propeller, and makes the airplane fly.

You can change the shape of a rubber band by stretching it. Stretching the rubber band takes a little effort. The energy you put into stretching it becomes elastic potential energy. Like the skateboarder at the top of the half-pipe, the stretched rubber band stores potential energy. When you let the rubber band go, it goes back to its original shape. It releases its stored-up potential energy as it does so, as you know if you have ever snapped a rubber band against your skin!

> **Reading Check** How is elastic potential energy stored and released? (*See the Appendix for answers to Reading Checks.*)

Conversions Involving Chemical Energy

You may have heard someone say, "Breakfast is the most important meal of the day." Why is eating breakfast so important? As shown in **Figure 3,** chemical energy comes from the food you eat. Your body uses chemical energy to function. Eating breakfast gives your body the energy needed to help you start the day.

Figure 2 *The wound-up rubber band in this model airplane has potential energy because its shape has been changed.*

Figure 3 Chemical energy of food is converted into kinetic energy when you are active. It is converted into thermal energy to maintain body temperature.

Is That a Fact!

One appliance that uses a great deal of electrical energy (4,200 to 4,800 kWh per year) is the water heater. At the other extreme, an electric toothbrush uses only about 5 kWh per year.

Energy from Food Students may assume that they get energy from the sun only when they eat plants or plant products. However, when a person eats meat, that person is still getting energy from the sun. For example, a cow gets energy from the sun by eating plants. The cow stores some of this energy in its cells. When a person eats beef, that person's body uses the energy that was stored in the cow's cells. This energy originally came from the sun.

CONNECTION ACTiViTY
Environmental Science ———— GENERAL

Photosynthesis in Rain Forests
Divide the class into two groups. Have one group research the rate of growth and the rate of photosynthesis in tropical rain forests. Have the second group research the rate of rain-forest destruction. Ask both groups to present their findings to the class. Encourage a discussion of the usefulness of photosynthesis versus the usefulness of clearing the land occupied by rain forests. **LS** Logical

Figure 4 From Light Energy to Chemical Energy

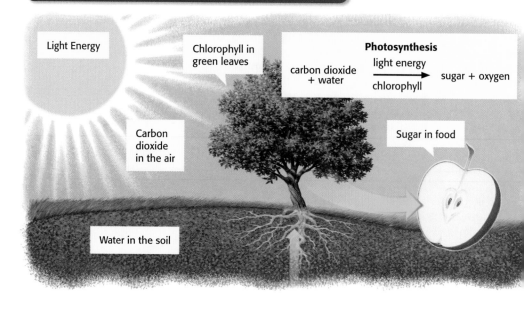

Light Energy

Chlorophyll in green leaves

Photosynthesis

$$\text{carbon dioxide} + \text{water} \xrightarrow[\text{chlorophyll}]{\text{light energy}} \text{sugar} + \text{oxygen}$$

Carbon dioxide in the air

Sugar in food

Water in the soil

CONNECTION TO Biology

WRITING SKILL **Energy from Plants** All living things need energy. Plants play a major role in providing sources of energy that our bodies use, from the oxygen we breathe to the food we eat. Research the different ways that plants help provide the energy requirements of all living things, and write a one-page report in your **science journal** describing what you learn.

Energy Conversions in Plants

Did you know that the chemical energy in the food you eat comes from the sun's energy? When you eat fruits, vegetables, or grains, you are taking in chemical energy. This energy comes from a chemical change that was made possible by the sun's energy. When you eat meat from animals that ate plants, you are also taking in energy that first came from the sun.

As shown in **Figure 4,** photosynthesis (FOHT oh SIN thuh sis) uses light energy to make new substances that have chemical energy. In this way, light energy is changed into chemical energy. The chemical energy from a tree can be changed into thermal energy when you burn the tree's wood. So, if you follow the conversion of energy back far enough, the energy from a wood fire actually comes from the sun!

Reading Check Where does the energy that plants use to grow come from?

The Process Continues

Let's trace where the energy goes. Plants change light energy into chemical energy. The chemical energy in the food you eat is changed into another kind of chemical energy that your body can use. Your body then uses that energy to give you the kinetic energy that you use in everything you do. It's an endless process—energy is always going somewhere!

Answer to Reading Check
Plants get their energy from the sun.

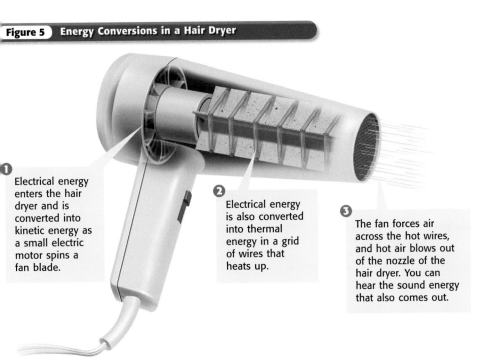

Figure 5 Energy Conversions in a Hair Dryer

1 Electrical energy enters the hair dryer and is converted into kinetic energy as a small electric motor spins a fan blade.

2 Electrical energy is also converted into thermal energy in a grid of wires that heats up.

3 The fan forces air across the hot wires, and hot air blows out of the nozzle of the hair dryer. You can hear the sound energy that also comes out.

Why Energy Conversions Are Important

Energy conversions are needed for everything we do. Heating our homes, getting energy from a meal, and many other things use energy conversions. Machines, such as the hair dryer shown in **Figure 5,** help harness energy and make that energy work for you. Electrical energy by itself won't dry your hair. But you can use a hair dryer to change electrical energy into the thermal energy that will help you dry your hair.

Conversions Involving Electrical Energy

You use electrical energy all of the time. When you listen to the radio, when you make toast, and when you take a picture with a camera, you use electrical energy. Electrical energy can easily be changed into other forms of energy. **Table 1** lists some common energy conversions that involve electrical energy.

Table 1 Some Conversions of Electrical Energy	
Alarm clock	electrical energy ⟶ light energy and sound energy
Battery	chemical energy ⟶ electrical energy
Light bulb	electrical energy ⟶ light energy and thermal energy
Blender	electrical energy ⟶ kinetic energy and sound energy

Science Bloopers

A Nuclear Car? The design for a nuclear-powered automobile was proposed by Ford automotive designers in the 1950s. The name of the car was to be the *Ford Nucleon,* and the car was to be propelled by a small atomic reactor located in the rear of the car. For several reasons, the car was never built.

Is That a Fact!

Only about 20% of the energy released by burning gasoline in a car engine is converted to kinetic energy to move the car forward. Most of the rest is converted to thermal energy, which is wasted.

Using the Figure — GENERAL

Concept Mapping Have students refer to **Figure 5** and **Table 1** to create a concept map of ways that electrical energy is converted. The map should begin with the nature of the work done on each object and end with the type(s) of energy produced. **LS** Visual

Cultural Awareness GENERAL

Bicycles for Daily Transportation There are more than 33 million cyclists in the United States. Most people in the United States ride bicycles for competition, recreation, or exercise, but people in other parts of the world use bicycles for daily transportation. For example, people in China often use a bicycle when they need to travel short distances, such as from home to work. How would U.S. traffic problems be different if most people in the United States rode bicycles to work? **LS** Logical

SUPPORT FOR

English Language Learners

Energy Conversions in the Home Show pictures of some common machines students might find at home one at a time. Have students note the name of the machine and the kind of energy conversion that may occur in it. Call on volunteers to share their responses with the class. **LS** Visual/Verbal

Section 2 • Energy Conversions **135**

Figure 6 *Some of the energy you transfer to a nutcracker is converted into sound energy as the nutcracker transfers energy to the nut.*

Energy and Machines

You've been learning about energy, its different form and the ways that it can change between forms. Anoth way to learn about energy is to look at how machin use energy. A machine can make work easier b changing the size or direction (or both) of the force neede to do the work.

Suppose you want to crack open a walnut. Using nutcracker, such as the one shown in **Figure 6,** woul be much easier (and less painful) than using you fingers. You transfer energy to the nutcracker, and transfers energy to the nut. The nutcracker allows yo to use less force over a greater distance to do the sam amount of work as if you had used your bare hand Another example of how energy is used by a machine shown in **Figure 7.** Some machines change the energy pu into them into other forms of energy.

✓ Reading Check What are two things that machines can do to force that is put into them?

| Figure 7 | Energy Conversions in a Bicycle |

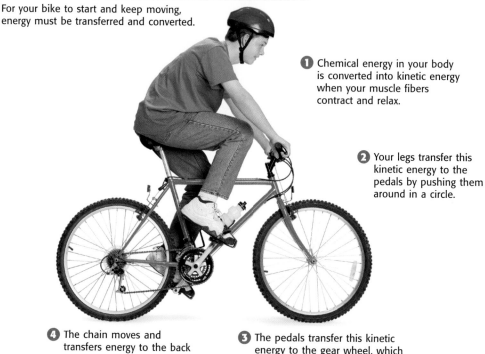

For your bike to start and keep moving, energy must be transferred and converted.

❶ Chemical energy in your body is converted into kinetic energy when your muscle fibers contract and relax.

❷ Your legs transfer this kinetic energy to the pedals by pushing them around in a circle.

❹ The chain moves and transfers energy to the back wheel, which gets you moving!

❸ The pedals transfer this kinetic energy to the gear wheel, which transfers kinetic energy to the chain.

Answer to Reading Check
Machines can change the size or direction of the input force.

Machines as Energy Converters

Machines help you use energy by converting it into the form that you need. **Figure 8** shows a device called a *radiometer*. It was invented to measure energy from the sun. Inside the glass bulb are four small vanes that absorb light energy. The vanes are dark on one side and light on the other. The dark sides absorb light energy better than the light sides do. As gases next to the dark sides of the vanes heat up, the gas molecules move faster, which causes the vanes to turn. The radiometer shows how a machine can convert energy from one form into another. It changes light energy into heat energy into kinetic energy.

Figure 8 *Machines can change energy into different forms. This radiometer converts light energy into kinetic energy.*

SECTION Review

Summary

- An energy conversion is a change from one form of energy to another. Any form of energy can be converted into any other form of energy.
- Kinetic energy is converted to potential energy when an object is moved against gravity.
- Elastic potential energy is another example of potential energy.
- Your body uses the food you eat to convert chemical energy into kinetic energy.
- Plants convert light energy into chemical energy.
- Machines can transfer energy and can convert energy into a more useful form.

Using Key Terms

1. In your own words, write a definition for the term *energy conversion.*

Understanding Key Ideas

2. In plants, energy is transformed from
   a. kinetic to potential.
   b. light to chemical.
   c. chemical to electrical.
   d. chemical to light.
3. Describe a case in which electrical energy is converted into thermal energy.
4. How does your body get the energy that it needs?
5. What is the role of machines in energy conversions?

Critical Thinking

6. **Applying Concepts** Describe the kinetic-potential energy conversions that occur when a basketball bounces.
7. **Applying Concepts** A car that brakes suddenly comes to a screeching halt. Is the sound energy produced in this conversion a useful form of energy? Explain your answer.

Interpreting Graphics

Look at the diagram below, and answer the following questions.

8. What kind of energy does the skier have at the top of the slope?
9. What happens to that energy after the skier races down the slope of the mountain?

For a variety of links related to this chapter, go to www.scilinks.org

Topic: Energy Conversions
SciLinks code: HSM0511

Answers to Section Review

1. Sample answer: a change from one kind of energy to another
2. b
3. Sample answer: a space heater, whose heating coils are given thermal energy from electrical energy when the heater is plugged in
4. Your body gets its energy from chemical energy found in food.
5. Machines can convert energy into more useful forms of energy.
6. The potential energy of a basketball is at a maximum when the ball is at its greatest height. The potential energy becomes converted to kinetic energy as the ball falls to the ground, and kinetic energy is at a maximum as the ball reaches the ground. When the ball bounces back up again, its kinetic energy is once again converted into potential energy, and so on.
7. No, the sound produced by screeching brakes is not a useful form of energy, because it does not contribute to stopping the car.
8. potential energy
9. It is converted to kinetic energy.

CHAPTER RESOURCES

Chapter Resource File

- Section Quiz GENERAL
- Section Review GENERAL
- Vocabulary and Section Summary GENERAL
- Reinforcement Worksheet BASIC

Technology

- Transparencies
  - LINK TO LIFE SCIENCE L46 Photosynthesis
  - P36 Energy Conversions in a Bicycle

Focus

Overview
This section introduces the law of conservation of energy. Students will learn how all energy is continuously being converted into other forms, and they will learn why the principle of energy conversion makes perpetual motion impossible.

🎧 Bellringer
Pose the following questions to students:

• Where does the energy that makes a roller coaster car move come from?

• Where does the energy go?

• What does "All of the energy put into a process still exists somewhere when the process has ended" mean?

Motivate

Demonstration ── GENERAL
Where Does the Energy Go?
Show students a high-density rubber ball. Explain that it was designed to bounce for a long time but that it must eventually stop. Allow the ball to begin bouncing. As it bounces, ask students to observe both the height and the number of bounces. Ask them to theorize why the ball eventually stops. Ask them what happens to the kinetic energy of the ball's movement. **LS** Logical

---

What You Will Learn
● Explain how energy is conserved within a closed system.
● Explain the law of conservation of energy.
● Give examples of how thermal energy is always a result of energy conversion.
● Explain why perpetual motion is impossible.

Vocabulary
friction
law of conservation of energy

READING STRATEGY
Paired Summarizing Read this section silently. In pairs, take turns summarizing the material. Stop to discuss ideas that seem confusing.

Conservation of Energy

Many roller coasters have a mechanism that pulls the cars up to the top of the first hill. But the cars are on their own for the rest of the ride.

As the cars go up and down the hills on the track, their potential energy is converted into kinetic energy and back again. But the cars never return to the same height at which they started. Does energy get lost somewhere along the way? No, it is just converted into other forms of energy.

Where Does the Energy Go?
To find out where a roller coaster's original potential energy goes, you have to think about more than just the hills of the roller coaster. Friction plays a part too. **Friction** is a force that opposes motion between two surfaces that are touching. For the roller coaster to move, energy must be used to overcome friction. There is friction between the cars' wheels and the track and between the cars and the air around them. As a result, not all of the potential energy of the cars changes into kinetic energy as the cars go down the first hill. Likewise, as you can see in **Figure 1,** not all of the kinetic energy of the cars changes back into potential energy.

Figure 1 **Energy Conversions in a Roller Coaster**

Not all of the cars' potential energy (*PE*) is converted into kinetic energy (*KE*) as the cars go down the first hill. In addition, not all of the cars' kinetic energy is converted into potential energy as the cars go up the second hill. Some of it is changed into thermal energy because of friction.

 PE is greatest at the top of the first hill.

 KE at the bottom of the first hill is less than the *PE* at the top was.

ⓒ *PE* at the top of the second hill is less than *KE* and *PE* from the first hill.

CHAPTER RESOURCES

Chapter Resource File
📁 • **Lesson Plan**
 • **Directed Reading A** BASIC
 • **Directed Reading B** SPECIAL NEEDS

Technology
🖥 **Transparencies**
 • Bellringer
 • P37 Energy Conversions in a Roller Coaster

MISCONCEPTION ALERT

Energy Lost as Friction Students may assume that all processes involving work and energy are 100% efficient. Remind students that all motion and all processes involving work are opposed by friction. Friction converts kinetic energy into thermal energy. Let students rub their palms together for 30 s. They will feel the thermal energy produced by friction.

Energy Is Conserved Within a Closed System

A *closed system* is a group of objects that transfer energy only to each other. For example, a closed system that involves a roller coaster consists of the track, the cars, and the air around them. On a roller coaster, some mechanical energy (the sum of kinetic and potential energy) is always converted into thermal energy because of friction. Sound energy also comes from the energy conversions in a roller coaster. If you add together the cars' kinetic energy at the bottom of the first hill, the thermal energy due to overcoming friction, and the sound energy made, you end up with the same total amount of energy as the original amount of potential energy. In other words, energy is conserved and not lost.

Law of Conservation of Energy

Energy is conserved in all cases. Because no exception to this rule has been found, this rule is described as a law. According to the **law of conservation of energy,** energy cannot be created or destroyed. The total amount of energy in a closed system is always the same. As **Figure 2** shows, energy can change from one form to another. But all of the different forms of energy in a system always add up to the same total amount of energy. It does not matter how many energy conversions take place.

Reading Check Why is the conservation of energy considered a scientific law? (*See the Appendix for answers to Reading Checks.*)

friction a force that opposes motion between two surfaces that are in contact

law of conservation of energy the law that states that energy cannot be created or destroyed but can be changed from one form to another

Figure 2 Energy Conservation in a Light Bulb

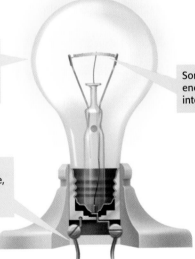

Some energy is converted into thermal energy, which makes the bulb feel warm.

Some electrical energy is converted into light energy.

As electrical energy is carried through the wire, some of it is converted into thermal energy.

Is That a Fact!
At extremely low temperatures, some materials become superconductors, materials that have no resistance to the flow of electrical energy. These materials are used to create giant electromagnets that generate strong magnetic fields with very little thermal-energy loss.

Section 3 • Conservation of Energy **139**

Close

Reteaching ——— BASIC

Conservation of Roller-Coaster Energy Revisit **Figure 1** by showing students the transparency of that figure. Ask students why each successive hill is smaller than the last, and make sure that they know where the energy went. **LS** Visual

Quiz ——— GENERAL

1. Think of an example other than the ones given in this section that illustrates the law of conservation of energy. (Answers may vary but should reflect an understanding of energy conservation.)

2. What condition would have to exist for perpetual motion to be possible? (no production of waste thermal energy; no friction)

Alternative Assessment ——— GENERAL

Energy Conservation Diagram Have students draw a diagram of a system in which energy conservation is demonstrated. The diagram should include labels that indicate the kinds of energy involved. **LS** Visual

SCHOOL to HOME

Energy Conversions
With an adult, find three examples of energy conversions that take place in your home. In your **science journal,** write down the kinds of energy that go into each conversion and the kinds of energy that result. For each type of energy that is output, indicate whether the energy is useful.

ACTIVITY

No Conversion Without Thermal Energy

Any time one form of energy is converted into another form, some of the original energy always gets converted into thermal energy. The thermal energy due to friction that results from energy conversions is not useful energy. That is, this thermal energy is not used to do work. Think about a car. You put gas into a car. But not all of the gasoline's chemical energy makes the car move. Some wasted thermal energy will always result from the energy conversions. Much of this energy leaves through the radiator and the exhaust pipe.

Perpetual Motion? No Way!

People have sometimes tried to make a machine that would run forever without any additional energy. This perpetual (puh PECH oo uhl) motion machine would put out exactly as much energy as it takes in. But that's impossible, because some waste thermal energy always results from energy conversions. The only way a machine can keep moving is to have a constant supply of energy. For example, the "drinking bird" shown in **Figure 3** uses thermal energy from the air to evaporate the water from its head. So, it is not a perpetual motion machine.

✓ Reading Check Why is "perpetual motion" impossible?

Figure 3 The "Drinking Bird"

❶ When the bird "drinks," the felt covering its head gets wet.

❷ When the bird is upright, water evaporates from the felt, which decreases the temperature and pressure in the head. Fluid is drawn up from the tail, where pressure is higher, and the bird tips downward.

❸ After the bird "drinks," fluid returns to the tail, the bird flips upright, and the cycle repeats.

Answer to Reading Check
Perpetual motion is impossible because energy conversions always result in the production of waste thermal energy.

Making Conversions Efficient

You may have heard that a car is energy efficient if it gets good gas mileage, and that your home may be energy efficient if it is well insulated. In terms of energy conversions, *energy efficiency* (e FISH uhn see) is a comparison of the amount of energy before a conversion with the amount of useful energy after a conversion. A car with high energy efficiency can go farther than other cars with the same amount of gas.

Energy conversions that are more efficient end up wasting less energy. Look at **Figure 4.** Newer cars tend to be more energy efficient than older cars. One reason is the smooth, aerodynamic (ER oh die NAM ik) shape of newer cars. The smooth shape reduces friction between the car and the surrounding air. Because these cars move through air more easily, they use less energy to overcome friction. So, they are more efficient. Improving the efficiency of machines, such as cars, is important because greater efficiency results in less waste. If less energy is wasted, less energy is needed to operate a machine.

Figure 4 *The shape of newer cars reduces friction between the body of the car and the air.*

More aerodynamic car

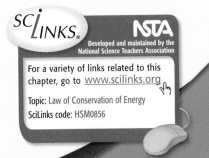

Less aerodynamic car

SECTION Review

Summary

- Because of friction, some energy is always converted into thermal energy during an energy conversion.

- Energy is conserved within a closed system. According to the law of conservation of energy, energy cannot be created or destroyed.

- Perpetual motion is impossible because some of the energy put into a machine is converted into thermal energy because of friction.

Using Key Terms

1. Use the following terms in the same sentence: *friction* and *the law of conservation of energy.*

Understanding Key Ideas

2. Perpetual motion is impossible because
   a. things tend to slow down.
   b. energy is lost.
   c. machines are very inefficient.
   d. machines have friction.

3. Describe the energy conversions that take place on a roller coaster, and explain how energy is conserved.

Math Skills

4. A bike is pedaled with 80 J of energy and then coasts. It does 60 J of work in moving forward until it stops. How much of the energy that was put into the bike became thermal energy?

Critical Thinking

5. **Evaluating Conclusions** Imagine that you drop a ball. It bounces a few times and then it stops. Your friend says that the energy that the ball had is gone. Where did the energy go? Evaluate your friend's statement based on energy conservation.

6. **Evaluating Assumptions** If someone says that a car has high energy output, can you conclude that the car is efficient? Explain.

SCILINKS

NSTA
Developed and maintained by the National Science Teachers Association

For a variety of links related to this chapter, go to www.scilinks.org

Topic: Law of Conservation of Energy
SciLinks code: HSM0856

CHAPTER RESOURCES

Chapter Resource File

- Section Quiz GENERAL
- Section Review GENERAL
- Vocabulary and Section Summary GENERAL

SECTION
4

Focus

Overview

Students will learn about renewable and nonrenewable energy resources and about advantages and disadvantages of energy resources.

 Bellringer

Write the names of several types of energy resources (such as sunlight, coal, and wind) on the board. Ask students to predict which resources are nonrenewable and which resources are renewable.

Motivate

ACTIVITY —————— GENERAL

Sources of Energy Tell students to pick an activity that they do every day. Ask them to trace the energy involved in their activity back to its source. For example, if their activity consists of playing computer games, they would trace the light and sound energy from the computer. Then, they would trace the production of the electrical energy used by the computer back to the energy's source. The power plant produced electrical energy from a fuel such as coal or natural gas. If they can, students should trace the fuel back to its source, too. **LS** Logical

What You Will Learn

- Name several energy resources.
- Explain how the sun is the source of most energy on Earth.
- Evaluate the advantages and disadvantages of using various energy resources.

Vocabulary

nonrenewable resource
fossil fuel
renewable resource

READING STRATEGY

Reading Organizer As you read this section, make a table comparing nonrenewable resources and renewable resources.

nonrenewable resource a resource that forms at a rate that is much slower than the rate at which it is consumed

fossil fuel a nonrenewable energy resource formed from the remains of organisms that lived long ago

Energy Resources

Energy is used to light and warm our homes. It is used to make food, clothing, and other things. It is also used to transport people and products from place to place. Where does all of this energy come from?

An *energy resource* is a natural resource that can be converted into other forms of energy in order to do useful work. In this section, you will learn about several energy resources, including the one that most other energy resources come from—the sun.

Nonrenewable Resources

Some energy resources, called **nonrenewable resources,** cannot be replaced or are replaced much more slowly than they are used. Fossil fuels are the most important nonrenewable resources.

Oil and natural gas, shown in **Figure 1,** as well as coal, are the most common fossil fuels. **Fossil fuels** are energy resources that formed from the buried remains of plants and animals that lived millions of years ago. These plants stored energy from the sun by photosynthesis. Animals used and stored this energy by eating the plants. So, fossil fuels are concentrated forms of the sun's energy. Now, millions of years later, energy from the sun is released when these fossil fuels are burned.

✓ **Reading Check** Why are fossil fuels considered nonrenewable resources? *(See the Appendix for answers to Reading Checks.)*

| Figure 1 | Formation of Fossil Fuels |

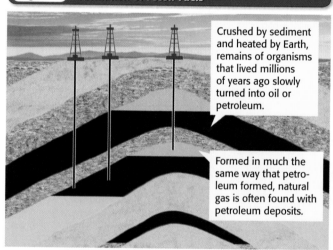

Crushed by sediment and heated by Earth, remains of organisms that lived millions of years ago slowly turned into oil or petroleum.

Formed in much the same way that petroleum formed, natural gas is often found with petroleum deposits.

CHAPTER RESOURCES

Chapter Resource File

- **Lesson Plan**
- **Directed Reading A** BASIC
- **Directed Reading B** SPECIAL NEEDS

Technology

- **Transparencies**
  - Bellringer
  - P38 Formation of Fossil Fuels
  - *LINK TO EARTH SCIENCE* E11 Porous Rocks as Reservoirs for Fossil Fuels

Workbooks

Interactive Textbook Struggling Readers

Answer to Reading Check

Fossil fuels are nonrenewable resources because they are used up more quickly than they are replaced.

Uses of Fossil Fuels

All fossil fuels contain stored energy from the sun, which can be converted into other kinds of energy. **Figure 2** shows some different ways that fossil fuels are used in our society.

People have been getting energy from the burning of coal, a fossil fuel, for hundreds of years. Today, burning coal is still a very common way to generate electrical energy. Many products, such as gasoline, wax, and plastics, are made from petroleum, another fossil fuel. A third kind of fossil fuel, natural gas, is often used in home heating.

Figure 2   Everyday Uses of Some Fossil Fuels

Coal

Most coal used in the United States is burned to produce steam to run electric generators.

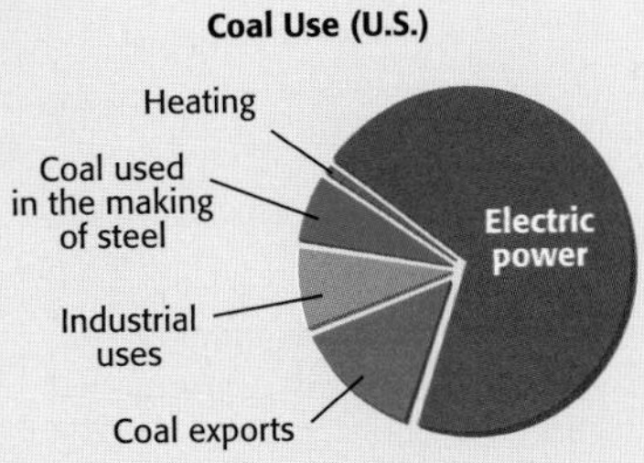

Coal Use (U.S.)
- Heating
- Coal used in the making of steel
- Industrial uses
- Coal exports
- Electric power

Petroleum

Gasoline, kerosene, wax, and petrochemicals come from petroleum.

Finding alternative energy resources will become more important in years to come.

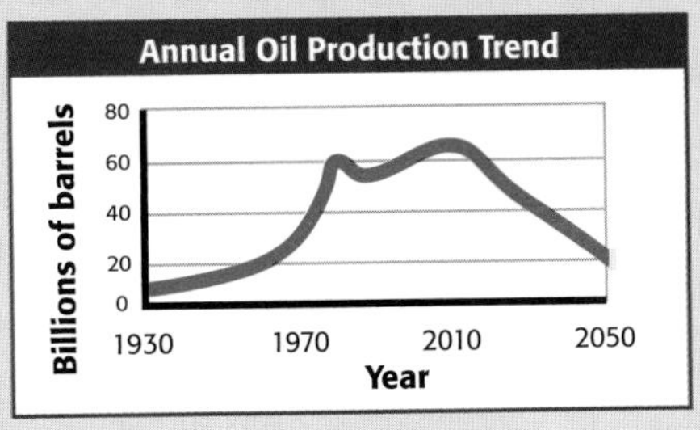

Annual Oil Production Trend

(graph: Billions of barrels vs Year, 1930–2050)

Natural Gas

Natural gas is used in heating systems, stoves, ovens, and vehicles.

Compared to other fossil fuels, natural gas has very low emission levels when burned.

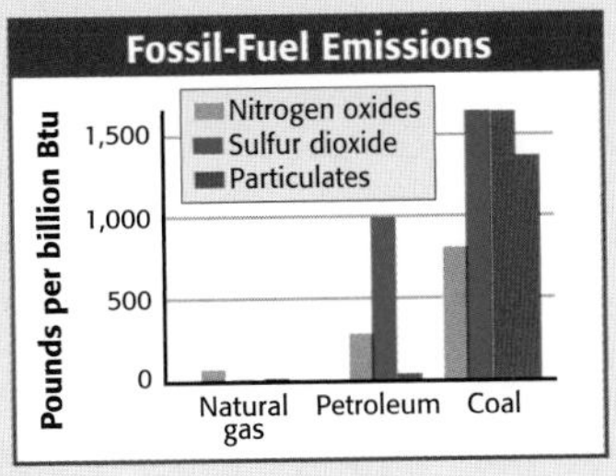

Fossil-Fuel Emissions

(bar graph: Pounds per billion Btu — Nitrogen oxides, Sulfur dioxide, Particulates for Natural gas, Petroleum, Coal)

Teach

CONNECTION ACTIVITY
Math —————————— GENERAL

Worldwide Coal Distribution
The worldwide distribution of coal reserves in billions of metric tons (1 metric ton = 1,000 kg) is as follows:

- 66 in Africa
- 695 in Asia
- 404 in Europe
- 271 in North America
- 7 in South and Central America

Help students construct both a pie chart and a bar graph to display this information. Discuss the two presentations, including when each might be useful.
LS Logical

CONNECTION ACTIVITY
History —————————— GENERAL

 Use of Fossil Fuels Ask students to write a short story about how a day in their life would be if no fossil-fuel energy (oil, gasoline, natural gas, and coal) were available. The story should include descriptions of when and how their daily activities would be performed, which things would be different, and which things might stay the same.
LS Intrapersonal   PORTFOLIO

Energy Density of Fossil Fuels It takes about 454 kg of lead-acid batteries (such as the one in most cars) to store the same amount of energy that about 4 L of gasoline contains.

Converting Fossil Fuels into Electrical Energy Have students study **Figure 3** on this page. Make sure that students understand each step for converting fossil fuels into electrical energy by discussing each step. Ask students to create a concept map explaining each of the steps.  **LS** Logical

INCLUSION Strategies

- *Hearing Impaired*
- *Learning Disabled*
- *Developmentally Delayed*

Simplification of information can help some students understand complicated details. To make sure that students understand the concepts of renewable energy and nonrenewable energy, put on the board a chart that has the following row headings: "Coal," "Petroleum," "Natural gas," "Nuclear energy," "Solar energy," "Wind energy," "Energy from water," "Geothermal energy," and "Biomass." Make columns that have the following headings: "Renewable" and "Nonrenewable." As a group, discuss each resource (row headings) and place a check in either the "Renewable" or "Nonrenewable" column. **LS** Verbal **English Language Learners**

Figure 3 Converting Fossil Fuels into Electrical Energy

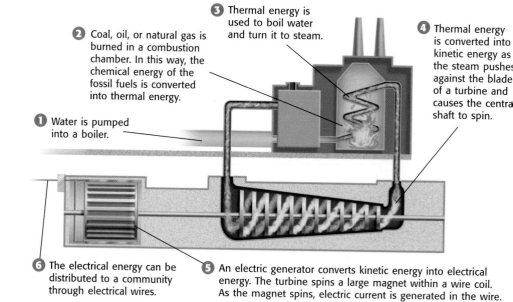

① Water is pumped into a boiler.

② Coal, oil, or natural gas is burned in a combustion chamber. In this way, the chemical energy of the fossil fuels is converted into thermal energy.

③ Thermal energy is used to boil water and turn it to steam.

④ Thermal energy is converted into kinetic energy as the steam pushes against the blade of a turbine and causes the central shaft to spin.

⑤ An electric generator converts kinetic energy into electrical energy. The turbine spins a large magnet within a wire coil. As the magnet spins, electric current is generated in the wire.

⑥ The electrical energy can be distributed to a community through electrical wires.

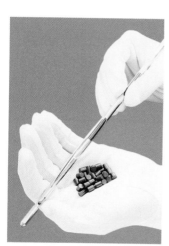

Figure 4 *A single uranium fuel pellet contains the energy equivalent of about 1 metric ton of coal.*

Electrical Energy from Fossil Fuels

One way to generate electrical energy is to burn fossil fuels. In fact, fossil fuels are the main source of electrical energy generated in the United States. *Electric generators* convert the chemical energy in fossil fuels into electrical energy by the process shown in **Figure 3.** The chemical energy in fossil fuels is changed into the electrical energy that you use every day.

Nuclear Energy

Another way to generate electrical energy is to use nuclear energy. Like fossil-fuel power plants, a nuclear power plant generates thermal energy that boils water to make steam. The steam then turns a turbine, which runs a generator. The spinning generator changes kinetic energy into electrical energy. However, the fuels used in nuclear power plants differ from fossil fuels. Nuclear energy is generated from radioactive elements, such as uranium, shown in **Figure 4.** In a process called *nuclear fission* (NOO klee uhr FISH uhn), the nucleus of a uranium atom is split into two smaller nuclei, which releases nuclear energy. Because the supply of these elements is limited, nuclear energy is a nonrenewable resource.

✓ **Reading Check** Where does nuclear energy come from?

Is That a Fact!

The First Electrical Generator In 1882 in Manhattan, Thomas Edison built the first electrical generating station designed to provide electrical energy to homes and businesses.

Answer to Reading Check

Nuclear energy comes from radioactive elements that give off energy during nuclear fission.

enewable Resources

ome energy resources, called **renewable resources,** are aturally replaced more quickly than they are used. ome renewable resources, such as solar energy and wind nergy, are considered practically limitless.

olar Energy

unlight can be changed into electrical energy through olar cells. These cells can be used in devices such as alculators. Solar cells can also be placed on the roof of house to provide electrical energy. Some houses can se solar energy by allowing sunlight into the house hrough large windows. The sun's energy can then be sed to heat the house.

nergy from Water

he sun causes water to evaporate and fall again as rain hat flows through rivers. The potential energy of water n a reservoir can be changed into kinetic energy as the vater flows through a dam. **Figure 5** shows a hydroelectric am. Falling water turns turbines in a dam. The turbines re connected to a generator that changes kinetic energy nto electrical energy.

Vind Energy

Vind is caused by the sun's heating of Earth's surface. Because Earth's surface is not heated evenly, wind is reated. The kinetic energy of wind can turn the blades f a windmill. Wind turbines are shown in **Figure 6.** A vind turbine changes the kinetic energy of the air into lectrical energy by turning a generator.

renewable resource a natural resource that can be replaced at the same rate at which the resource is consumed

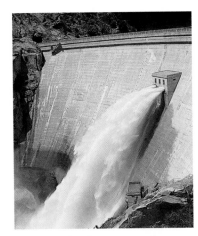

Figure 5 *This dam converts the energy from water going downstream into electrical energy.*

Figure 6 *These wind turbines are converting wind energy into electrical energy.*

BRAIN FOOD

Of the total energy used by a standard incandescent light bulb, only one-tenth is converted to light energy. The rest is converted to thermal energy. That's why light bulbs are so hot after they have been on for a while!

ACTIVITY — ADVANCED

The Ozone Layer Have students research and prepare a presentation about the importance of the ozone layer of the atmosphere and the effects of ozone layer depletion on the environment and on solar energy. Students should answer the following questions: "How might the amount of thermal energy received from the sun be affected? How do holes in the ozone layer affect the efficiency of solar energy as an energy resource?" Encourage students to be creative in their presentations. **LS Logical**

Debate — GENERAL

Oil from Shale and Tar Sands It is estimated that Earth has reserves of shale oil and tar sands that are about 500 times larger than the known crude-oil reserves. Shale oil and tar sands could provide the world with petroleum products long after crude oil reserves have been exhausted. However, the production of petroleum from shale oil and tar sands is much more expensive than the production of crude oil is. Have students debate whether resources should be spent to produce petroleum from shale oil and tar sands or to develop renewable energy resources. **LS Interpersonal**

Reteaching — BASIC
Renewable and Nonrenewable
Challenge the class to name each energy resource mentioned in this section. Prompt students to tell whether each resource is renewable or nonrenewable and why. **LS** Logical

Quiz — GENERAL
1. Explain the process of fossil-fuel formation. (Organisms that lived millions of years ago died and were covered by layers of sediment. The pressure and the temperatures produced by the overlying layers caused chemical reactions that changed the organic matter into fossil fuel.)

2. Name the five types of energy that are considered renewable resources. (solar energy, energy from water, wind energy, geothermal energy, and biomass)

Alternative Assessment — GENERAL
When Fossil Fuels Run Out Ask students to think about how life will change when fossil fuels run out. How will the environment, jobs, travel, sports, and industry be affected? Ask students to write or illustrate a short story that describes a day in such a time. **LS** Verbal

Geothermal Energy

Thermal energy caused by the heating of Earth's crust is called *geothermal energy*. Some geothermal power plants pump water underground next to hot rock. The water returns to the surface as steam, which can then turn the turbine of a generator.

Reading Check Where does geothermal energy come from?

Biomass

Plants use and store energy from the sun. Organic matter such as plants, wood, and waste, that can be burned to release energy is called *biomass*. **Figure 7** shows an example. Some countries depend on biomass for energy.

Figure 7 *Plants capture the sun's energy. When wood is burned, it releases the energy it got from the sun, which can be used to generate electrical energy.*

The Two Sides to Energy Resources

All energy resources have advantages and disadvantages. How can you decide which energy resource to use? **Table 1** compares several energy resources. Depending on where you live, what you need energy for, and how much energy you need, one energy resource may be a better choice than another.

Table 1 Advantages and Disadvantages of Energy Resources

Energy Resource	Advantages	Disadvantages
Fossil fuels	• provide a large amount of thermal energy per unit of mass • are easy to get and transport • can be used to generate electricity and to make products such as plastic	• are nonrenewable • produce smog • release substances that can cause acid precipitation • create a risk of oil spills
Nuclear	• is a very concentrated form of energy • does not produce air pollution	• produces radioactive waste • is nonrenewable
Solar	• is an almost limitless source of energy • does not produce pollution	• is expensive to use for large-scale energy production • is practical only in sunny areas
Water	• is renewable • does not produce air pollution	• requires dams, which disrupt a river's ecosystem • is available only where there are rivers
Wind	• is renewable • is relatively inexpensive to generate • does not produce air pollution	• is practical only in windy areas
Geothermal	• is an almost limitless source of energy • power plants require little land	• is practical only in areas near hot spots • produces wastewater, which can damage soil
Biomass	• is renewable • is inexpensive	• requires large areas of farmland • produces smoke

Answer to Reading Check
Geothermal energy comes from the thermal energy given off by underground areas of hot rock.

Choosing the Right Energy Resource

As **Table 1** shows, each source of energy that we know about on Earth has advantages and disadvantages. For example, you have probably heard that fossil fuels pollute the air. They will also run out after they are used up. Even renewable resources have their drawbacks. Generating lots of energy from solar energy is difficult. So it cannot be used to meet the energy needs of large cities. Geothermal energy is limited to the "hot spots" in the world where it is available. Hydroelectric energy requires large dams, which can affect the ecology of river life. Energy planning in all parts of the world requires careful consideration of energy needs and the availability and responsible use of resources.

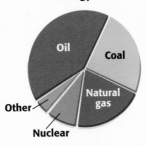

CONNECTION TO
Social Studies

WRITING SKILL **Earth's Energy Resources** Find examples of places in the world where the various energy resources mentioned in this chapter are used. List them in your **science journal.** Discuss any patterns that you notice, such as which regions of the world use certain energy resources.

SECTION Review

Summary

- An energy resource is a natural resource that can be converted into other forms of energy in order to do useful work.
- Nonrenewable resources cannot be replaced after they are used or can be replaced only after long periods of time. They include fossil fuels and nuclear energy.
- Renewable resources can be replaced in nature over a relatively short period of time. They include energy from the sun, wind, and water; geothermal energy; and biomass.
- The sun is the source of most energy on Earth.
- Choices about energy resources depend on where you live and what you need energy for.

Using Key Terms

1. In your own words, write a definition for the term *fossil fuel*.

Complete each of the following sentences by choosing the correct term from the word bank.

nonrenewable resources
renewable resources

2. There is a practically limitless supply of ___.

3. ___ are used up more quickly than they are being replaced.

Understanding Key Ideas

4. Which of the following is a renewable resource?
   a. wind
   b. coal
   c. nuclear energy
   d. petroleum

5. Compare fossil fuels and biomass as energy resources.

6. Trace electrical energy back to the sun.

Critical Thinking

7. **Making Comparisons** Describe the similarities and differences between transforming energy in a hydroelectric dam and a wind turbine.

8. **Analyzing Ideas** Name an energy resource that does NOT depend on the sun.

Interpreting Graphics

9. Use the pie chart below to explain why renewable resources are becoming more important to the United States.

U.S. Energy Sources

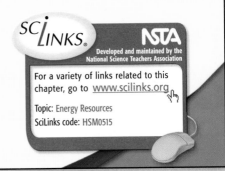

Oil | Coal | Natural gas | Other | Nuclear

SCI LINKS
NSTA
Developed and maintained by the National Science Teachers Association

For a variety of links related to this chapter, go to www.scilinks.org

Topic: Energy Resources
SciLinks code: HSM0515

CHAPTER RESOURCES

Chapter Resource File

- • Section Quiz **GENERAL**
- • Section Review **GENERAL**
- • Vocabulary and Section Summary **GENERAL**
- • Critical Thinking **ADVANCED**

Technology

- Interactive Explorations CD-ROM
  • The Generation Gap

Finding Energy

Teacher's Notes

Time Required
Two 45-minute class periods

Lab Ratings

EASY ——————→ HARD

Teacher Prep 🧪
Student Set-Up 🧪
Concept Level 🧪🧪🧪
Clean Up 🧪

MATERIALS
The materials listed for this lab are enough for each group of 2–3 students. Rolling carts are available from suppliers of science classroom materials. The ramp should be at least 1 m long.

Procedure Notes
Use one day to set up and collect data. Use the second day for calculations, or assign the calculations as homework.

Ask a Question
1. Sample answer: The kinetic energy comes from the potential energy that you had at the top of the hill.

Form a Hypothesis
2. Accept all testable hypotheses.

OBJECTIVES

Form a hypothesis about where kinetic energy comes from.

Test your hypothesis by collecting and analyzing data.

MATERIALS

- books (2 or 3)
- masking tape
- meterstick
- metric balance
- rolling cart
- stopwatch
- wooden board

Finding Energy

When you coast down a hill on a bike or skateboard, you may notice that you pick up speed, or go faster and faster. Because you are moving, you have kinetic energy—the energy of motion. Where does that energy come from? When you pedal the bike or push the skateboard, you are the source of the kinetic energy. But where does the kinetic energy come from when you roll down a hill without making any effort? In this lab, you will find out where such kinetic energy comes from.

Ask a Question

1. Where does the kinetic energy come from when you roll down a hill?

Form a Hypothesis

2. Write a hypothesis that is a possible answer to the question above. Explain your reasoning.

Test the Hypothesis

3. Copy the Data Collection Table below.

				Time of trial (s)			
Data Collection Table							
Height of ramp (m)	Length of ramp (m)	Mass of cart (kg)	Weight of cart (N)	1	2	3	Average time (s)
		DO NOT WRITE IN BOOK					

Holt Lab Generator CD-ROM

Search for any lab by topic, standard, difficulty level, or time. Edit any lab to fit your needs, or create your own labs. Use the Lab Materials QuickList software to customize your lab materials list.

Rebecca Ferguson
North Ridge Middle School
North Richland Hills, Texas

CHAPTER RESOURCES

Chapter Resource File

- **Datasheet for Chapter Lab**
- **Lab Notes and Answers**

Technology
📹 Classroom Videos
- Lab Video

- Energy of a Pendulum

4. Use your books and board to make a ramp.

5. Use masking tape to mark a starting line at the top of the ramp. Be sure the starting line is far enough down from the top of the ramp to allow the cart to be placed behind the line.

6. Use masking tape to mark a finish line at the bottom of the ramp.

7. Find the height of the ramp by measuring the height of the starting line and subtracting the height of the finish line. Record the height of the ramp in your Data Collection Table.

8. Measure the distance in meters between the starting line and the finish line. In the Data Collection Table, record this distance as the length of the ramp.

9. Use the balance to find the mass of the cart in grams. Convert this measurement to kilograms by dividing it by 1,000. In your Data Collection Table, record the mass in kilograms.

10. Multiply the mass by 10 to get the weight of the cart in newtons. Record this weight in your Data Collection Table.

11. Set the cart behind the starting line, and release it. Use a stopwatch to time how long the cart takes to reach the finish line. Record the time in your Data Collection Table.

12. Repeat step 11 twice more, and average the results. Record the average time in your Data Collection Table.

Analyze the Results

1. **Organizing Data** Copy the Calculations Table shown at right onto a separate sheet of paper.

2. **Analyzing Data** Calculate and record the quantities for the cart in the Calculations Table by using your data and the four equations that follow.

Calculations Table			
Average speed (m/s)	Final speed (m/s)	Kinetic energy at bottom (J)	Gravitational potential energy at top (J)
DO NOT WRITE IN BOOK			

$$\text{average speed} = \frac{\text{length of ramp}}{\text{average time}}$$

Final speed = 2 × average speed
(This equation works because the cart accelerates smoothly from 0 m/s.)

$$\text{kinetic energy} = \frac{\text{mass} \times (\text{final speed})^2}{2}$$

(Remember that 1 kg · m²/s² = 1 J, the unit used to express energy.)

Gravitational potential energy = weight × height
(Remember that 1 N = 1 kg · m/s², so 1 N × 1 m = 1 kg · m²/s² = 1 J)

Draw Conclusions

3. **Drawing Conclusions** How does the cart's gravitational potential energy at the top of the ramp compare with its kinetic energy at the bottom? Does this support your hypothesis? Explain your answer.

4. **Evaluating Data** You probably found that the gravitational potential energy of the cart at the top of the ramp was almost, but not exactly, equal to the kinetic energy of the cart at the bottom of the ramp. Explain this finding.

5. **Applying Conclusions** Suppose that while riding your bike, you coast down both a small hill and a large hill. Compare your final speed at the bottom of the small hill with your final speed at the bottom of the large hill. Explain your answer.

Draw Conclusions

3. The magnitude of the cart's gravitational potential energy at the top of the ramp is nearly identical to the magnitude of its kinetic energy at the bottom of the ramp. Whether this finding supports the original hypothesis will depend on the original hypothesis.

4. The cart's gravitational potential energy at the top of the ramp is slightly greater than its kinetic energy at the bottom of the ramp because some of the energy is used to do work against friction. Without friction, the two energy measurements would be the same.

5. You would have a greater final speed at the bottom of the large hill than at the bottom of the small hill. The amount of gravitational potential energy depends on the height of the starting position. Starting from a greater height means starting with more gravitational potential energy, which is converted into kinetic energy as you coast down the hill.

Assignment Guide	
SECTION	**QUESTIONS**
1	1, 6, 11, 15, 17, 23–25
2	2, 7, 9–10, 12, 16, 18, 20
3	3, 13, 21–22
4	4–5, 8, 14, 19

ANSWERS

Using Key Terms

1. Sample answer: Potential energy is the energy of position of an object. Kinetic energy is the energy of motion of an object.

2. Sample answer Mechanical energy is the total kinetic and potential energy of an object. Energy conversion is the change of energy from one form to another.

3. Sample answer: Friction is a force that opposes motion between two surfaces that are in contact. The law of conservation of energy states that energy is never created or lost; it simply changes form.

4. Sample answer: Renewable resources are replaced naturally more quickly than they are used up. Nonrenewable resources are not replaced— or are replaced very slowly— after they are used up.

USING KEY TERMS

For each pair of terms, explain how the meanings of the terms differ.

1. *potential energy* and *kinetic energy*

2. *mechanical energy* and *energy conversion*

3. *friction* and *the law of conservation of energy*

4. *renewable resources* and *nonrenewable resources*

5. *energy resources* and *fossil fuels*

UNDERSTANDING KEY IDEAS

Multiple Choice

6. Kinetic energy depends on
    a. mass and volume.
    b. velocity and weight.
    c. weight and height.
    d. velocity and mass.

7. Gravitational potential energy depends on
    a. mass and velocity.
    b. weight and height.
    c. mass and weight.
    d. height and distance.

8. Which of the following types of energy is not a renewable resource?
    a. wind energy
    b. nuclear energy
    c. solar energy
    d. geothermal energy

9. Which of the following sentences describes a conversion from chemical energy to thermal energy?
    a. Food is digested and used to regulate body temperature.
    b. Charcoal is burned in a barbecue pit
    c. Coal is burned to produce steam.
    d. All of the above

10. When energy changes from one form to another, some of the energy always changes into
    a. kinetic energy.
    b. potential energy.
    c. thermal energy.
    d. mechanical energy.

Short Answer

11. Name two forms of energy, and relate them to kinetic or potential energy.

12. Give three examples of one form of energy being converted into another form.

13. Explain what a closed system is, and how energy is conserved within it.

14. How are fossil fuels formed?

Math Skills

15. A box has 400 J of gravitational potential energy.
    a. How much work had to be done to give the box that energy?
    b. If the box weighs 100 N, how far above the ground is it?

5. Sample answer: Energy resources are natural sources of energy that can be converted into other forms of energy to do useful work. Fossil fuels are energy resources that come from decayed organic matter from plants and animals that lived millions of years ago.

Understanding Key Ideas

6. d
7. b
8. b
9. d
10. c

11. Sample answer: Thermal energy depends partly on the kinetic energy of the particles that make up an object. Chemical energy is a kind of potential energy because it depends on the arrangement of atoms in a molecule, which is energy of position.

12. Sample answer: When a person jumps off a diving board, his or her potential energy is converted into kinetic energy. When steam turns the blades of a turbine, the thermal energy of the steam is converted into the kinetic energy of the moving turbine.

CRITICAL THINKING

6 Concept Mapping Use the following terms to create a concept map: *energy, machines, sound energy, hair dryer, electrical energy, energy conversions, thermal energy,* and *kinetic energy.*

17 Applying Concepts Describe what happens in terms of energy when you blow up a balloon and release it.

18 Identifying Relationships After you coast down a hill on your bike, you will eventually come to a complete stop. Use this fact to explain why perpetual motion is impossible.

19 Predicting Consequences Imagine that the sun ran out of energy. What would happen to our energy resources on Earth?

20 Analyzing Processes Look at the photo below. Beginning with the pole vaulter's breakfast, trace the energy conversions necessary for the event shown to take place.

21 Forming Hypotheses Imagine two cars, one of which is more efficient than the other. Suggest two possible reasons one car is more efficient.

22 Evaluating Hypotheses Describe how you would test the two hypotheses you proposed in item 21. How would you determine whether one, both, or neither hypothesis is a factor in the car's efficiency?

INTERPRETING GRAPHICS

Use the graphic below to answer the questions that follow.

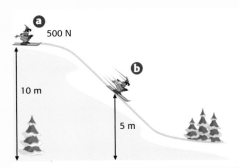

23 What is the skier's gravitational potential energy at point *a*?

24 What is the skier's gravitational potential energy at point *b*?

25 What is the skier's kinetic energy at point *b*? (Hint: mechanical energy = potential energy + kinetic energy)

When a hair dryer is turned on, electrical energy is converted into kinetic energy of the turning fan and thermal energy of the hot coils inside the hair dryer.

13. Within a closed system, objects transfer energy only to each other. Energy is conserved in a closed system because energy only changes form and is neither created nor destroyed.

14. Fossil fuels formed from decayed organic matter of plants and animals, which was subjected to millions of years of pressure under Earth's crust.

15. **a.** 400 J
    b. 400 J ÷ 100 N = 4 m

Critical Thinking

16. An answer to this exercise can be found at the end of this book.

17. The compression of the air in the balloon is a kind of potential energy, which is released in the form of kinetic energy when you let the balloon go.

18. As the potential energy you had on top of the hill is converted into kinetic energy, some of the kinetic energy is converted to thermal energy because of friction, so you eventually come to a stop. In the same way, perpetual motion is impossible because energy conversions always result in energy being "lost" as heat.

19. We would no longer have a source of solar, wind, or hydroelectric energy.

20. The food that the pole vaulter ate for breakfast contained chemical energy, which his body turned into a different kind of chemical energy, which was then used as kinetic energy when he pole-vaulted.

21. Sample answer: One car may be more aerodynamic than the other, causing less energy to be lost because of friction. One car may have fewer moving parts than the other does, causing less energy to be lost because of friction. (Other answers, including a difference in weight, are possible.)

22. Sample answer: To test the effect of aerodynamics, measure the efficiency of a slower car that has the more aerodynamic design and compare it with the efficiency of a slower car that has the less aerodynamic design. (Answers should include controlled experiments.)

Interpreting Graphics

23. 500 N × 10 m = 5,000 J
24. 500 N × 5 m = 2,500 J
25. 5,000 J − 2,500 J = 2,500 J

Standardized Test Preparation

Teacher's Note

To provide practice under more realistic testing conditions, give students 20 minutes to answer all of the questions in this Standardized Test Preparation.

MISCONCEPTION ALERT

Answers to the standardized test preparation can help you identify student misconceptions and misunderstandings.

READING

Passage 1

1. D
2. G
3. C
4. G

✚ TEST DOCTOR

Question 3: Students may misread the passage to say that there is 70 times the amount of natural gas used by the United States in 1 year in each of the two gas deposits mentioned and so may choose answer D.

READING

Read each of the passages below. Then, answer the questions that follow each passage.

Passage 1 Gas hydrates are icy formations of water and methane. Methane is the main component of natural gas. The methane in gas hydrates is made by bacteria in the ocean. Large areas of hydrates have been found off the coasts of North Carolina and South Carolina in marine sediments. In just two areas that are each about the size of Rhode Island, scientists think there may be 70 times the amount of natural gas used by the United States in 1 year. The energy from gas hydrates could be used to drive machinery or generate electrical energy.

1. How large are each of the two gas hydrate deposits mentioned in this article?
   A about the size of the United States
   B about the size of South Carolina
   C about the size of North Carolina
   D about the size of Rhode Island

2. What are gas hydrates mainly made of?
   F bacteria and sediments
   G water and methane
   H natural gas and water
   I ice and sediments

3. How long could U.S. natural gas needs be met by all the gas in both deposits mentioned?
   A 1 year
   B 2 years
   C 70 years
   D 140 years

4. Where do methane gas hydrates come from?
   F ocean water
   G bacteria
   H sediments
   I ice

Passage 2 Two new technologies may reduce the price of electric cars. One is called a *hybrid electric vehicle*. This vehicle has a small gasoline engine that provides extra power and recharges the batteries. The other technology uses hydrogen fuel cells instead of batteries. These cells use the hydrogen present in more-conventional fuels, such as gasoline or ethanol, to produce an electric current that powers the car.

1. In this passage, what does *vehicle* mean?
   A electric
   B hybrid
   C car
   D current

2. Which of the following are conventional fuels?
   F gasoline and ethanol
   G hydrogen and ethanol
   H gasoline and hydrogen
   I only hydrogen

3. Which of the following is a fact in this passage?
   A A hybrid electric vehicle runs partly on gasoline.
   B All electric cars are hybrid.
   C All electric cars use hydrogen fuel cells.
   D Hydrogen fuel cells use conventional fuel.

4. What do the two new technologies described in the passage have in common?
   F They do not use conventional fuels.
   G They may reduce the price of electric cars.
   H They use hybrid engines.
   I They use hydrogen to produce an electric current.

Passage 2

1. C
2. F
3. A
4. G

✚ TEST DOCTOR

Question 3: Answer D may be chosen by students if they incorrectly infer from the last sentence of the passage that hydrogen is a conventional fuel.

The pie chart below shows U.S. energy use source of energy. Use the chart below answer the questions that follow.

U.S. Energy Sources

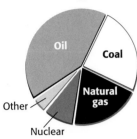

According to the graph, the United States relies on fossil fuels for about what percentage of its energy?

A 30%

B 45%

C 60%

D 80%

Nuclear energy represents about what percentage of U.S. energy sources?

F 15%

G 30%

H 50%

I 70%

Which energy source accounts for about 25% of U.S. energy?

A oil

B coal

C natural gas

D nuclear energy

MATH

Read each question below, and choose the best answer.

1. Gerald bought 2.5 kg of apples. How many grams of apples did he buy?

   A 0.0025 g

   B 0.25 g

   C 25 g

   D 2,500 g

2. Which group contains ratios that are equivalent to 3/8?

   F 6/16, 9/24, 12/32

   G 6/16, 12/24, 12/32

   H 6/24, 12/32, 15/40

   I 6/9, 9/24, 15/40

3. Carmen went to a bookstore. She bought three books for $7.99 each and four books for $3.35 each. Which number sentence can be used to find c, the total cost of the books?

   A $c = 3 + (7.99 \times 1) + (4 \times 3.35)$

   B $c = (1 \times 7.99) + (3 \times 3.35)$

   C $c = (3 \times 7.99) + (4 \times 3.35)$

   D $c = (3 \times 7.99) \times (4 \times 3.35)$

4. Rhonda's Mobile Car Washing charges $15 to wash a customer's car. Vacuuming the car costs an extra $10. Rhonda wants to know how much money she earned last week. When she looks at her appointment book, Rhonda finds that she washed a total of 50 cars. Only 20 of these cars were vacuumed after being washed. How much money did Rhonda earn last week?

   F $500

   G $750

   H $950

   I $1050

1. D

2. F

3. B

TEST DOCTOR

Question 1: Correctly answering this question requires a recognition that oil, coal, and natural gas are fossil fuels. According to the pie chart, together they constitute about 80% of U.S. energy sources.

MATH

1. D

2. F

3. C

4. H

TEST DOCTOR

Question 4: Rhonda earned $950: $750 from 50 cars being charged $15 each for a wash, plus $200 for 20 of the cars being charged $10 each for a vacuum.

Standardized Test Preparation

CHAPTER RESOURCES

Chapter Resource File

• Standardized Test Preparation GENERAL

State Resources

For specific resources for your state, visit **go.hrw.com** and type in the keyword **HSMSTR**.

Science, Technology, and Society

Discussion ——— GENERAL

Have students name different kinds of water-propulsion technology that people have used over the ages. Oars, sails, and propellers should be discussed, and students should recognize that each is a different kind of technology. Draw students' attention to the design features of the underwater jet engine, and ask students to state the similarities and differences between the underwater jet engine and propellers. Have students offer opinions about whether the underwater jet engine is a completely new technology or an improvement on the propeller design.

Scientific Discoveries

Background

Einstein's famous equation stating the equivalence of mass and energy was a direct result of his theory of special relativity. The theory and implications of relativity were his life's work, and the results of that work have been confirmed by numerous experiments.

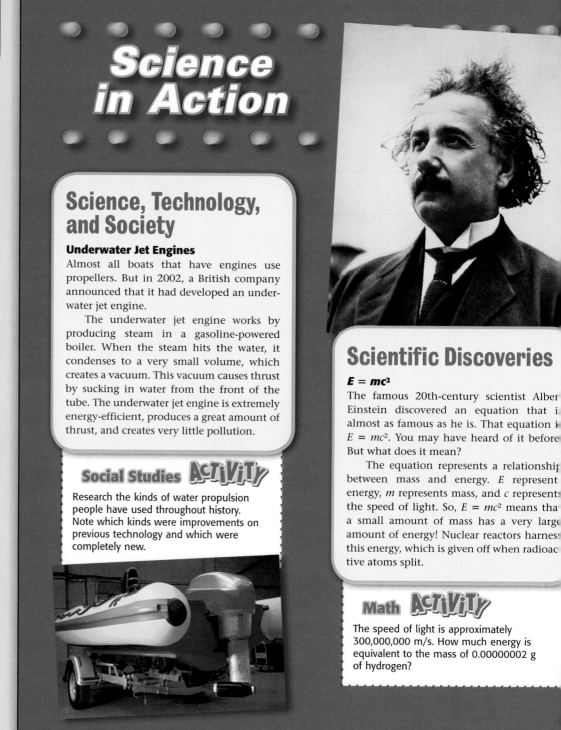

Science in Action

Science, Technology, and Society

Underwater Jet Engines

Almost all boats that have engines use propellers. But in 2002, a British company announced that it had developed an underwater jet engine.

The underwater jet engine works by producing steam in a gasoline-powered boiler. When the steam hits the water, it condenses to a very small volume, which creates a vacuum. This vacuum causes thrust by sucking in water from the front of the tube. The underwater jet engine is extremely energy-efficient, produces a great amount of thrust, and creates very little pollution.

Social Studies ACTIVITY

Research the kinds of water propulsion people have used throughout history. Note which kinds were improvements on previous technology and which were completely new.

Scientific Discoveries

$E = mc^2$

The famous 20th-century scientist Albert Einstein discovered an equation that is almost as famous as he is. That equation is $E = mc^2$. You may have heard of it before. But what does it mean?

The equation represents a relationship between mass and energy. E represents energy, m represents mass, and c represents the speed of light. So, $E = mc^2$ means that a small amount of mass has a very large amount of energy! Nuclear reactors harness this energy, which is given off when radioactive atoms split.

Math ACTIVITY

The speed of light is approximately 300,000,000 m/s. How much energy is equivalent to the mass of 0.00000002 g of hydrogen?

Answer to Social Studies Activity

Oars were a very early—and probably the first—technology to be used in water propulsion. Later boat designs utilized long rows of oars on either side of the ship. Sails, which harness wind power, have also been used since ancient times. Sail technology progressed from a single sail to a series of different types of sails on a single ship. With the industrial age and the steam engine came paddleboats and then propellers.

Answer to Math Activity

2×10^{-8} g $= 2 \times 10^{-11}$ kg
$(2 \times 10^{-11}$ kg$) \times (3 \times 10^8$ m/s$)^2 =$
$(2 \times 10^{-11}$ kg$) \times (9 \times 10^{16}$ m/s$) = 1,800,000$ J

Careers

Cheryl Mele

Power-Plant Manager Cheryl Mele is the manager of the Decker Power Plant in Austin, Texas, where she is in charge of almost 1 billion watts of electric power generation. Most of the electric power is generated by a steam-driven turbine system that uses natural gas fuel. Gas turbines are also used. Together, the systems make enough electrical energy for many homes and businesses.

Cheryl Mele says her job as plant manager is to do "anything that needs doing." Her training as a mechanical engineer allows her to run tests and to find problems in the plant. Previously, Mele had a job helping to design more-efficient gas turbines. That job helped prepare her for the job of plant manager.

Mele believes that engineering and power-plant management are interesting jobs because they allow you to work with many new technologies. Mele thinks young people should pursue what interests them. "Be sure to connect the math you learn to the science you are doing," she says. "This will help you to understand both."

Language Arts ACTIVITY

Look up the word *energy* in a dictionary. Compare the different definitions you find to the definition given in this chapter.

go.hrw.com
To learn more about these Science in Action topics, visit go.hrw.com and type in the keyword **HP5ENGF.**

Current Science
Check out Current Science® articles related to this chapter by visiting go.hrw.com. Just type in the keyword **HP5CS09.**

Heat and Heat Technology
Chapter Planning Guide

Compression guide:
To shorten instruction because of time limitations, omit Section 4.

OBJECTIVES	LABS, DEMONSTRATIONS, AND ACTIVITIES	TECHNOLOGY RESOURCES
PACING • 90 min pp. 156–163 **Chapter Opener**	SE **Start-up Activity**, p. 157 GENERAL	OSP **Parent Letter** ■ CD **Student Edition on CD-ROM** CD **Guided Reading Audio CD** ■ TR **Chapter Starter Transparency*** VID **Brain Food Video Quiz**
Section 1 Temperature • Describe how temperature relates to kinetic energy. • Compare temperatures on different temperature scales. • Give examples of thermal expansion.	TE **Demonstration** Ball-and-Ring Heat Expansion, p. 158 ◆ GENERAL SE **Quick Lab** Hot or Cold?, p. 159 GENERAL TE **Connection Activity** Math, p. 161 GENERAL LB **Whiz-Bang Demonstrations** Cool It* BASIC LB **Calculator-Based Labs** A Hot Hand* ADVANCED LB **Calculator-Based Labs** How Low Can You Go?* ADVANCED	OSP **Lesson Plans** (also in print) TR **Bellringer Transparency*** TR **P39 Three Temperature Scales*** SE **Internet Activity**, p. 159 GENERAL CD **Science Tutor**
PACING • 90 min pp. 164–171 **Section 2 What Is Heat?** • Define *heat* as thermal energy transferred between objects at different temperatures. • Compare conduction, convection, and radiation. • Use specific heat capacity to calculate heat.	TE **Demonstration** Heat and Thermal Energy, p. 165* ◆ GENERAL SE **Quick Lab** Heat Exchange, p. 166 GENERAL TE **Demonstration** Convection Currents, p. 167 ◆ GENERAL SE **Connection to Social Studies** Living near Coastlines, p. 169 GENERAL TE **Connection Activity** Home Economics, p. 169 GENERAL SE **Skills Practice Lab** Feel the Heat, p. 184 GENERAL SE **Inquiry Lab** Save the Cube!, p. 206 GENERAL LB **Calculator-Based Labs** Feel the Heat* ADVANCED	OSP **Lesson Plans** (also in print) TR **Bellringer Transparency*** TR **LINK TO EARTH SCIENCE** E61 The Greenhouse Effect* TR **P40 Transfer of Thermal Energy** TR **P41 Conduction and Convection*** TR **P42 The Greenhouse Effect** CRF **SciLinks Activity*** GENERAL VID **Lab Videos for Physical Science** CD **Science Tutor**
PACING • 45 min pp. 172–175 **Section 3 Matter and Heat** • Identify three states of matter. • Explain how heat affects matter during a change of state. • Describe how heat affects matter during a chemical change. • Explain what a calorimeter is used for.	TE **Demonstration** Thermal Energy and Matter, p. 172 GENERAL TE **Activity** Rates of Cooling, p. 173 ◆ GENERAL LB **Labs You Can Eat** Baked Alaska* BASIC LB **Calculator-Based Labs** Counting Calories* ADVANCED SE **Model-Making Lab** Counting Calories, p. 207 GENERAL	OSP **Lesson Plans** (also in print) TR **Bellringer Transparency*** TR **P43 Bomb Calorimeter*** CD **Science Tutor**
PACING • 45 min pp. 176–183 **Section 4 Heat Technology** • Analyze several kinds of heating systems. • Describe how a heat engine works. • Explain how a refrigerator keeps food cold. • List some effects of heat technology on the environment.	SE **School-to-Home Activity** Home Heating and Cooling, p. 178 GENERAL TE **Group Activity** Solar Heating Models, p. 178 GENERAL TE **Activity** Flow of Air Through a Heating System, p. 178 BASIC TE **Activity** Types of Heat Engines, p. 180 ADVANCED LB **EcoLabs & Field Activities** Energy-Efficient Home* BASIC LB **Long-Term Projects & Research Ideas** Firewalking Exposed* ADVANCED LB **Calculator-Based Labs** Solar Homes* ADVANCED	OSP **Lesson Plans** (also in print) TR **Bellringer Transparency*** TR **P44 Solar Heating Systems*** CD **Science Tutor**

PACING • 90 min

CHAPTER REVIEW, ASSESSMENT, AND STANDARDIZED TEST PREPARATION

CRF **Vocabulary Activity*** GENERAL
SE **Chapter Review**, pp. 186–187 GENERAL
CRF **Chapter Review*** ■ GENERAL
CRF **Chapter Tests** A* ■ GENERAL, B* ADVANCED, C* SPECIAL NEEDS
SE **Standardized Test Preparation**, pp. 188–189 GENERAL
CRF **Standardized Test Preparation*** GENERAL
CRF **Performance-Based Assessment*** GENERAL
OSP **Test Generator, Test Item Listing**

Online and Technology Resources

go.hrw.com
Holt Online Learning

Visit **go.hrw.com** for access to Holt Online Learning, or enter the keyword **HP7 Home** for a variety of free online resources.

One-Stop Planner® CD-ROM

This CD-ROM package includes:
• Lab Materials QuickList Software
• Holt Calendar Planner
• Customizable Lesson Plans
• Printable Worksheets
• ExamView® Test Generator
• Interactive Teacher's Edition
• Holt PuzzlePro®
• Holt PowerPoint® Resources

SKILLS DEVELOPMENT RESOURCES	SECTION REVIEW AND ASSESSMENT	CORRELATIONS
SE Pre-Reading Activity, p. 156 `GENERAL` **OSP** Science Puzzlers, Twisters & Teasers `GENERAL`		National Science Education Standards SAI 1, 2; PS 3a
CRF Directed Reading A* ■ `BASIC`, B* `SPECIAL NEEDS` **IT** Interactive Textbook* `Struggling Readers` **CRF** Vocabulary and Section Summary* ■ `GENERAL` **SE** Reading Strategy Prediction Guide, p. 158 `GENERAL` **SE** Math Practice Converting Temperatures, p. 161 `GENERAL` **TE** Support for English Language Learners, p. 161 **MS** Math Skills for Science Using Temperature Scales* `GENERAL`	**SE** Reading Checks, pp. 159, 160, 162 `GENERAL` **TE** Reteaching, p. 162 `BASIC` **TE** Quiz, p. 162 `GENERAL` **TE** Alternative Assessment, p. 162 `GENERAL` **TE** Homework, p. 162 `GENERAL` **SE** Section Review,* p. 163 ■ `GENERAL` **CRF** Section Quiz* ■ `GENERAL`	UCP 1, 2, 3; SAI 1, 2; PS 3a, 3b
CRF Directed Reading A* ■ `BASIC`, B* `SPECIAL NEEDS` **IT** Interactive Textbook* `Struggling Readers` **CRF** Vocabulary and Section Summary* ■ `GENERAL` **SE** Reading Strategy Paired Summarizing, p. 164 `GENERAL` **TE** Reading Strategy Prediction Guide, p. 165 `GENERAL` **TE** Inclusion Strategies, p. 167 **CRF** Reinforcement Worksheet Feel the Heat* `BASIC` **TE** Support for English Language Learners, p. 169	**SE** Reading Checks, pp. 165, 167, 168, 169 `GENERAL` **TE** Homework, p. 165 `GENERAL` **TE** Reteaching, p. 170 `BASIC` **TE** Quiz, p. 170 `GENERAL` **TE** Alternative Assessment, p. 170 `GENERAL` **SE** Section Review,* p. 171 ■ `GENERAL` **CRF** Section Quiz* ■ `GENERAL`	UCP 2, 3; SAI 1; PS 3a, 3b; *LabBook:* SAI 1, 2; PS 3a, 3b; *Chapter Lab:* SAI; PS 3a, 3b
CRF Directed Reading A* ■ `BASIC`, B* `SPECIAL NEEDS` **IT** Interactive Textbook* `Struggling Readers` **CRF** Vocabulary and Section Summary* ■ `GENERAL` **SE** Reading Strategy Brainstorming, p. 172 `GENERAL` **TE** Inclusion Strategies, p. 173 **MS** Math Skills for Science Knowing Nutrition* `GENERAL` **TE** Support for English Language Learners, p. 173	**SE** Reading Checks, pp. 173, 174 `GENERAL` **TE** Reteaching, p. 174 `BASIC` **TE** Quiz, p. 174 `GENERAL` **TE** Alternative Assessment, p. 174 `GENERAL` **SE** Section Review,* p. 175 `GENERAL` **CRF** Section Quiz* ■ `GENERAL`	UCP 2, 3; PS 3a, 3b; *LabBook:* SAI 1, 2; PS 3a, 3b
CRF Directed Reading A* ■ `BASIC`, B* `SPECIAL NEEDS` **IT** Interactive Textbook* `Struggling Readers` **CRF** Vocabulary and Section Summary* ■ `GENERAL` **SE** Reading Strategy Reading Organizer, p. 176 `GENERAL` **TE** Reading Strategy Prediction, p. 177 `GENERAL` **TE** Support for English Language Learners, p. 177 **CRF** Critical Thinking Try and Try Again* `ADVANCED`	**SE** Reading Checks, pp. 177, 179, 181, 182 `GENERAL` **TE** Reteaching, p. 182 `BASIC` **TE** Quiz, p. 182 `GENERAL` **TE** Alternative Assessment, p. 182 `GENERAL` **SE** Section Review,* p. 183 ■ `GENERAL` **CRF** Section Quiz* ■ `GENERAL`	UCP 1; ST 2; SPSP 2; PS 3a, 3b

SCILINKS.
NSTA
www.scilinks.org
Maintained by the **National Science Teachers Association.** See Chapter Enrichment pages that follow for a complete list of topics.

Current Science®
Check out **Current Science** articles and activities by visiting the HRW Web site at **go.hrw.com.** Just type in the keyword **HP5CS10T.**

 Classroom Videos
• **Lab Videos** demonstrate the chapter lab.
• **Brain Food Video Quizzes** help students review the chapter material.

 Classroom CD-ROMs
• **Guided Reading Audio CD** (Also in Spanish)
• **Interactive Explorations**
• **Virtual Investigations**
• **Visual Concepts**
• **Science Tutor**

 Holt Lab Generator CD-ROM
Search for any lab by topic, standard, difficulty level, or time. Edit any lab to fit your needs, or create your own labs. Use the Lab Materials QuickList software to customize your lab materials list.

6 · Chapter Resources

Visual Resources

CHAPTER STARTER TRANSPARENCY

Heat and Heat Technology — CHAPTER STARTER

Strange but True!

Would you want to live in a house without a heating system? You could if you lived in an Earthship! Earthships are the brainchild of Michael Reynolds, an architect in Taos, New Mexico. These houses are designed to make the most of our planet's most abundant source of energy, the sun.

Each Earthship takes full advantage of passive solar heating. For example, large windows face south in order to maximize the amount of energy the house receives from the sun. Each home is partially buried in the ground, with the excavated soil piled almost to the roof. The energy-absorbing soil helps keep the windows inside the house.

To absorb the sun's energy, the outer walls of Earthships are massive and thick. The walls may be made with crushed aluminum cans or stacks of old

automobile tires filled with dirt. These materials absorb the sun's energy during daylight hours and naturally heat the house from the walls inward. Because an Earthship maintains a temperature around 15°C (about 60°F), it can keep its occupants comfortable through all but the coldest winter nights.

Technology that keeps you warm or cool is very important. In this chapter, you'll learn about temperature and heat, the transfer of energy by different materials, and the use of heat technology in everyday life.

BELLRINGER TRANSPARENCIES

Heat and Heat Technology — BELLRINGER TRANSPARENCY

Section: Temperature
The temperature of boiling water is 100° on the Celsius scale and 212° on the Fahrenheit scale. Look at each of the following temperatures carefully, and decide whether you think that it is hot or cold:
60°F, 60°C, 37°F, 37°C, 0°C, 100°F, 70°F

Write your responses in your **science journal**. Now think about how these temperatures would feel to you if you were living in northern Alaska. What about if you were living in North Africa?

Section: What Is Heat?
Imagine the following:
You walk into the bathroom in your bare feet. The temperature in there is 23°C. You step onto the tile floor, and it feels very cold. Quickly, you step onto the throw rug in front of the sink, and the rug feels warmer.

Answer these questions in your **science journal**:
Is the floor really colder than the rug? Why do they seem to be at different temperatures when your bare feet touch them?

TEACHING TRANSPARENCIES

Three Temperature Scales

Heat and Heat Technology — TEACHING TRANSPARENCY

Bomb Calorimeter

TEACHING TRANSPARENCIES

Heat and Heat Technology — TEACHING TRANSPARENCY

Conduction

Convection

Solar Heating Systems

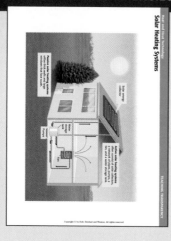

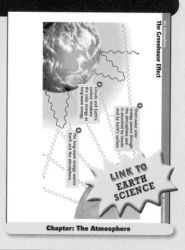

The Greenhouse Effect

LINK TO EARTH SCIENCE

Chapter: The Atmosphere

CONCEPT MAPPING TRANSPARENCY

Heat and Heat Technology — CONCEPT MAPPING TRANSPARENCY

Use the following terms to complete the concept map below:
thermometer, conduction, thermal energy, thermal expansion, temperature, heat, radiation

Planning Resources

LESSON PLANS

Lesson Plan — SAMPLE

Section: Waves

Pacing
Regular Schedule: with lab(s):2 days   without lab(s):1 days
Block Schedule: with lab(s):1 1/2 days   without lab(s):1 day

Objectives
1. Relate the seven properties of life to a living organism.
2. Describe seven themes that can help you to organize what you learn about biology.
3. Identify the tiny structures that make up all living organisms.
4. Differentiate between reproduction and heredity and between metabolism and homeostasis.

National Science Education Standards Covered
LSInter1c:Cells have particular structures that underlie their functions.
LSMat1:Most cell functions involve chemical reactions.
LSBeh1:Cells store and use information to guide their functions.
UCP1:Cell functions are regulated.
SI1: Cells can differentiate and form complete multicellular organisms.
PS1: Species evolve over time.
ESS1: The great diversity of organisms is the result of more than 3.5 billion years of evolution.
ESS2: Natural selection and its evolutionary consequences provide a scientific explanation for the fossil record of ancient life forms as well as for the striking molecular similarities observed among the diverse species of living organisms.
ST1: The millions of different species of plants, animals, and microorganisms that live on Earth today are related by descent from common ancestors.
ST2: The energy for life primarily comes from the sun.
SPSP1: The complexity and organization of organisms accommodate the need for obtaining, transforming, transporting, releasing, and eliminating the matter and energy used to sustain the organisms.
SPSP6: As matter and energy flows through different levels of organization of living systems—cells, organs, communities—and between living systems and the physical environment, chemical elements are reconditioned in different ways.
HNS1: Organisms have behavioral responses to internal changes and to external stimuli.

PARENT LETTER

SAMPLE

Dear Parent,

Your son's or daughter's science class will soon begin exploring the chapter entitled "The World of Physical Science." In this chapter, students will learn about how the scientific method applies to the world of physical science and the role of physical science in the world. By the end of the chapter, students should demonstrate a clear understanding of the chapter's main ideas and be able to discuss the following topics:

1. physical science is the study of energy and matter (Section 1)
2. the role of physical science in the world around them (Section 1)
3. careers that rely on physical science (Section 1)
4. the steps used in the scientific method (Section 2)
5. examples of technology (Section 2)
6. how the scientific method is used to answer questions and solve problems (Section 2)
7. how our knowledge of science changes over time (Section 2)
8. how models represent real objects or systems (Section 3)
9. examples of different ways models are used in science (Section 3)
10. the importance of the International System of Units (Section 4)
11. the appropriate units to use for particular measurements (Section 4)
12. how area and density are derived quantities (Section 4)

Questions to Ask Along the Way

You can help your son or daughter learn about these topics by asking interesting questions such as the following:

• What are some surprising careers that use physical science?
• What is a characteristic of a good hypothesis?
• When is it a good idea to use a model?
• Why do Americans measure things in terms of inches and yards and meters ?

ALSO IN SPANISH

TEST ITEM LISTING

TEST ITEM LISTING
The World of Science — SAMPLE

MULTIPLE CHOICE

1. A limitation of models is that
   a. they are large enough to use.
   b. they do not act exactly like the things that they model.
   c. they are smaller than the things that they model.
   d. they model unfamiliar things.
   Answer: B   Difficulty: 1   Section: 3   Objective: 2

2. The length 10 m is equal to
   a. 100 cm.   c. 10,000 mm.
   b. 1,000 cm.   d. Both (b) and (c)
   Answer: D   Difficulty: 1   Section: 3   Objective: 3

3. To be valid, a hypothesis must be
   a. testable.   c. make into a law.
   b. supported by evidence.   d. Both (a) and (b)
   Answer: B   Difficulty: 1   Section: 2   Objective: 2   1

4. The statement "Sheila has a stain on her shirt" is an example of a(n)
   a. loss   c. observation.
   b. hypothesis.   d. prediction.
   Answer: A   Difficulty: 1   Section: 2   Objective: 2

5. A hypothesis is often developed out of
   a. observations.   c. laws.
   b. experiments.   d. Both (a) and (b)
   Answer: D   Difficulty: 1   Section: 2   Objective: 2

6. How many milliliters are in 3.5 kL?
   a. 3,500 mL   c. 3,500,000 mL
   b. 0.0035 mL   d. 35,000 mL
   Answer: C   Difficulty: 1   Section: 3   Objective: 3

7. A map of Seattle is an example of a
   a. law.   c. model.
   b. theory.   d. unit.
   Answer: C   Difficulty: 1   Section: 3   Objective: 2

8. A lab has the safety icons shown below. These icons mean that you should wear
   a. only safety goggles.   c. safety goggles and a lab apron.
   b. only a lab apron.   d. safety goggles, a lab apron, and gloves.
   Answer: B   Difficulty: 1   Section: 3   Objective: 2

9. The law of conservation of mass says the lot of mass before a chemical change is
   a. more than the total mass after the change.
   b. less than the total mass after the change.
   c. the same as the total mass after the change.
   d. not the same as the total mass after the change.
   Answer: C   Difficulty: 1   Section: 3   Objective: 2

10. In which of the following areas might you find a geochemist at work?
    a. studying the chemistry of rocks   c. studying fishes
    b. studying forestry   d. studying the atmosphere
    Answer: A   Difficulty: 1   Section: 3   Objective: 2

One-Stop Planner® CD-ROM

This CD-ROM includes all of the resources shown here and the following time-saving tools:

• Lab Materials QuickList Software
• Customizable lesson plans
• Holt Calendar Planner
• The powerful ExamView® Test Generator

155C Chapter 6 · Heat and Heat Technology

Meeting Individual Needs

DIRECTED READING A
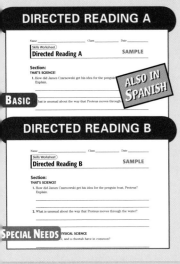
BASIC — ALSO IN SPANISH

DIRECTED READING B
SPECIAL NEEDS

VOCABULARY ACTIVITY
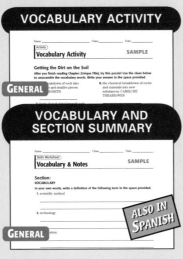
GENERAL

VOCABULARY AND SECTION SUMMARY
GENERAL — ALSO IN SPANISH

REINFORCEMENT
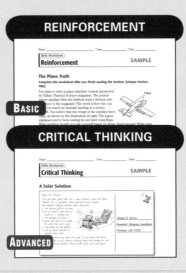
BASIC

CRITICAL THINKING
ADVANCED

SCILINKS ACTIVITY

GENERAL

SCIENCE PUZZLERS, TWISTERS & TEASERS
GENERAL

Labs and Activities

ECOLABS & FIELD ACTIVITIES

BASIC

LONG-TERM PROJECTS & RESEARCH IDEAS
ADVANCED

WHIZ-BANG DEMONSTRATIONS
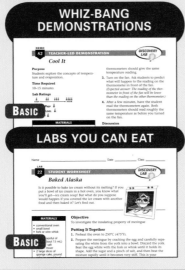
BASIC

LABS YOU CAN EAT
BASIC

CALCULATOR-BASED LABS
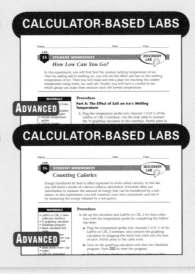
ADVANCED

CALCULATOR-BASED LABS
ADVANCED

DATASHEETS FOR QUICK LABS

DATASHEETS FOR CHAPTER LABS

DATASHEETS FOR LABBOOK

Review and Assessments

SECTION QUIZ

GENERAL — ALSO IN SPANISH

SECTION REVIEW
GENERAL — ALSO IN SPANISH

CHAPTER REVIEW
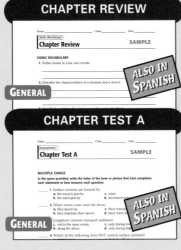
GENERAL — ALSO IN SPANISH

CHAPTER TEST A
GENERAL — ALSO IN SPANISH

CHAPTER TEST B
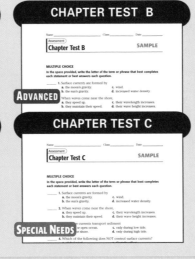
ADVANCED

CHAPTER TEST C
SPECIAL NEEDS

STANDARDIZED TEST PREPARATION
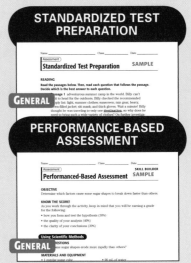
GENERAL

PERFORMANCE-BASED ASSESSMENT
GENERAL

This Chapter Enrichment provides relevant and interesting information to expand and enhance your presentation of the chapter material.

Section 1

Temperature

Temperature Scales

- Daniel Gabriel Fahrenheit (1686–1736) developed the first mercury thermometer in 1714. His scale used the temperature of a brine solution of ice and salt as 0°. He chose 30° for the freezing temperature of water and 90° for the temperature of the human body. These were later adjusted to 32° and 98.6°.

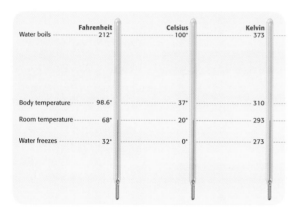

	Fahrenheit	Celsius	Kelvin
Water boils	212°	100°	373
Body temperature	98.6°	37°	310
Room temperature	68°	20°	293
Water freezes	32°	0°	273

- Anders Celsius (1701–1744) developed the centigrade temperature scale assigning 0° to the freezing point of pure water and 100° to the boiling point of pure water. The Celsius scale is used by the scientific community.

- In 1848, British physicist and mathematician William Thomson (1824–1907), later Lord Kelvin, developed the absolute temperature scale. Using J.A.C. Charles's (1746–1823) work with gases, Kelvin realized that a gas decreased by 1/273 of its volume for each Celsius-degree decrease in temperature. Kelvin theorized that a substance would lose all energy at a temperature of –273°C, so he assigned that point a value of zero on his scale.

Is That a Fact!

◆ How much energy does the human body radiate in 1 s? It radiates about as much energy as a 60 W light bulb in the same amount of time.

Section 2

What Is Heat?

Benjamin Thompson (1753–1814)

- In the eighteenth century, most scientists defined heat as an invisible and weightless fluid, called "caloric," that soaked into an object as it was heated and left an object as it cooled.

- Benjamin Thompson, also known as Count Rumford, an American-born British physicist, noticed that metal became very hot during the process of boring cannons. He set up an experiment to find out why.

- In his experiment, Thompson encased the cannon form in a wooden barrel filled with water. After hours of drilling, the water began to boil. The water continued to boil for as long as the drill was turned. If heat had been a material substance, it would have run out eventually; and the cannon would have become cold—no matter how much drilling was done. Thompson decided that heat was actually a form of energy supplied by the work of turning the drill.

Section 3

Matter and Heat

Water and Heat

- When thermal energy is added to substances, they usually expand. When thermal energy is subtracted, they usually contract. Water behaves this way until it reaches the temperature range between 4°C and 0°C. In this range, water expands as it cools and freezes, making its solid form (ice) less dense than its liquid form.

Latent Heat

- The amount of thermal energy that is lost or gained during a phase change is called *latent heat.* During a phase change, there is no change in temperature. The energy that is absorbed or released is used to break or to form intermolecular bonds.

Is That a Fact!

◆ More than 2 million joules of thermal energy are lost from a mammal's body as 1 L of perspiration is evaporated.

Section 4

Heat Technology

Radiant Heating

- Radiant heating refers to systems in which floors, walls, and ceilings are used as radiant-heating units. Steam or hot-water pipes can be placed in the floors or the walls during the construction of the building. If electrical resistance is used, panels containing coils are placed in the baseboard or the ceiling.

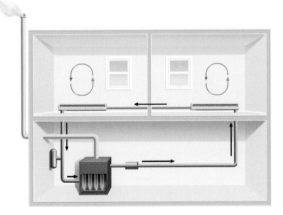

Steam Engines

- Heron of Alexandria (second or third century CE) invented a type of steam engine, but the French physicist Denis Papin (c. 1647–1712) designed the first piston steam engine in 1690. Thomas Savery (c. 1650–1715) and Thomas Newcomen (1663–1729) made improvements on Papin's design, but it was James Watt (1736–1819) who produced the modern steam engine.

Internal Combustion Engines

- Jean-Joseph Étienne Lenoir (1822–1900) is given credit for inventing the first practical internal combustion engine. Nikolaus August Otto (1832–1891) and Rudolf Diesel (1858–1913) also did extensive work with internal combustion engines. Gottlieb Daimler (1834–1900) assisted Otto with this engine. Daimler, who developed both two- and four-cycle engines, patented his own engine in 1887.

- Karl Benz (1844–1929), a German engineer, developed a two-cycle internal combustion engine and a light four-cycle engine. In 1886, Benz patented a vehicle that had his engine.

- Benz and Daimler, who worked independently of each other and who never met, were each credited with building the first automobile.

Is That a Fact!

◆ Heating, cooling, and breathing can produce hazardous waste gases and vapors. An adequate ventilation system provides about 280 L to 850 L of outside air per minute for each person in a room.

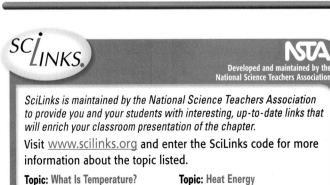

SciLinks is maintained by the National Science Teachers Association to provide you and your students with interesting, up-to-date links that will enrich your classroom presentation of the chapter.

Visit www.scilinks.org and enter the SciLinks code for more information about the topic listed.

Topic: What Is Temperature?
SciLinks code: HSM1664

Topic: Heat Energy
SciLinks code: HSM0727

Topic: What Is Heat?
SciLinks code: HSM1661

Topic: Heating Systems
SciLinks code: HSM0733

Overview

This chapter will help students learn about the nature of heat and thermal energy. They will learn about the difference between heat and temperature, relationships between matter and heat, and heat technology.

Assessing Prior Knowledge

Students should be familiar with the following topics:

• matter

• energy

Identifying Misconceptions

Students often believe that heat makes things rise and that heat and cold are opposites. They also believe that heat is a sub-stance like air or steam. Most students have considerable diffi-culty distinguishing between heat and temperature even after instruction. The belief that tem-perature is a measurement of heat is particularly hard to change. They will conclude that larger ice cubes have a colder temperature and so on. They also believe that metal is colder than plastic because cold passes through metal more quickly. Students have a hard time understanding heating and cooling as processes of thermal energy transfer. Students often believe that both hot and cold are transferred.

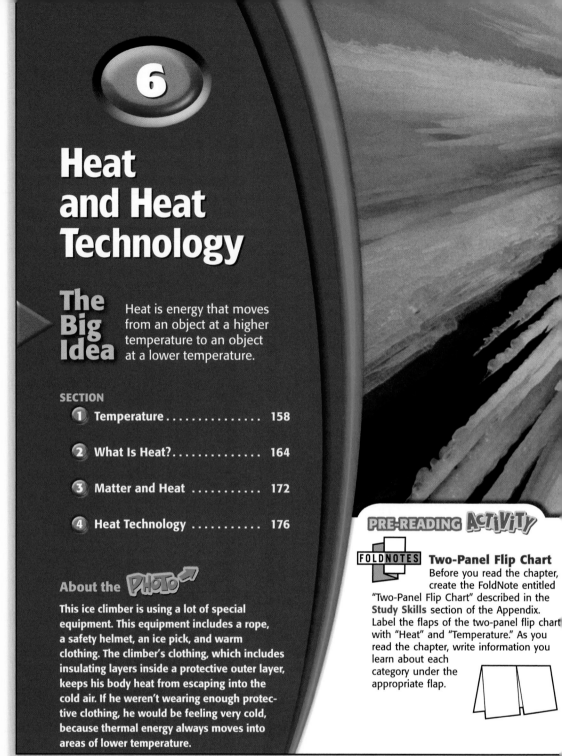

Heat and Heat Technology

The Big Idea Heat is energy that moves from an object at a higher temperature to an object at a lower temperature.

About the PHOTO

This ice climber is using a lot of special equipment. This equipment includes a rope, a safety helmet, an ice pick, and warm clothing. The climber's clothing, which includes insulating layers inside a protective outer layer, keeps his body heat from escaping into the cold air. If he weren't wearing enough protec-tive clothing, he would be feeling very cold, because thermal energy always moves into areas of lower temperature.

PRE-READING ACTIVITY

FOLDNOTES Two-Panel Flip Chart
Before you read the chapter, create the FoldNote entitled "Two-Panel Flip Chart" described in the **Study Skills** section of the Appendix. Label the flaps of the two-panel flip chart with "Heat" and "Temperature." As you read the chapter, write information you learn about each category under the appropriate flap.

Standards Correlations

National Science Education Standards

The following codes indicate the National Science Education Standards that correlate to this chapter. The full text of the standards is at the front of the book.

Chapter Opener
SAI 1, 2; PS 3a

Section 1 Temperature
UCP 1, 2, 3; SAI 1, 2; PS 3a, 3b

Section 2 What Is Heat?
UCP 2, 3; SAI 1; PS 3a, 3b; *LabBook:* SAI 1, 2; PS 3a, 3b

Section 3 Matter and Heat
UCP 2, 3; PS 3a, 3b; *LabBook:* SAI 1, 2; PS 3a, 3b

Section 4 Heat Technology
UCP 1; ST 2; SPSP 2; PS 3a, 3b

Chapter Lab
SAI 1; PS 3a, 3b

Chapter Review
PS 3a, 3b

Science in Action
ST 2; PS 3a

START-UP ACTIVITY

MATERIALS

FOR EACH GROUP
- small pieces of metal, wood, plastic foam, rock, plastic, cardboard
- thermometer strip (You can use bulb thermometers, but liquid crystal thermometer strips or cards, available from a science store or supply house, may measure the temperature of the materials more accurately.)

Answers

1. Sample answer: The plastic foam felt the warmest.
2. Students should find that the materials were all about the same temperature.
3. Answers may vary.
4. Sample answer: My hand was not a good thermometer because some materials felt warmer than others, even though they were all about the same temperature.

START-UP ACTIVITY

Some Like It Hot

Sometimes, you can estimate an object's temperature by touching the object. In this activity, you will find out how well your hand works as a thermometer!

Procedure

1. Gather small pieces of the following materials: **metal, wood, plastic foam, rock, plastic,** and **cardboard.** Allow the materials to sit untouched on a table for a few minutes.

2. Put the palms of your hands on each of the materials. List the materials in order from coolest to warmest.

3. Place a **thermometer strip** on the surface of each material. Record the temperature of each material.

Analysis

1. Which material felt the warmest to your hands?
2. Which material had the highest temperature? Was it the same material that felt the warmest?
3. Why do you think some materials felt warmer than others?
4. Was your hand a good thermometer? Explain why or why not.

Strange but True!

Would you want to live in a house without a heating system? You could if you lived in an Earthship! Earthships are the brainchild of Michael Reynolds, an architect in Taos, New Mexico. These houses are designed to make the most of our planet's most abundant source of energy, the sun.

Each Earthship takes full advantage of passive solar heating. For example, large windows face south in order to maximize the amount of energy the house receives from the sun. Each home

automobile tires filled with dirt. These materials absorb the sun's energy during daylight hours and naturally heat the house from the walls inward. Because an Earthship maintains a temperature around 15°C (about 60°F), it can keep its occupants comfortable through all but the coldest winter nights.

Technology that keeps you warm or cool is very important. In this chapter, you'll learn about temperature and heat, the transfer of energy by different materials, and the use of heat technology

Chapter Starter Transparency
Use this transparency to help students begin thinking about heat and heat technology.

CHAPTER RESOURCES

Technology

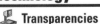 **Transparencies**
- Chapter Starter Transparency

READING SKILLS

Student Edition on CD-ROM

Guided Reading Audio CD
- English or Spanish

Classroom Videos
- Brain Food Video Quiz

Workbooks

 **Science Puzzlers, Twisters & Teasers**
- Heat and Heat Technology GENERAL

Focus

Overview

This section explains temperature and how it is measured. Students learn how temperature relates to kinetic energy. They will explore thermal expansion and learn how to convert between temperature scales.

 Bellringer

Write the following on the board:

The temperature of boiling water is 100° on the Celsius scale and 212° on the Fahrenheit scale.

Look at each of the following temperatures carefully, and decide whether you think that it is hot or cold:

60°F, 60°C, 37°F, 37°C, 0°C, 100°F, 70°F

Write your responses in your **science journal.**

Motivate

Demonstration — GENERAL

Ball-and-Ring Heat Expansion
Obtain a metal ball-and-ring set. Show students that the ball can pass through the ring. Heat the ball for a minute or two, and then try to pass the ball through the ring. Be sure to use protective gloves. Ask students why the ball no longer passes through the ring. **LS** Visual

---

Temperature

You probably put on a sweater or a jacket when it's co[l]. Likewise, you probably wear shorts in the summer when [it] gets hot. But how hot is hot, and how cold is cold?

Think about the knobs on a water faucet: they are labeled "[H]" for hot and "C" for cold. But does only hot water come o[ut] when the hot-water knob is on? You may have noticed th[at] when you first turn on the hot water, the water is warm [or] even cool. Is the label on the knob wrong? The terms *hot* a[nd] *cold* are not scientific terms. If you really want to specify h[ow] hot or cold something is, you must use temperature.

What Is Temperature?

You probably think of temperature as a measure of how h[ot] or cold something is. But using the terms *hot* and *cold* c[an] be confusing. Imagine that you are outside on a hot day. Y[ou] step onto a shady porch where a fan is blowing. You think [it] feels cool there. Then, your friend comes out onto the por[ch] from an air-conditioned house. She thinks it feels warm! Usi[ng] the word *temperature* instead of words such as *cool* or *war[m]* avoids confusion. Scientifically, **temperature** is a measure of th[e] average kinetic energy of the particles in an object.

Temperature and Kinetic Energy

All matter is made of atoms or molecules that are alwa[ys] moving, even if it doesn't look like they are. Because th[e] particles are in motion, they have kinetic energy. The fast[er] the particles are moving, the more kinetic energy they hav[e.] Look at **Figure 1**. The more kinetic energy the particles of a[n] object have, the higher the temperature of the object is.

What You Will Learn

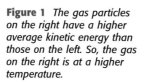

● Describe how temperature relates to kinetic energy.
● Compare temperatures on different temperature scales.
● Give examples of thermal expansion.

Vocabulary
temperature
thermal expansion
absolute zero

READING STRATEGY

Prediction Guide Before reading this section, write the title of each heading in this section. Next, under each heading, write what you think you will learn.

temperature a measure of how hot (or cold) something is; specifically, a measure of the average kinetic energy of the particles in an object

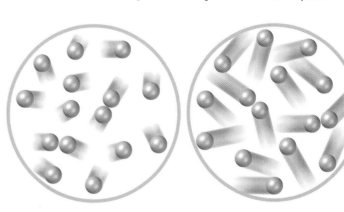

Figure 1 *The gas particles on the right have a higher average kinetic energy than those on the left. So, the gas on the right is at a higher temperature.*

CHAPTER RESOURCES

Chapter Resource File

 • **Lesson Plan**
  • **Directed Reading A** BASIC
  • **Directed Reading B** SPECIAL NEEDS

Technology

 Transparencies
  • Bellringer

Workbooks

 Interactive Textbook Struggling Readers

MISCONCEPTION
////ALERT\\\\

Heat and Temperature Students often think that heat and temperature are the same. Stress that temperature is the measure of the average kinetic energy of the molecules in a substance. Heat is the transfer of thermal energy between objects that are at different temperatures. These concepts are covered in Section 2 of this chapter.

Hot or Cold?

1. Put both your hands into a **bucket of warm water,** and note how the water feels.

2. Now, put one hand into a **bucket of cold water** and the other into a **bucket of hot water.**

3. After a minute, take your hands out of the hot and cold water and put them back in the warm water. Note how the water feels to each hand.

4. Can you rely on your hands to determine temperature? Explain your observations.

Average Kinetic Energy of Particles

Particles of matter are always moving. But they move in different directions and at different speeds. The motion of particles is random. Because particles are moving at different speeds, individual particles have different amounts of kinetic energy. But the *average* kinetic energy of all the particles in an object can be measured. When you measure an object's temperature, you measure the average kinetic energy of all the particles in the object.

The temperature of a substance depends on the average kinetic energy of all its particles. Its temperature does not depend on how much of it you have. Look at **Figure 2.** A pot of tea and a cup of tea each have a different amount of tea. But their atoms have the same average kinetic energy. So, the pot of tea and the cup of tea are at the same temperature.

Reading Check How is temperature related to kinetic energy? (*See the Appendix for answers to Reading Checks.*)

For another activity related to this chapter, go to **go.hrw.com** and type in the keyword **HP5HOTW.**

Figure 2 *There is more tea in the teapot than in the mug. But the temperature of the tea in the mug is the same as the temperature of the tea in the teapot.*

Answer to Reading Check
Temperature is a measure of the average kinetic energy of the particles of a substance.

Converting Between Temperature Scales Ask students to use **Figure 3** to determine human body temperature on the Kelvin scale (310 K), the Celsius scale (37°C), and the Fahrenheit scale (98.6°F). At what temperature does water boil on the Celsius scale? (100°C) on the Kelvin scale? (373 K) **LS** Visual

Discussion ———— GENERAL

Difference Between Temperature Scales The Fahrenheit scale defines the freezing point of water as 32°F. By the time 0°F is reached, the temperature is well below the freezing point of water. Human body temperature is 98.6°F. Discuss with the class what would happen if normal human body temperature suddenly shot up to 98.6°C. Ask students, "Would air temperatures of 70°C–75°C feel comfortable? Why do doctors worry more about a fever of a couple of degrees Celsius than a fever of a couple of degrees Fahrenheit?" **LS** Logical

Answer to Reading Check
Thermal expansion makes thermometers work.

Measuring Temperature

How would you measure the temperature of a steaming cup of hot chocolate? Would you take a sip of it or stick your finger in it? You probably would not. You would use a thermometer.

Using a Thermometer

Many thermometers are thin glass tubes filled with a liquid. Mercury and alcohol are often used in thermometers because they remain in liquid form over a large temperature range.

Thermometers can measure temperature because of a property called thermal expansion. **Thermal expansion** is the increase in volume of a substance because of an increase in temperature. As a substance's temperature increases, its particles move faster and spread out. So, there is more space between them, and the substance expands. Mercury and alcohol expand by constant amounts for a given change in temperature.

Look at the thermometers in **Figure 3.** They are all at the same temperature. So, the alcohol in each thermometer has expanded the same amount. But the number for each thermometer is different because a different temperature scale is marked on each one.

✔ **Reading Check** What property makes thermometers work?

thermal expansion an increase in the size of a substance in response to an increase in the temperature of the substance

absolute zero the temperature at which molecular energy is at a minimum (0 K on the Kelvin scale or −273.16°C on the Celsius scale)

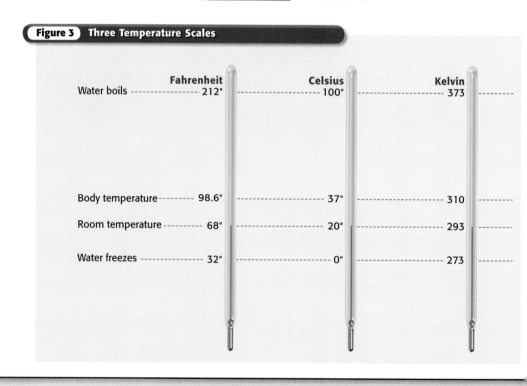

Figure 3 Three Temperature Scales

	Fahrenheit	Celsius	Kelvin
Water boils	212°	100°	373
Body temperature	98.6°	37°	310
Room temperature	68°	20°	293
Water freezes	32°	0°	273

Science Bloopers

Reversal of Scale When Anders Celsius invented his temperature scale, he set the freezing point of water as 100° and the boiling point of water as 0°. Apparently, the person who made thermometers for Celsius got the two numbers reversed, and ever since, 0° has been the freezing point of water and 100° has been the boiling point of water.

Temperature Scales

Look at **Figure 4.** When a weather report is given, you will probably hear the temperature given in degrees Fahrenheit (°F). Scientists, however, often use the Celsius scale. In the Celsius scale, the temperature range between the freezing point and boiling point of water is divided into 100 equal parts, called degrees Celsius (°C). A third scale, the Kelvin (or absolute) scale, is the official SI temperature scale. The Kelvin scale is divided into units called kelvins (K)—not degrees kelvin.

The lowest temperature on the Kelvin scale is 0 K, which is called **absolute zero.** Absolute zero (about −459°F) is the temperature at which all molecular motion stops. It is not possible to actually reach absolute zero, although temperatures very close to 0 K have been reached in laboratories.

Temperature Conversion

As shown by the thermometers on the previous page, a given temperature is represented by different numbers on the three temperature scales. For example, the freezing point of water is 32°F, 0°C, or 273 K.

The temperature 0°C is actually much higher than 0 K. But a *change* of one kelvin is equal to a change of one Celsius degree. The temperature 0°C is higher than 0°F, but a change of one Fahrenheit degree is *not* equal to a change of one Celsius degree. You can convert from one scale to another using the equations shown in **Table 1** below.

Table 1 Converting Between Temperature Units

To convert	Use the equation	Example
Celsius to Fahrenheit °C ⟶ °F	$°F = \left(\dfrac{9}{5} \times °C\right) + 32$	Convert 45°C to degrees Fahrenheit. $°F = \left(\dfrac{9}{5} \times 45°C\right) + 32 = 113°F$
Fahrenheit to Celsius °F ⟶ °C	$°C = \dfrac{5}{9} \times (°F - 32)$	Convert 68°F to degrees Celsius. $°C = \dfrac{5}{9} \times (68°F - 32) = 20°C$
Celsius to Kelvin °C ⟶ K	$K = °C + 273$	Convert 45°C to Kelvins. $K = 45°C + 273 = 318\ K$
Kelvin to Celsius K ⟶ °C	$°C = K - 273$	Convert 32 K to degrees Celsius. $°C = 32\ K - 273 = -241°C$

Figure 4 *Weather reports that you see on the news usually give temperatures in degrees Fahrenheit (°F).*

Research ——— GENERAL

Temperature Innovators
Encourage students to research the lives and work of Anders Celsius, Gabriel Fahrenheit, William Rankine, and William Thomson (Lord Kelvin). Students can present their findings on posters, by writing a story or skit, or in a report. **LS** Verbal

CONNECTION ACTIVITY
Math——— GENERAL

Order of Operations When solving equations, it is important to follow the order of operations. Remind students to do what is inside the parentheses first, then to multiply or divide from left to right, and finally to add or subtract from left to right.

Have students do the following conversion problems:

- Normal body temperature is 98.6°F. Marie has a temperature of 38.5°C. Does Marie have a fever? (yes; 38.5°C = 101.3°F)

- The temperature tonight is supposed to be 265 K. Will water left in a bucket outside freeze? (yes; 265 K = −8°C, which is below water's freezing point, 0°C) **LS** Logical

Reteaching — BASIC

Concept Mapping Have students make a concept map of the terms *temperature, thermal energy, kinetic energy, thermal expansion,* and *thermometer.*
LS Visual

Quiz — GENERAL

1. Most substances _____ when they are cooled. (contract)
2. Scientists use either the _____ scale or the _____ scale. (Celsius, Kelvin)
3. Temperature _____ as average kinetic energy decreases. (decreases)

Alternative Assessment — GENERAL

Expansion Joints Ask students to theorize why large buildings and sidewalks are constructed with expansion joints. (to allow for thermal expansion) Ask them to explain what would happen in hot or cold weather if there were no expansion joints. **LS** Logical

Homework — GENERAL

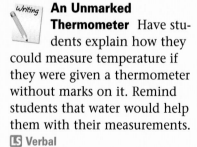

An Unmarked Thermometer Have students explain how they could measure temperature if they were given a thermometer without marks on it. Remind students that water would help them with their measurements.
LS Verbal

Figure 5 *This gap in the bridge allows the concrete to expand and contract without breaking.*

More About Thermal Expansion

You have learned about how thermal expansion works in the liquids that fill thermometers. Thermal expansion has many other applications. Below, you will read about a case in which thermal expansion can be dangerous, one in which it can be useful, and one in which it can carry you into the air!

Expansion Joints on Highways

Have you ever gone across a highway bridge in a car? You probably heard and felt a "thuh-thunk" every couple of seconds as you went over the bridge. That sound is made when the car goes over small gaps called *expansion joints,* shown in **Figure 5.**

If the weather is very hot, the bridge can heat up enough to expand. As it expands, there is a danger of the bridge breaking. Expansion joints keep segments of the bridge apart so that they have room to expand without the bridge breaking.

✓ Reading Check What is the purpose of expansion joints in a bridge?

Bimetallic Strips in Thermostats

Thermal expansion also occurs in a thermostat, the device that controls the heater in your home. Some thermostats have a bimetallic strip inside. A *bimetallic strip* is made of two different metals stacked in a thin strip. Because different materials expand at different rates, one of the metals expands more than the other when the strip gets hot. This makes the strip coil and uncoil in response to changes in temperature. This coiling and uncoiling closes and opens an electric circuit that turns the heater on and off in your home, as shown in **Figure 6.**

Figure 6   How a Thermostat Works

Electrical contacts   Bimetallic strip

a As the room temperature drops below the desired level, the bimetallic strip coils more tightly, and the glass tube tilts. A drop of mercury closes an electric circuit that turns the heater on.

b As the room temperature rises above the desired level, the bimetallic strip uncoils slightly, becoming larger. The drop of mercury rolls back in the tube, opening the electric circuit, and the heater turns off.

Answer to Reading Check
Expansion joints on a bridge allow the bridge to undergo thermal expansion without breaking.

hermal Expansion in Hot-Air Balloons

ou may have heard the expression "Hot air rises." If ou have ever seen hot-air balloons peacefully gliding rough the sky, you have seen this principle at work. ut why does hot air rise?

When a gas is heated, as shown in **Figure 7**, its articles have more kinetic energy. They move around ore quickly, so there is more space between them. The as is then able to expand if it is not kept at the same olume by its container. When air (which is a mixture of ases) inside a hot-air balloon is heated, the air expands. s it expands, it becomes less dense than the air outside e balloon. So, the balloon goes up, up, and away!

Figure 7 *Thermal expansion helps get these hot-air balloons off the ground.*

SECTION Review

Summary

- Temperature is a measure of the average kinetic energy of the particles of a substance.

- Fahrenheit, Celsius, and Kelvin are three temperature scales.

- Thermal expansion is the increase in volume of a substance due to an increase in temperature.

- Absolute zero (0 K, or −273°C) is the lowest possible temperature.

- A thermostat works because of the thermal expansion of a bimetallic strip.

Using Key Terms

1. In your own words, write a definition for the term *temperature*.

2. Use each of the following terms in a separate sentence: *thermal expansion* and *absolute zero*.

Understanding Key Ideas

3. Which of the following is the coldest temperature possible?
   a. 0 K
   b. 0°C
   c. 0°F
   d. −273°F

4. Does temperature depend on the amount of the substance? Explain.

5. Describe the process of thermal expansion.

Math Skills

6. Convert 35°C to degrees Fahrenheit.

7. Convert 34°F to degrees Celsius.

8. Convert 0°C to kelvins.

9. Convert 100 K to degrees Celsius.

Critical Thinking

10. **Predicting Consequences** Why do you think heating a full pot of soup on the stove could cause the soup to overflow?

11. **Analyzing Processes** During thermal expansion, what happens to the density of a substance?

12. **Forming Hypotheses** A glass of cold water whose particles had a low average kinetic energy was placed on a table. The average kinetic energy in the cold water increased, while the average kinetic energy of the part of the table under the glass decreased. What do you think happened?

SCiLINKS® NSTA
Developed and maintained by the
National Science Teachers Association

For a variety of links related to this chapter, go to www.scilinks.org

Topic: What Is Temperature?
SciLinks code: HSM1664

Answers to Section Review

1. Sample answer: Temperature is a direct measure of the average kinetic energy of the particles in an object.

2. Sample answer: Thermal expansion causes mercury in a thermometer to change volume, allowing it to measure temperature. Absolute zero is the temperature at which there is no thermal energy at all.

3. a

4. no; Temperature is the average kinetic energy of particles of a substance. If the individual particles of two objects have the same average kinetic energy, they are at the same temperature regardless of how much matter is in each object.

5. When the temperature of an object is raised, its particles move around more, so they take up more space. This causes the entire object to expand.

6. (9/5 × 35°C) + 32 = 95°F

7. 5/9 × (34°F − 32) = 1.1°C

8. 0°C + 273 = 273 K

9. 100 K − 273 = −173°C

10. The soup could overflow its pot as it cooks because of thermal expansion. The soup will expand in volume as its temperature increases. If the cold soup is too close to the top of the pot, it will likely overflow as it expands.

11. Thermal expansion causes the density of a substance to decrease, because the same mass takes up more volume.

12. Thermal energy was transferred from the table to the glass of cold water.

Focus

Overview

In this section, students learn that heat is the transfer of energy between objects at different temperatures. They also learn the three methods of heating objects and how to calculate heat using specific heat capacity. Finally, they learn about the differences between temperature, thermal energy, and heat.

Bellringer

Ask students to imagine the following:

> You walk into the bathroom in your bare feet. The temperature in there is 23°C. You step onto the tile floor, and it feels very cold. Quickly, you step onto the throw rug in front of the sink, and the rug feels warmer.

Ask students to answer these questions in their **science journal:**

> Is the floor really colder than the rug? Why do they seem to be at different temperatures when your bare feet touch them?

What Is Heat?

It's time for your annual physical. The doctor comes in an begins her exam by placing a metal stethoscope on your back You jump a little and say, "Whoa! That's cold!"

What is it about the stethoscope that made it feel cold? The answer has to do with how energy moves between the meta and your skin. In this section, you'll learn about this kind c energy transfer.

Transferred Thermal Energy

You might think of the word *heat* as having to do with thing that feel hot. But heat also has to do with things that fee cold—such as the stethoscope. In fact, heat is what cause objects to feel hot or cold or to get hot or cold under the righ conditions. You probably use the word *heat* every day to mean different things. However, in this chapter, you will use onl` one specific meaning for *heat*. **Heat** is the energy transferred between objects that are at different temperatures.

Why do some things feel hot, while others feel cold When two objects at different temperatures come into contact energy is always transferred from the object that has the highe temperature to the object that has the lower temperature Look at **Figure 1.** The doctor's stethoscope touches your back Energy is transferred from your back to the stethoscope because your back has a higher temperature (about 37°C) than the stethoscope (probably room temperature, about 20°C) has This energy is transferred quickly, so the stethoscope feel cold to you.

What You Will Learn

- Define *heat* as thermal energy transferred between objects at different temperatures.
- Compare conduction, convection, and radiation.
- Use specific heat capacity to calculate heat.

Vocabulary

heat	convection
thermal energy	radiation
thermal conduction	specific
thermal conductor	heat
thermal insulator	

READING STRATEGY

Paired Summarizing Read this section silently. In pairs, take turns summarizing the material. Stop to discuss ideas that seem confusing.

heat the energy transferred between objects that are at different temperatures

Figure 1 *The metal stethoscope feels cold because of heat!*

CHAPTER RESOURCES

Chapter Resource File

- **Lesson Plan**
- **Directed Reading A** (BASIC)
- **Directed Reading B** (SPECIAL NEEDS)

Technology

Transparencies
- Bellringer
- *LINK TO **EARTH SCIENCE*** E61 The Greenhouse Effect
- P40 Transfer of Thermal Energy

Workbooks

Interactive Textbook Struggling Readers

MISCONCEPTION ALERT

The Meaning of Heat In everyday usage, the word *heat* has in a variety of meanings, such as "warmth" or "the energy contained in a hot object." However, a much narrower definition of *heat* is used in this chapter. Students should understand that heat is a transfer of energy between objects that are at different temperatures. The example described on this page is a useful introduction to this concept.

Heat and Thermal Energy

If heat is transferred energy, what form of energy is being transferred? The answer is thermal energy. **Thermal energy** is the total kinetic energy of the particles that make up a substance. Thermal energy, which is measured in joules (J), depends partly on temperature. Something at a high temperature has more thermal energy than it would have at a lower temperature. Thermal energy also depends on how much of a substance there is. Look at **Figure 2**. The more particles there are in a substance at a given temperature, the greater the thermal energy of the substance is.

Figure 2 *Although both soups are at the same temperature, there is more soup in the pan. So, the soup in the pan has more thermal energy than the soup in the bowl.*

Reaching the Same Temperature

Look at **Figure 3**. When objects that have different temperatures come into contact, energy will always be transferred. Energy will pass from the warmer object to the cooler object until both have the same temperature. When objects that are touching each other have the same temperature, there is no net change in the thermal energy of either one. Although one object may have more thermal energy than the other object, both objects will be at the same temperature.

thermal energy the kinetic energy of a substance's atoms

✓ **Reading Check** What will happen if two objects at different temperatures come into contact? (*See the Appendix for answers to Reading Checks.*)

Figure 3 **Transfer of Thermal Energy**

① Energy is transferred from the particles in the juice to the particles in the bottle. These particles transfer energy to the particles in the ice water, causing the ice to melt.

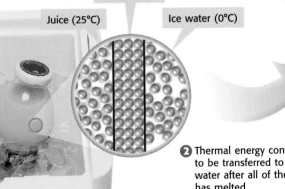

Bottle (25°C)

Juice (25°C)

Ice water (0°C)

Bottle (9°C)

Juice (9°C)

Water (9°C)

② Thermal energy continues to be transferred to the water after all of the ice has melted.

③ Eventually, the juice, bottle, and water have the same temperature. The juice and bottle have become colder, and the water has become warmer.

Answer to Reading Check

If two objects at different temperatures come into contact, thermal energy will be transferred from the higher-temperature object to the lower-temperature object until both objects are at the same temperature.

Homework ——— GENERAL

Transferred Energy Ask students this question:

When energy has been transferred by heat, what happens to it? Explain your answer.
(Energy transferred by heat moves from a higher-temperature object to a lower-temperature object. The thermal energy of the lower-temperature object increases, as does its temperature. The thermal energy of the higher-temperature object decreases, as does its temperature.) **LS** Logical

Teach, continued

MATERIALS

FOR EACH GROUP
- beaker, 250 mL
- film canister
- paper, graph
- thermometers (2)
- water, hot and cool

Safety Caution: Remind students to handle thermometers carefully. Caution students to wear safety goggles during this activity.

Teacher's Notes: Prepare the film canister lids in advance. Make a hole in each canister lid with an awl or a pair of sharp scissors. The thermometer should fit tightly enough in the lid that water will not drip out when the assembly is turned upside down. (One-hole stoppers can also be used.)

Students should graph both sets of data on the same grid. You may wish to assist students in adjusting the scales of their graph to show all their data.

Answer

5. Students should see that the rate of energy transfer decreases as the two water samples approach the same temperature.

Heat Exchange

1. Fill a **film canister** with **hot water**. Insert the **thermometer apparatus** prepared by your teacher. Record the temperature.

2. Fill a **250 mL beaker** two-thirds full with **cool water**. Insert **another thermometer** into the cool water, and record its temperature.

3. Place the canister in the cool water. Record the temperature measured by each thermometer every 30 s.

4. When the thermometers read nearly the same temperature, stop and graph your data. Plot temperature (*y*-axis) versus time (*x*-axis).

5. Describe what happens to the rate of energy transfer as the two temperatures get closer.

thermal conduction the transfer of energy as heat through a material

Conduction, Convection, and Radiation

You already know several examples of energy transfer. You know that stoves transfer energy to soup in a pot. You adjust the temperature of your bath water by adding cold or hot water to the tub. And the sun warms your skin. In the next few pages, you'll learn about three ways to transfer thermal energy: *conduction, convection,* and *radiation.*

Conduction

Imagine that you have put a cold metal spoon in a bowl of hot soup, as shown in **Figure 4.** Soon, the handle of the spoon warms up—even though it is not in the soup! The entire spoon gets warm because of conduction. **Thermal conduction** is the transfer of thermal energy from one substance to another through direct contact. Conduction can also occur within a substance, such as the spoon in **Figure 4.**

How does conduction work? When objects touch each other, their particles collide. Thermal energy is transferred from the higher-temperature substance to the lower-temperature substance. Remember that particles of substances at different temperatures have different average kinetic energies. So, when particles collide, particles with higher kinetic energy transfer energy to those with lower kinetic energy. This transfer makes some particles slow down and other particles speed up until all particles have the same average kinetic energy. As a result, the substances have the same temperature.

Figure 4 *The end of this spoon will warm up because conduction, the transfer of energy through direct contact, occurs all the way up the handle.*

Q: Why did the music teacher bring a metal pole to orchestra rehearsal?

A: He wanted the orchestra to have a good conductor.

Is That a Fact!

Special ceramic tiles were created for use on the underside of the space shuttle. These tiles transfer so little energy that one side can be exposed to a welder's torch while the other side remains cool to the touch.

166 Chapter 6 • Heat and Heat Technology

Conductors and Insulators

Substances that conduct thermal energy very well are called **thermal conductors.** For example, the metal in a doctor's stethoscope is a conductor. Energy is transferred rapidly from your warm skin to the cool stethoscope. That's why the stethoscope feels cold. Substances that do not conduct thermal energy very well are called **thermal insulators.** For example, a doctor's wooden tongue depressor is an insulator. It is at the same temperature as the stethoscope. But the tongue depressor doesn't feel cold. The reason is that thermal energy is transferred very slowly from your tongue to the wood. Some typical conductors and insulators are shown in **Table 1** at right.

Reading Check How can two objects that are the same temperature feel as if they are at different temperatures?

Convection

A second way thermal energy is transferred is **convection,** the transfer of thermal energy by the movement of a liquid or a gas. Look at **Figure 5.** When you boil water in a pot, the water moves in roughly circular patterns because of convection. The water at the bottom of a pot on a stove burner gets hot because it is touching the pot (conduction). As it heats, the water becomes less dense because its higher-energy particles spread apart. The warmer water rises through the denser, cooler water above it. At the surface, the warm water begins to cool. The particles move closer together, making the water denser. The cooler water then sinks back to the bottom. It is heated again, and the cycle begins again. This circular motion of liquids or gases due to density differences that result from temperature differences is called a *convection current.*

Table 1	Conductors and Insulators
Conductors	**Insulators**
Curling iron	Flannel shirt
Cookie sheet	Oven mitt
Iron skillet	Plastic spatula
Copper pipe	Fiberglass insulation
Stove coil	Ceramic bowl

thermal conductor a material through which energy can be transferred as heat

thermal insulator a material that reduces or prevents the transfer of heat

convection the transfer of thermal energy by the circulation or movement of a liquid or gas

Figure 5 *The repeated rising and sinking of water during boiling are due to convection.*

CHAPTER RESOURCES

Technology

 Transparencies
• P41 Conduction and Convection

Demonstration ——— GENERAL

Convection Currents Fill a 250 mL beaker about two-thirds full of water. Place the beaker on a hot plate turned on low or medium. Roll some very small pieces of aluminum foil into small, tightly packed balls. Drop the foil balls into the water, and direct students to observe what happens to the balls as the water warms up. Ask students what the movement of the foil balls suggests about the movement of water within the beaker. (The circulation of the foil balls suggests that the water in the beaker is circulating, too.) Then, ask what method of heating is shown in this demonstration. (convection) **LS** Visual

Answer to Reading Check

Two objects that are at the same temperature can feel as though they are at different temperatures if one object is a better thermal conductor than the other is. The better conductor will feel colder because it will draw thermal energy away from your hand faster.

CONNECTION to Earth Science ——— GENERAL

Convection Currents in the Atmosphere Convection currents caused by the uneven heating of Earth's surface are responsible for Earth's winds, weather patterns, and ocean currents. Without these currents, Earth's climates would be very different.

INCLUSION Strategies

• *Gifted and Talented*
• *Behavior Control Issues*
Students may benefit from expanding on a topic. Ask these students to make a list of 30 items in the classroom, 15 of which would work as thermal conductors and 15 that would work as thermal insulators. **LS** Logical   English Language Learners

CONNECTION to
Astronomy ————— GENERAL

The Atmosphere of Venus The very dense atmosphere of Venus is composed mostly of carbon dioxide. The high amount of carbon dioxide results in a greenhouse effect that traps most of the thermal energy from sunlight. The surface temperature of Venus is therefore the hottest of any planet in the solar system. It remains at about 460°C—hot enough to melt zinc metal.

Using the Figure — GENERAL

The Greenhouse Effect Draw students' attention to **Figure 7.** Ask students why they think clouds would keep an area of Earth from heating up as much as it would on a clear day. (Clouds prevent some radiation from reaching Earth.) Then, ask what would happen if greenhouse gases kept most of the thermal energy that reaches Earth from escaping into space. (Earth would gradually warm up.) Use the teaching transparency "The Greenhouse Effect" to help students understand how the atmospheres of Venus and Earth can act like greenhouses. English Language
Learners
LS Visual

radiation the transfer of energy as electromagnetic waves

Radiation

A third way thermal energy is transferred is **radiation,** the transfer of energy by electromagnetic waves, such as visible light and infrared waves. Unlike conduction and convection, radiation can involve either an energy transfer between particles of matter or an energy transfer across empty space.

All objects, including the heater in **Figure 6,** radiate electromagnetic waves. The sun emits visible light, which you can see, and waves of other frequencies, such as infrared and ultraviolet waves, which you cannot see. When your body absorbs infrared waves, you feel warmer.

Radiation and the Greenhouse Effect

Earth's atmosphere acts like the windows of a greenhouse. It allows the sun's visible light to pass through it. A greenhouse also traps heat energy, keeping the inside warm. The atmosphere traps some energy, too. This process, called the *greenhouse effect,* is illustrated in **Figure 7.** If our atmosphere did not trap the sun's energy in this way, most of the sun's energy that reached Earth would be radiated immediately back into space. Earth would be a cold, lifeless planet.

The atmosphere traps the sun's energy because of *greenhouse gases,* such as water vapor, carbon dioxide, and methane, which trap energy especially well. Some scientists are concerned that high levels of greenhouse gases in the atmosphere may trap too much energy and make Earth too warm.

✓ **Reading Check** What is the greenhouse effect?

Figure 6 *The coils of this portable heater warm a room partly by radiating visible light and infrared waves.*

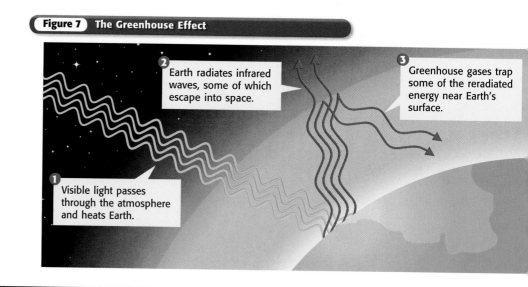

Figure 7 **The Greenhouse Effect**

2 Earth radiates infrared waves, some of which escape into space.

3 Greenhouse gases trap some of the reradiated energy near Earth's surface.

1 Visible light passes through the atmosphere and heats Earth.

CHAPTER RESOURCES
Technology
Transparencies
• P42 The Greenhouse Effect

Answer to Reading Check
The greenhouse effect is the trapping of thermal energy from the sun in Earth's atmosphere.

Heat and Temperature Change

Have you ever fastened your seat belt on a hot summer day? If so, you may have noticed that the metal buckle felt hotter than the cloth belt did. Why?

Thermal Conductivity

Different substances have different thermal conductivities. *Thermal conductivity* is the rate at which a substance conducts thermal energy. The metal buckle of a seat belt, such as the one shown in **Figure 8,** has a higher thermal conductivity than the cloth belt has. Because of its higher thermal conductivity, the metal transfers energy more rapidly to your hand when you touch it than the cloth does. So, even if the cloth and metal are at the same temperature, the metal feels hotter.

Specific Heat

Another difference between the metal and the cloth is how easily each changes temperature when it absorbs or loses energy. When equal amounts of energy are transferred to or from equal masses of different substances, the change in temperature for each substance will differ. **Specific heat** is the amount of energy needed to change the temperature of 1 kg of a substance by 1°C.

Look at **Table 2.** The specific heat of the cloth of a seat belt is more than twice that of the metal buckle. So, for equal masses of metal and cloth, the same thermal energy will increase the temperature of the metal twice as much as the cloth. The higher the specific heat of something is, the more energy it takes to increase its temperature. **Table 2** shows that most metals have very low specific heats. On the other hand, the specific heat of water is very high. This is why swimming-pool water usually feels cool, even on a hot day. The same energy heats up the air more than it heats up the water.

Figure 8 *The cloth part of a seat belt does not feel as hot as the metal part.*

specific heat the quantity of heat required to raise a unit mass of homogeneous material 1 K or 1°C in a specified way given constant pressure and volume

Table 2 Specific Heat of Some Common Substances

Substance	Specific heat (J/kg•°C)	Substance	Specific heat (J/kg•°C)
Lead	128	Glass	837
Gold	129	Aluminum	899
Copper	387	Cloth of seat belt	1,340
Iron	448	Ice	2,090
Metal of seat belt	500	Water	4,184

CONNECTION TO Social Studies

WRITING SKILL **Living near Coastlines** Water has a higher specific heat than land does. Because of water's high specific heat, the ocean has a moderating effect on the weather of coastal areas. The mild weather of coastal areas is one reason they tend to be heavily populated. Find out what the weather is like in various coastal areas in the world. Research the various reasons why coastal areas tend to be heavily populated, and write a brief report in your **science journal.**

WEIRD SCIENCE

You can boil water in a paper cup (Tell students NOT to try this at home, though!). The water removes the thermal energy—water boils at 100°C—from the paper before the cup reaches its kindling temperature (more than 230°C).

Close

Reteaching — BASIC
Thermal Energy Transfer

Review the three ways thermal energy is transferred by revisiting the teaching transparencies "Conduction and Convection" and "The Greenhouse Effect" (which shows heating by radiation). Make sure students know how thermal energy is being transferred in each picture.

LS Visual

Quiz — GENERAL

Ask students whether the following statements are true or false.

1. Heat is the transfer of energy between two objects with different temperatures. (true)

2. Convection currents result from temperature differences in liquids and gases. (true)

3. Radiation is the means by which the energy from the sun is transferred to Earth. (true)

4. Water stays warm or cool longer than land does because water has a lower specific heat than land does. (false)

Alternative Assessment — GENERAL

Concept Mapping Have the students construct a concept map using the following terms:

temperature, thermal energy, heat, conduction, radiation, convection, solids, liquids, gases, and *vacuum*

LS Visual

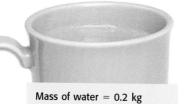

Mass of water = 0.2 kg
Temperature (before) = 25°C
Temperature (after) = 80°C
Specific heat of water = 4,184 J/kg•°C

Figure 9 *Information used to calculate heat, the amount of energy transferred to the water, is shown above.*

Heat, Temperature, and Amount

Unlike temperature, energy transferred between objects cannot be measured directly. Instead, it must be calculated. When calculating energy transferred between objects, you can use the definition of *heat* as the amount of energy that is transferred between two objects that are at different temperatures. Heat can then be expressed in joules (J).

How much energy is needed to heat a cup of water to make tea? To answer this question, you have to consider the water's mass, its change in temperature, and its specific heat. These are all listed in **Figure 9**. In general, if you know an object's mass, its change in temperature, and its specific heat, you can use the equation below to calculate heat.

$$heat \ (J) = specific\ heat \ (J/kg•°C) \times mass \ (kg) \times change\ in\ temperature \ (°C)$$

Calculating Heat

Using the equation above, you can calculate the heat transferred to the water. Because the water's temperature increases, the value of heat is positive. You can also use this equation to calculate the heat transferred from an object when it cools down. The value for heat would then be negative because the temperature decreases.

✓ **Reading Check** What are the three pieces of information needed to calculate heat?

Calculating Heat Calculate the heat transferred to a mass of 0.2 kg of water to change the temperature of the water from 25°C to 80°C. (The specific heat of water is 4,184 J/kg•°C.)

Step 1: Write the equation for calculating heat.

$$heat = specific\ heat \times mass \times change\ in\ temperature$$

Step 2: Replace the specific heat, mass, and temperature change with the values given in the problem, and solve.

$$heat = 4,184 \ J/kg•°C \times 0.2 \ kg \times (80°C - 25°C)$$
$$heat = 46,024 \ J$$

Now It's Your Turn

1. Imagine that you heat 2.0 kg of water to make pasta. The temperature of the water before you heat it is 40°C, and the temperature after is 100°C. How much heat was transferred to the water?

Answer to Reading Check

Specific heat, mass, and the change in temperature are needed to calculate heat.

Answer to Math Focus

1. $heat$ = 4,184 J/kg•°C × 2.0 kg × (100°C − 40°C) = 502,000 J

SECTION Review

Summary

- Heat is energy transferred between objects that are at different temperatures.
- Thermal energy is the total kinetic energy of the particles that make up a substance.
- Thermal energy will always be transferred from higher to lower temperature.
- Transfer of thermal energy ends when two objects that are in contact are at the same temperature.
- Conduction, convection, and radiation are three ways thermal energy is transferred.

- Specific heat is the amount of energy needed to change the temperature of 1 kg of a substance by 1°C.
- Energy transferred by heat cannot be measured directly. It must be calculated using specific heat, mass, and change in temperature.
- Energy transferred by heat is expressed in joules (J) and is calculated as follows: heat (J) = specific heat (J/kg•°C) × mass (kg) × change in temperature (°C).

Using Key Terms

For each pair of terms, explain how the meanings of the terms differ.

1. *thermal conductor* and *thermal insulator*

2. *convection* and *radiation*

Understanding Key Ideas

3. Two objects at different temperatures are in contact. Which of the following happens to their thermal energy?
   a. Their thermal energies remain the same.
   b. Thermal energy passes from the cooler object to the warmer object.
   c. Thermal energy passes from the warmer object to the cooler object.
   d. Thermal energy passes back and forth equally between the two objects.

4. What is heat?

Math Skills

5. The specific heat of lead is 128 J/kg•°C. How much heat is needed to raise the temperature of a 0.015 kg sample of lead by 10°C?

Critical Thinking

6. **Making Inferences** Two objects have the same total thermal energy. They are different sizes. Are they at the same temperature? Explain.

7. **Applying Concepts** Why do many metal cooking utensils have wooden handles?

Interpreting Graphics

8. Look at the photo below. It shows examples of heat transfer by conduction, convection, and radiation. Indicate which type of heat transfer is happening next to each letter.

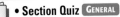

For a variety of links related to this chapter, go to www.scilinks.org

Topic: What Is Heat?
SciLinks code: HSM1661

Answers to Section Review

1. Sample answer: A thermal conductor is a substance through which thermal energy passes easily. A thermal insulator is a substance through which thermal energy passes only slowly.

2. Sample answer: Convection is the transfer of thermal energy by currents in a fluid caused by temperature differences within that fluid. Radiation is the transfer of thermal energy by electromagnetic waves moving through space.

3. c

4. Heat is the transfer of thermal energy between objects at different temperatures.

5. 128 J/kg•°C × 0.015 kg × 10°C = 19 J

6. no; They will not be at the same temperature, because in order for a larger object to have the same total thermal energy as a smaller object, the larger object must be at a lower temperature.

7. Because wood is a poor conductor of heat, you can hold the wooden handle of a hot pot, for instance, without being burned.

8. a: conduction; b: convection; c: radiation

CHAPTER RESOURCES

Chapter Resource File

- Section Quiz GENERAL
- Section Review GENERAL
- Vocabulary and Section Summary GENERAL
- Reinforcement Worksheet BASIC
- SciLinks Activity GENERAL
- Datasheet for Quick Lab

Focus

Overview

In this section, students learn how substances change from state to state and how heat affects matter during changes of state. They also learn how heat affects matter during chemical changes.

Bellringer

Ask students to predict what changes would occur if they added an equal number of ice cubes to a glass of cold water and a glass of warm water. Ask them to explain their answer.

Motivate

Demonstration — GENERAL

Thermal Energy and Matter On an overhead projector, place a beaker half-full of very hot water. Place a second beaker half-full of very cold water next to the first. Before turning on the projector, ask students to watch the screen. As you drop food coloring into each beaker, have students describe what they see happening in the beaker. Ask them these questions:

From your observations, which beaker contained the hotter water? How did you come to this conclusion? Predict what will happen to the molecules of a liquid if more thermal energy is added. Visual

What You Will Learn

● Identify three states of matter.
● Explain how heat affects matter during a change of state.
● Describe how heat affects matter during a chemical change.
● Explain what a *calorimeter* is used for.

Vocabulary
states of matter
change of state

READING STRATEGY

Brainstorming The key idea of this section is the relationship between matter and heat. Brainstorm words and phrases related to matter and heat.

Matter and Heat

Have you ever eaten a frozen juice bar outside on a hot summer day? It's pretty hard to finish the entire thing before it starts to drip and make a big mess!

The juice bar melts because the sun radiates energy to the frozen juice bar. The energy absorbed by the juice bar increases the kinetic energy of the molecules in the juice bar, which starts to change to a liquid.

States of Matter

The matter that makes up a frozen juice bar has the same identity whether the juice bar is frozen or has melted. The matter is just in a different form, or state. The **states of matter** are the physical forms in which a substance can exist. Matter consists of particles that can move around at different speeds. The state a substance is in depends on the speed of its particles, the attraction between them, and the pressure around them. Three familiar states of matter are solid, liquid, and gas, shown in **Figure 1.**

Thermal energy is the total energy of all the particles that make up a substance. Suppose that you have equal masses of a substance in its three states, each at a different temperature. The substance will have the most thermal energy as a gas and the least thermal energy as a solid. The reason is that the particles of a gas move around fastest.

Figure 1 Particles of a Solid, a Liquid, and a Gas

Particles of a gas, such as carbon dioxide, move fast enough to overcome nearly all of the attraction between them. The particles move independently of one another.

Particles of a liquid move fast enough to overcome some of the attraction between them. The particles are able to slide past one another.

Particles of a solid, such as ice, do not move fast enough to overcome the strong attraction between them, so they are held tightly together. The particles vibrate in place.

CHAPTER RESOURCES

Chapter Resource File
- Lesson Plan
- Directed Reading A BASIC
- Directed Reading B SPECIAL NEEDS

Technology
- Transparencies
  - Bellringer

Workbooks
- Interactive Textbook Struggling Readers

CONNECTION to Life Science — GENERAL

States of Matter and Life on Earth Life on Earth would end if there were no water. Water occurs in three states—solid, liquid, and gas—and all three are critical to survival. Even though water vapor (a gas) is invisible, it is just as important as the water we can see.

Changes of State

When you melt cheese to make a cheese dip, such as that shown in **Figure 2,** the cheese changes from a solid to a thick, gooey liquid. A **change of state** is a change of a substance from one state of matter to another. A change of state is a *physical change* that affects one or more physical properties of a substance without changing the identity of the substance. Changes of state include *freezing* (liquid to solid), *melting* (solid to liquid), *boiling* (liquid to gas), and *condensing* (gas to liquid).

Energy and Changes of State

Suppose that you put an ice cube in a pan and set the pan on a stove burner. Soon, the ice will turn to water and then to steam. If you made a graph of the temperature of the ice versus the energy involved during this process, it would look something like the graph in **Figure 3.**

As the ice is heated, its temperature increases from –25°C to 0°C. As the ice melts, its temperature remains at 0°C even as more energy is added. This added energy changes the arrangement of the molecules in the ice. The temperature of the ice remains the same until all of the ice has become liquid water. At that point, the water's temperature starts to increase from 0°C to 100°C. At 100°C, the water begins to change to steam. Even as more energy is added, the water's temperature stays at 100°C as long as there is liquid water present. When all of the water has become steam, the temperature again increases.

✓ **Reading Check** What happens to the temperature of a substance while it is undergoing a change of state? (*See the Appendix for answers to Reading Checks.*)

Figure 2 *When you melt cheese, you change the state of the cheese but not its identity.*

states of matter the physical forms of matter, which include solid, liquid, and gas

change of state the change of a substance from one physical state to another

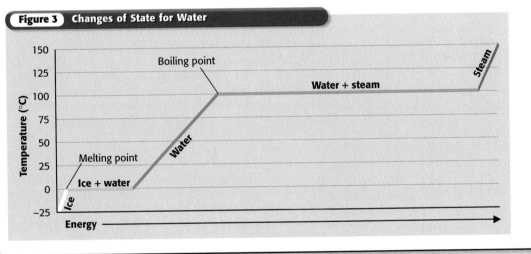

Figure 3 Changes of State for Water

MATERIALS

FOR EACH GROUP
- test tubes (3)
- thermometers (3)
- water, nail polish remover, and isopropyl alcohol,10 mL each, in the test tubes

Safety Caution: Caution students to wear safety goggles and gloves for this activity. Nail polish remover and alcohol should be handled with care.

Rates of Cooling Have students insert the thermometers into the liquids and wait for the temperatures to stabilize before taking readings. Have them record the temperatures on a chart. Then, have them remove one thermometer, carefully wave it in the air, and take another temperature reading. Instruct them to record the new temperature and then for the other liquids. Ask students what caused the temperature to decrease as the thermometer was waved around. (As it evaporated, the liquid absorbed energy from the thermometer.) ⬜ Visual/Logical

Answer to Reading Check

While a substance is undergoing a change of state, the temperature of the substance remains the same.

SUPPORT FOR

English Language Learners
Energy and State Changes
Have students study the graph on this page. Tell them that adding energy to a substance may cause a change in state. Ask students if ice can be warmer than 0° C. (No, if it's warmer than that, it will become water.) Summarize by pointing out that additional energy causes a change of state, not of temperature. ⬜ Visual/Auditory

🔵 INCLUSION Strategies

- *Learning Disabled*
- *Hearing Impaired*
- *Developmentally Delayed*

Many students will better understand new ideas if the ideas are repeated and related to familiar information. Write these four states on the board: freezing, melting, boiling, condensing. Ask students to identify each of these situations with one of the four states: ice cubes turn to water, dew covers a windshield, soup bubbles on the stove, winter road becomes slippery after the sun goes down, water in a pan on the stove slowly disappears, and bathroom mirror fogs over when you take a shower. ⬜ Intrapersonal English Language Learners

Section 3 • Matter and Heat **173**

Matter and Heat Relationships
Help students to tie the material in this section together by revisiting the change-of-state graph in **Figure 3** and relating it to the chemical energy discussion on this and the facing page. Students should realize that both topics deal with quantifying heat in matter changes, both physical and chemical. **LS** Logical

Quiz — GENERAL

Ask students whether these statements are true or false.

1. When ice changes to a liquid, it absorbs energy. (true)

2. When a liquid evaporates, it absorbs energy. (true)

3. When a vapor condenses to a liquid, energy is given off. (true)

4. When a liquid boils, energy is absorbed. (true)

Alternative Assessment — GENERAL

Concept Mapping Have students make a concept map showing how heat affects matter during a change of state and during a chemical change. **LS** Visual

Figure 4 In a natural-gas fireplace, the methane in natural gas and the oxygen in air change into carbon dioxide and water. As a result of the change, energy is given off, making a room feel warmer.

Figure 5 A serving of this fruit contains 120 Cal (502,080 J) of energy, which becomes available when the fruit is eaten.

Heat and Chemical Changes

Heat is involved not only in changes of state, which are physical changes, but also in *chemical changes*—changes that occur when one or more substances are changed into entirely new substances that have different properties. During a chemical change, new substances are formed.

For a new substance to form, old bonds between particles must be broken, and new bonds must be formed. The breaking and creating of bonds between particles involves energy. Sometimes, a chemical change requires that thermal energy be put into substances for a reaction to occur. Other times, a chemical change, such as the one shown in **Figure 4**, will result in a release of energy.

Food and Chemical Energy

Food contains substances from which your body gets energy. Energy that your body can use is released when chemical compounds such as carbohydrates are broken down in your body. The energy is released in chemical reactions.

You have probably seen Nutrition Facts labels, such as the one shown in **Figure 5** on the left. Among other information, such labels show how much chemical energy is in a certain amount of the food. The Calorie is the unit of energy that is often used to measure chemical energy in food. One Calorie is equivalent to 4,184 J.

How do you measure how many Calories of energy are in a certain amount of food? Because the Calorie is a measure of energy, it is also a measure of heat. The amount of energy in food can therefore be measured by a device that measures heat.

✓ **Reading Check** What is the unit of energy in food?

Answer to Reading Check
The unit of energy in food is the Calorie.

Calorimeters

A *calorimeter* (KAL uh RIM uht uhr) is a device that measures heat. When one object transfers thermal energy to another object, the energy lost by one object is gained by the other object. This the key to how a calorimeter works. Inside a calorimeter, shown in **Figure 6,** thermal energy transferred from a known mass of a test substance to a known mass of another substance, usually water.

The energy of food, in Calories, is found in this way. In a special kind of calorimeter called a *bomb calorimeter,* a food sample is burned. The energy that is released is transferred to the water. By measuring the temperature change of the water and using water's specific heat, you can determine the exact amount of energy transferred by the food sample to the water. This amount of energy (heat) equals the energy content of the food.

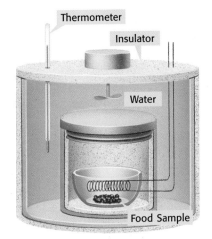

Figure 6 *A bomb calorimeter can measure energy content in food by measuring how much heat is given off by a food sample when it is burned.*

Using Key Terms

1. Use each of the following terms in a separate sentence: *states of matter* and *change of state.*

Understanding Key Ideas

2. What determines a substance's state?
   a. the size of its particles
   b. the amount of the substance
   c. the speed of its particles and the attraction between them
   d. the chemical energy that the substance has

3. During a change of state, why doesn't the temperature of the substance change?

Math Skills

4. When burned in a calorimeter, a sample of popcorn released 627,600 J. How much energy, in Calories, did the popcorn have?

Critical Thinking

5. **Applying Concepts** Many cold packs used for sports injuries are activated by bending the package, causing the substances inside to chemically react. How is heat involved in this process?

6. **Analyzing Processes** When water evaporates (changes from a liquid to a gas), the air near the water's surface becomes cooler. Explain why.

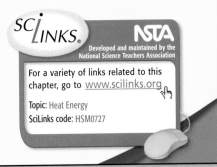

For a variety of links related to this chapter, go to www.scilinks.org

Topic: Heat Energy
SciLinks code: HSM0727

Developed and maintained by the National Science Teachers Association

Focus

Overview

In this section, students learn about different kinds of heating systems, heat engines, and cooling systems. They also learn about some effects of heat on the environment.

 Bellringer

Write the following on the board:

Predict whether leaving the refrigerator door open on a hot summer day will help to cool the kitchen. Explain your answer.

Have students write their responses in their **science journal.** Review these predictions after students have read this section.

Motivate

Discussion ——— GENERAL

Have students work together to hypothesize about how an air conditioner works and how heat is involved in an appliance that cools. Have the groups share their hypotheses with the class. Discuss some ways people may have cooled their homes before air conditioners were invented, and have them imagine what their lives would be like today without heating or air conditioning.

 Logical/Interpersonal

SECTION 4

Heat Technology

You probably wouldn't be surprised to learn that the heater in your home is an example of heat technology. But did you know that automobiles, refrigerators, and air conditioners are also examples of heat technology?

It's true! You can travel long distances, you can keep your food cold, and you can feel comfortable indoors during the summer—all because of heat technology.

Heating Systems

Many homes and buildings have a central heating system that controls the temperature in every room. On the next few pages, you will see some different central heating systems.

Hot-Water Heating

The high specific heat of water makes it useful for heating systems. A hot-water heating system is shown in **Figure 1.** A hot-water heater raises the temperature of water, which is pumped through pipes that lead to radiators in each room. The radiators then heat the colder air surrounding them. The water returns to the hot-water heater to be heated again.

What You Will Learn

- Analyze several kinds of heating systems.
- Describe how a heat engine works.
- Explain how a refrigerator keeps food cold.
- List some effects of heat technology on the environment.

Vocabulary
insulation
heat engine
thermal pollution

READING STRATEGY

Reading Organizer As you read this section, create an outline of the section. Use the headings from the section in your outline.

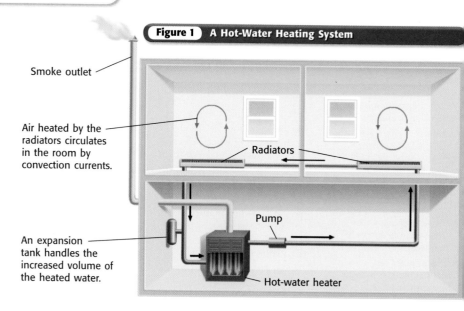

Figure 1 A Hot-Water Heating System

Smoke outlet

Air heated by the radiators circulates in the room by convection currents.

Radiators

Pump

An expansion tank handles the increased volume of the heated water.

Hot-water heater

CHAPTER RESOURCES

Chapter Resource File

- Lesson Plan
- Directed Reading A **BASIC**
- Directed Reading B **SPECIAL NEEDS**

Technology

 Transparencies
- Bellringer

Workbooks

 Interactive Textbook Struggling Readers

CONNECTION to History ——— GENERAL

Early Heating Systems The first heating systems developed by people were probably open fires in caves. When people found a way to make a hole in the side or top of the cave to let the smoke out, a type of fireplace was created. Fireplaces with a chimney tall enough to provide adequate draft for fires were first built in the 12th century.

Figure 2 — A Warm-Air Heating System

- Smoke outlet
- Warm air is circulated in the rooms by convection currents.
- Vent
- Filter
- Fan
- Furnace
- Duct

Warm-Air Heating

Air cannot hold as much thermal energy as water can. But warm-air heating systems are used in many homes and offices in the United States. In a warm-air heating system, shown in **Figure 2,** air is heated by burning fuel (usually natural gas) in a furnace. The warm air travels through ducts to different rooms. The warm air heats air in the rooms. Cooler air sinks below the warm air and enters a vent near the floor. Then, a fan forces the cooler air into the furnace. The air is heated and returned to the ducts. An air filter cleans the air as it moves through the system.

Heating and Insulation

Heat may quickly escape out of a house during cold weather, and during hot weather a house may heat up. To keep the house comfortable, a heating system must run much of the time during the winter. Air conditioners often must run most of the time in the summer to keep a house cool. This can be wasteful. Insulation can help reduce the energy needed to heat and cool buildings. Fiberglass insulation is shown in **Figure 3. Insulation** is a material that reduces the transfer of thermal energy. When insulation is used in walls, ceilings, and floors, less heat passes into or out of the building. Insulation helps a house stay warm in the winter and cool in the summer.

insulation a substance that reduces the transfer of electricity, heat, or sound

Figure 3 *Millions of tiny air pockets in this insulation help prevent thermal energy from flowing into or out of a building.*

✔ **Reading Check** How does insulation help reduce energy costs? (*See the Appendix for answers to Reading Checks.*)

READING STRATEGY — GENERAL

Prediction Before students read this section, have them predict the answers to the following questions about heating and cooling systems:

- Where should a heat register or heating vent be placed for maximum effect? (on the floor)
- Where should the cold-air return be placed? (on the floor)
- If you were cooling a house with central air conditioning, where would you place the cold-air register? (on the ceiling) the warm-air return? (on the ceiling)

LS Logical

MISCONCEPTION ALERT

Thermal Blankets Students often believe that blankets provide thermal energy. Explain that blankets insulate the body; the air pockets in the blanket material slow the escape of thermal energy from the body into the air, and the feeling of warmth results. Electric blankets are an exception.

Answer to Reading Check

Insulation helps save energy costs by keeping thermal energy from passing into or escaping from a building.

SUPPORT FOR

English Language Learners

Expanded Vocabulary As students read this section, they will encounter words to which they may not have had any previous exposure. Ask them to keep a running list of these words for the section. When they have finished reading the section, ask them to read it again with a partner and try to define the unknown words on their lists from context. If there are still undefined words left after the second reading, allow them access to a dictionary to

copy the definition onto their lists. Unfamiliar words may include: *central heating system, radiator, circulate, current, expansion, ducts, furnace, cent, filter, fiberglass, passive, solar, collector, combustion, exhaust, refrigerant.* Check lists for accuracy and spelling, and have students make corrections if necessary. Encourage students to keep their lists for future reference. **LS** Verbal/ Interpersonal

Using the Figure — GENERAL

Passive/Active Solar Heating
Draw students' attention to
Figure 4. Ask which parts of the
house are part of the passive
solar heating system and which
are part of the active solar heating system. (passive: large, south-
facing windows and thick walls;
active: solar collectors, network of
pipes, fan, and water storage
tank) **LS** Visual/Logical

Group ACTIVITY — GENERAL

Solar Heating Models Provide
groups with shoe boxes painted
flat black inside and out, jars or
cans painted white and black,
water, thermometers, and tubing. Challenge students to construct a model of a solar heating
system. **LS** Interpersonal

ACTIVITY — BASIC

**Flow of Air Through a Heating
System** Help students draw diagrams of the heating systems
shown in **Figures 1, 2,** and **4.**
Have them use red arrows to
indicate the flow of hot air and
blue arrows to indicate the flow
of cold air. English Language Learners
LS Visual

SCHOOL to HOME

WRITING SKILL **Home Heating and Cooling**

Find out from an adult what
kinds of systems are used in
your home for heating and
cooling. In your **science
journal,** describe how these
systems work. Also, describe
any energy-saving methods
used in your home.

ACTIVITY

Figure 4 *Passive and active
solar heating systems work
together to use the sun's energy
to heat an entire house.*

Solar Heating

The sun gives off a huge amount of energy. Solar heating
systems use this energy to heat houses and buildings. A
passive solar heating system does not have moving parts. It relies
on a building's structural design and materials to use energy
from the sun as a means of heating. An *active solar heating
system* has moving parts. It uses pumps and fans to distribute
the sun's energy throughout a building.

Look at the house in **Figure 4.** The large windows on the
south side of the house are part of the passive solar heating
system. These windows receive a lot of sunlight, and energy
enters through the windows into the rooms. Thick concrete
walls absorb energy and keep the house warm at night or
during cloudy days. In an active solar heating system, water
is pumped to the solar collector, where it is heated. The hot
water is pumped through pipes and transfers its energy to them.
A fan blowing over the pipes helps the pipes transfer their
thermal energy to the air. Warm air is then sent into rooms
through vents. Cooler water returns to the water storage tank
to be pumped back through the solar collector.

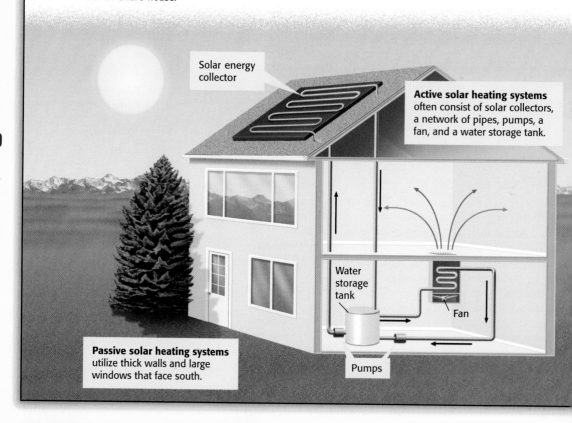

Solar energy collector

Active solar heating systems
often consist of solar collectors,
a network of pipes, pumps, a
fan, and a water storage tank.

Water storage tank

Fan

Pumps

Passive solar heating systems
utilize thick walls and large
windows that face south.

CHAPTER RESOURCES

Technology

 Transparencies
• P44 Solar Heating Systems

Is That a Fact!

Earth receives enough energy from the
sun in 1 min to meet the planet's
energy demands for an entire year. If
humans could find better ways to capture and use solar energy, dependence
on fossil fuels for energy sources could
be reduced.

Heat Engines

Did you know that automobiles work because of heat? A car has a **heat engine,** a machine that uses heat to do work. In a heat engine, fuel combines with oxygen in a chemical change that releases thermal energy. Heat engines burn fuel through this process, called *combustion.* Heat engines that burn fuel outside the engine are called *external combustion engines.* Heat engines that burn fuel inside the engine are called *internal combustion engines.* In both types of engines, fuel is burned to release thermal energy that can be used to do work.

Reading Check What kind of energy do combustion engines use?

External Combustion Engines

A simple steam engine, shown in **Figure 5,** is an example of an external combustion engine. Coal is burned to heat water in a boiler and change the water to steam. The steam expands, which pushes a piston. The piston can be attached to other parts of the machine that do work.

Modern steam engines, such as those used to generate electrical energy at a power plant, drive turbines instead of pistons. In the case of generators that use steam to do work, thermal energy is converted into electrical energy.

heat engine a machine that transforms heat into mechanical energy, or work

CONNECTION TO Oceanography

Energy from the Ocean
Ocean engineers are developing a new technology called *Ocean Thermal Energy Conversion,* or OTEC. OTEC uses temperature differences between surface water and deep water in the ocean to generate electrical energy. Research more information about OTEC, and make a model or a poster demonstrating how it works.

ACTIVITY

Figure 5 • An External Combustion Engine

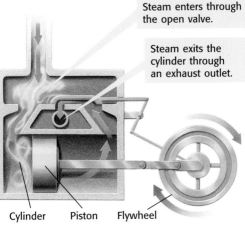

Steam enters through the open valve.

Steam exits the cylinder through an exhaust outlet.

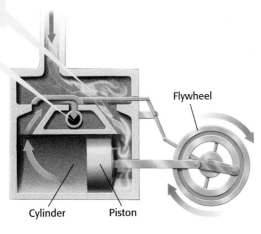

Flywheel

Cylinder   Piston   Flywheel

Cylinder   Piston

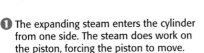

❶ The expanding steam enters the cylinder from one side. The steam does work on the piston, forcing the piston to move.

❷ As the piston moves to the other side, a second valve opens, and steam enters. The steam does work on the piston and moves it back. The motion of the piston turns a flywheel.

CONNECTION to History — GENERAL

Steam-Powered Tractor In 1769, Nicolas-Joseph Cugnot (1725–1804), a French army engineer, built a three-wheeled, steam-powered tractor. It traveled very slowly (3.6 km/h) and had to stop every 20 min to build up a fresh head of steam. Cugnot's tractor was hard to drive and not very practical, but his ideas led others to create better self-propelled vehicles.

Answer to Reading Check
Combustion engines use thermal energy.

Using the Figure — GENERAL
Concept Mapping Ask students to study **Figures 5** and **6.** Have them create a concept map that shows the similarities and differences between an external combustion engine and an internal combustion engine. The concept map should show the source of the energy, what the energy does, where the combustion takes place, and any other features of the two types of engines.
LS Visual

Science Bloopers

Horseless Carriages When automobiles were first built, they shared the roads with horses. Horses were often quite frightened by the cars. Uriah Smith, founder of a "horseless carriage" company in Michigan, came up with a solution to this problem: He made an automobile with a wooden, life-size horse head on the front. Unfortunately, this did nothing to quiet the noise of the engine, and horses were still frightened by cars.

ACTiViTY ———— **ADVANCED**

Types of Heat Engines Encourage interested students to research different types of heat engines, such as external and internal heat engines, the Carnot engine, and Heron's engine. Encourage them to include information on the laws of thermodynamics, perpetual motion machines, and entropy and chaos. **LS** Logical

CONNECTION to
Real World ———— **GENERAL**

Swamp Coolers Swamp coolers, or evaporative cooling systems, are used in areas of hot, dry weather, such as the southwestern United States. Swamp coolers work in a manner similar to the way evaporating sweat cools the body. A swamp cooler consists of a simple fan that draws in hot, dry outside air and passes it through wet filters. The evaporation process lowers the temperature of the indoor air, which the fan then distributes throughout the building.

Using the Figure— **GENERAL**

Cylinder Strokes Have students draw a series of cylinders similar to the ones in **Figure 6,** showing the four-stroke process. The strokes should be labeled to indicate the intake stroke, compression stroke, power stroke, and exhaust stroke. Ask students to then write a brief description of the processes that are occurring during each stroke. **LS** Visual

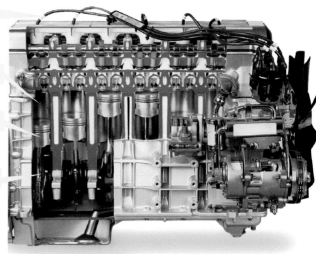

Wire to spark plug

Cylinder

Piston

Crankshaft

Figure 6 *The continuous cycling of the four strokes in the cylinders converts thermal energy into the kinetic energy needed to make a car move.*

Internal Combustion Engines

The six-cylinder car engine shown in **Figure 6** is an internal combustion engine. Fuel is burned inside the engine. The fuel used is gasoline, which is burned inside the cylinders. The cylinders go through a series of steps in burning the fuel.

First, a mixture of gasoline and air enters each cylinder as the piston moves down. This step is called the *intake stroke.* Next, the crankshaft turns and pushes the piston up, compressing the fuel mixture. This step is called the *compression stroke.* Next comes the *power stroke,* in which the spark plug uses electrical energy to ignite the compressed fuel mixture. As the mixture of fuel and air burns, it expands and forces the piston down. Finally, during the *exhaust stroke,* the crankshaft turns, and the piston is forced back up, pushing exhaust gases out of the cylinder.

Cooling Systems

When the summer gets hot, an air-conditioned room can feel very refreshing. Cooling systems are used to transfer thermal energy out of a particular area so that it feels cooler. An air conditioner, shown in **Figure 7,** is a cooling system that transfers thermal energy from a warm area inside a building or car to an area outside. Thermal energy naturally tends to go from areas of higher temperature to areas of lower temperature. So, to transfer thermal energy outside where it is warmer, the air-conditioning system must do work. It's like walking uphill: if you are going against gravity, you must do work.

Figure 7 *This air-conditioning unit keeps a building cool by moving thermal energy from inside the building to the outside.*

Is That a Fact!

A heat pump is a "refrigerator" that can be run in two directions. When a heat pump is used for cooling, energy is extracted from the air in the house and is pumped outside. When a heat pump is used for heating, energy is taken from the air outside and is pumped inside.

Figure 8 How a Refrigerator Works

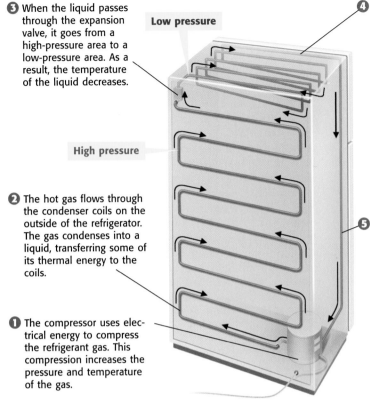

❸ When the liquid passes through the expansion valve, it goes from a high-pressure area to a low-pressure area. As a result, the temperature of the liquid decreases.

Low pressure

High pressure

❹ As the cold liquid refrigerant moves through the evaporating coils, it absorbs thermal energy from the refrigerator compartment, making the inside of the refrigerator cold. As a result, the temperature of the refrigerant increases, and it changes into a gas.

❷ The hot gas flows through the condenser coils on the outside of the refrigerator. The gas condenses into a liquid, transferring some of its thermal energy to the coils.

❺ The gas is then returned to the compressor, and the cycle repeats.

❶ The compressor uses electrical energy to compress the refrigerant gas. This compression increases the pressure and temperature of the gas.

...ooling and Energy

...ost cooling systems require electrical energy to do the work ...f cooling. The electrical energy is used by a device called a ...ompressor. The *compressor* does the work of compressing the ...efrigerant. The *refrigerant* is a gas that has a boiling point ...elow room temperature, which allows it to condense easily.

To keep many foods fresh, you store them in a refrigerator. ... refrigerator is another example of a cooling system. **Figure 8** ...hows how a refrigerator continuously transfers thermal energy ...rom inside the refrigerator to the condenser coils on the ...utside of the refrigerator. That's why the area near the back ...f a refrigerator feels warm.

Reading Check How does the inside of a refrigerator stay ...t a temperature that is cooler than the temperature outside ...he refrigerator?

Answer to Reading Check
The inside of a refrigerator is able to stay cooler than the outside because thermal energy inside the refrigerator is continuously being transferred outside of the refrigerator.

Is That a Fact!
A German scientist named Carl von Linde (1842–1934) made the first practical refrigerator, which used ammonia as the refrigerant.

Using the Figure—GENERAL
Refrigeration After students have studied **Figure 8,** discuss with them how refrigeration has affected food storage and the kinds of foods we eat. Ask them, "What did refrigeration allow that had never been possible before?" **LS** Logical

Going Further——GENERAL
Freon and the Environment Have interested students investigate the controversy about the effect of Freon™ on the environment. Students should also research the alternatives to Freon. Explain that Freon used to be a commonly used refrigerant in the United States. **LS** Logical

CONNECTION to History———GENERAL

Air Conditioning and Refrigeration The air conditioning systems we use today evolved from commercial refrigeration systems. In 1902, a young engineer named Willis Carrier helped a printing company that was having a problem with its color printing. Humidity caused the paper to expand or shrink. The colored inks would not align correctly, which caused fuzzy pictures. Carrier intended to control humidity with his device. To his surprise, the air was not only drier but also cooler. Carrier patented his machine in 1906 and made his first international sale to a silk mill in Japan in 1907. In this country, textile mills in the southern states were among the first to use Carrier's machines. The Carrier Corporation still manufactures air conditioners for homes and businesses today.

Reteaching — BASIC

Section Main Ideas Ask students what three ways in which heat is used in technology are discussed in this section. (heating, cooling, heat engines) Then, ask students to give examples of each. (heating: solar heating, hot-water heating, gas heating; cooling: air conditioning, refrigerators; heat engines: external combustion engines, internal combustion engines) **LS** Logical

Quiz — GENERAL

Ask students whether the following statements are true or false:

1. You can cool the kitchen by leaving the refrigerator door open. (false)

2. Refrigeration is possible because of energy absorbed and released during changes in state. (true)

3. A radiator heats a room by heating the air, which circulates in convection currents. (true)

Alternative Assessment — GENERAL

Heat and Appliances Refrigerators and air conditioners seem to produce colder temperatures rather than warmer temperatures. Have students explain how heat is involved in the lowering of temperatures. Then, have students make a list of household objects that are useful because they radiate or absorb thermal energy. **LS** Logical

Heat Technology and Thermal Pollution

Heating systems, car engines, and cooling systems all transf thermal energy to the environment. Unfortunately, too muc thermal energy released to the environment can have a neg tive effect.

Thermal Pollution

One of the negative effects of excess thermal energy **thermal pollution,** the excessive heating of a body of wate Thermal pollution can happen near large power plants, whic are often located near a body of water. Many electric-pow plants burn fuel to release thermal energy that is used generate electrical energy. Unfortunately, it is not possible f all of that thermal energy to do work. So, some thermal energ waste results and must be released to the environment.

Figure 9 shows how cool water is circulated through a pow plant to absorb waste thermal energy. As the cool water absorl energy, the water heats up. Sometimes the heated water dumped into the same body of water that it came from. result, the temperature of the water can increase. Increase water temperature in lakes and streams can harm animals tha live there. In extreme cases, the increase in temperature down stream from a power plant can adversely affect the ecosystem the river or lake. Some power plants reduce thermal pollutio by cooling the water before it is returned to the river.

✓ **Reading Check** Give an example of thermal pollution.

thermal pollution a temperature increase in a body of water that is caused by human activity and that has a harmful effect on water quality and on the ability of that body of water to support life

Figure 9 Thermal pollution from power plants can result if the plant raises the water temperature of lakes and streams.

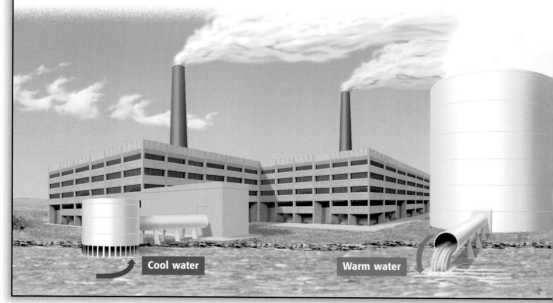

Cool water   Warm water

Answer to Reading Check

Sample answer: Thermal pollution can take place when heated water from an electrical generating plant is returned to the river from which the water came. The heated water that is returned to the river raises the temperature of the river water.

SECTION
Review

Summary

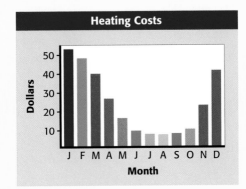

- Central heating systems include hot-water heating systems and warm-air heating systems.
- Solar heating systems can be passive or active. In passive solar heating, a building takes advantage of the sun's energy without the use of moving parts. Active solar heating uses moving parts to aid the flow of solar energy throughout a building.
- Heat engines use heat to do work.

- The two kinds of heat engines are external combustion engines, which burn fuel outside the engine, and internal combustion engines, which burn fuel inside the engine.
- A cooling system transfers thermal energy from cooler temperatures to warmer temperatures by doing work.
- Transferring excess thermal energy to lakes and rivers can result in thermal pollution.

Using Key Terms

1. Use each of the following terms in a separate sentence: *insulation, heat engine,* and *thermal pollution.*

Understanding Key Ideas

2. Which of the following describes how cooling systems transfer thermal energy?
   a. Thermal energy naturally flows from cooler areas to warmer areas.
   b. Thermal energy naturally flows from warmer areas to cooler areas.
   c. Work is done to transfer thermal energy from warmer areas to cooler areas.
   d. Work is done to transfer thermal energy from cooler areas to warmer areas.

3. Compare a hot-water heating system with a warm-air heating system.

4. What is the difference between an external combustion engine and an internal combustion engine?

Critical Thinking

5. **Identifying Relationships** How are changes of state important in how a refrigerator works?

6. **Expressing Opinions** Compare the advantages and disadvantages of solar heating systems. What do you think their overall benefits are, compared with those of other heating systems?

Interpreting Graphics

7. Look at the graph below. It shows the cost of heating a certain house month by month over the course of a year. During which times of the year is the most energy used for heating? Explain your answer.

Heating Costs

Dollars / Month

For a variety of links related to this chapter, go to www.scilinks.org

Topic: Heating Systems
SciLinks code: HSM0733

Answers to Section Review

1. Sample answer: A layer of insulation in building materials prevents the passage of thermal energy into or out of a building. A heat engine uses thermal energy to do work. Thermal pollution results when waste thermal energy changes the temperature of a natural body of water.

2. d

3. In a hot-water heating system, hot water is circulated into rooms, where it heats the air. In a warm-air heating system, air is heated by a central furnace and then circulated into rooms.

4. In an external combustion engine, fuel is burned outside the engine. In an internal combustion engine, fuel is burned inside the engine.

5. The exchange of thermal energy involved in evaporation and condensation is what makes a refrigerator work.

6. Sample answer: Solar heating systems are energy-efficient, but the amount of heating they can accomplish would not be much use in cold climates. Overall, it seems they could be put to good use in a lot of places in the world and could save a lot of energy.

7. Most energy is used for heating during the winter months. This is because in cold weather, thermal energy inside the house escapes more quickly as a result of the temperature difference between the inside and outside.

CHAPTER RESOURCES

Chapter Resource File

- Section Quiz GENERAL
- Section Review GENERAL
- Vocabulary and Section Summary GENERAL
- Critical Thinking ADVANCED

Feel the Heat

Teacher's Notes

Time Required

One or two 45-minute class periods

Lab Ratings

EASY —————→ HARD

Teacher Prep 🧪🧪🧪
Student Set-Up 🧪🧪
Concept Level 🧪🧪🧪
Clean Up 🧪🧪

MATERIALS

Materials listed are for each group of 2–4 students.

Safety Caution

Remind students that a thermometer should never be used for stirring. The container of hot water should be located where it cannot spill on students. Caution students to handle the nails carefully.

Procedure Notes

Heat water before class. Do not let the water temperature exceed 60°C. You may want to keep a large container of water heating on a hot plate. For step 5, the nails are set aside for about 5 min so that they will warm up to the same temperature as the water.

Feel the Heat

Heat is the energy transferred between objects at different temperatures. Energy moves from objects at higher temperatures to objects at lower temperatures. If two objects are left in contact for a while, the warmer object will cool down and the cooler object will warm up until they eventually reach the same temperature. In this activity, you will combine equal masses of water and nails at different temperatures to determine which has a greater effect on the final temperature.

Ask a Question

① When you combine substances at two different temperatures, will the final temperature be closer to the initial temperature of the warmer substance or of the colder substance, or halfway in between?

Form a Hypothesis

② Write a prediction that answers the question in item 1.

Test the Hypothesis

③ Copy the table below onto a separate sheet of paper.

④ Use the rubber band to bundle the nails together. Find and record the mass of the bundle. Tie a length of string around the bundle, leaving one end of the string 15 cm long.

⑤ Put the bundle of nails into one of the cups, letting the string dangle outside the cup. Fill the cup with enough hot water to cover the nails, and set it aside for at least 5 min.

OBJECTIVES

Measure the temperature change when hot and cold objects come into contact.

Compare materials for their ability to hold thermal energy.

MATERIALS

- balance, metric
- cups, plastic-foam, 9 oz (2)
- cylinder, graduated, 100 mL
- nails (10 to 12)
- string, 30 cm length
- paper towels
- rubber band
- thermometer
- water, cold
- water, hot

SAFETY

Data Collection Table					
Trial	Mass of nails (g)	Volume of water that equals mass of nails (mL)	Initial temp. of water and nails (°C)	Initial temp. of water to which nails will be transferred (°C)	Final temp. of water and nails combined (°C)
1					
2			DO NOT WRITE IN BOOK		

 Holt Lab Generator CD-ROM

Search for any lab by topic, standard, difficulty level, or time. Edit any lab to fit your needs, or create your own labs. Use the Lab Materials QuickList software to customize your lab materials list.

 Dennis Hanson
Big Bear Middle School
Big Bear Lake, California

Use the graduated cylinder to measure enough cold water to exactly equal the mass of the nails (1 mL of water = 1 g). Record this volume in the table.

Measure and record the temperature of the hot water with the nails and the temperature of the cold water.

Use the string to transfer the bundle of nails to the cup of cold water. Use the thermometer to monitor the temperature of the water-nail mixture. When the temperature stops changing, record this final temperature in the table.

Empty the cups, and dry the nails.

For Trial 2, repeat steps 4 through 9, but switch the hot and cold water. Record all of your measurements.

Analyze the Results

Analyzing Results In Trial 1, you used equal masses of cold water and nails. Did the final temperature support your initial prediction? Explain.

Analyzing Results In Trial 2, you used equal masses of hot water and nails. Did the final temperature support your initial prediction? Explain.

Explaining Events In Trial 1, which material—the water or the nails—changed temperature the most after you transferred the nails? What about in Trial 2? Explain your answers.

Draw Conclusions

Drawing Conclusions The cold water in Trial 1 gained energy. Where did the energy come from?

5 **Evaluating Results** How does the energy gained by the nails in Trial 2 compare with the energy lost by the hot water in Trial 2? Explain.

6 **Applying Conclusions** Which material seems to be able to hold energy better? Explain your answer.

7 **Interpreting Information** Specific heat is a property of matter that indicates how much energy is required to change the temperature of 1 kg of a material by 1°C. Which material in this activity has a higher specific heat (changes temperature less for the same amount of energy)?

8 **Making Predictions** Would it be better to have pots and pans made from a material with a high specific heat or a low specific heat? Explain your answer.

Communicating Your Data

Share your results with your classmates. Discuss how you would change your prediction to include your knowledge of specific heat.

Form a Hypothesis

2. Sample answer: The final temperature will be halfway in between the two initial temperatures. (Accept all testable hypotheses.)

Analyze the Results

1. Answers will vary depending on the initial prediction.
2. Answers will vary depending on the initial prediction.
3. The nails changed temperature more in both trials. Explanations should include references to initial and final temperatures.

Draw Conclusions

4. from the heated nails
5. The energy gained by the nails should be about the same as the energy lost by the hot water. (there might be some difference because of energy transfer to the cup and air.) The energy changes are the same because energy is conserved. Any energy gained by the nails must come from somewhere—in this case, from the water.
6. The water appears to hold energy better. Students' explanations should include that the temperature of the water changed less than the temperature of an equal mass of iron.
7. water
8. Pots and pans should be made from a material with a low specific heat so that more energy from the stove will be transferred to the food than to the pots and pans.

Communicating Your Data

Accept all reasonable answers. Sample revised prediction: The final temperature would be closer to the original temperature of the substance that has the higher specific heat.

Chapter Review

Assignment Guide

SECTION	QUESTIONS
1	1, 6, 10–11, 14, 17, 20–22
2	2–3, 7, 12, 15, 16, 18, 23
3	4, 9, 13, 24–26
4	5, 8, 19

ANSWERS

Using Key Terms

1. Temperature is a measure of the average kinetic energy of the particles of a substance. Thermal energy is the total kinetic energy of the particles of a substance.

2. Conduction is the transfer of thermal energy between objects that are touching. Heat is the transfer of thermal energy between objects that are at different temperatures.

3. A conductor is a substance that transfers thermal energy rapidly by conduction. An insulator is a substance that does not conduct thermal energy well.

4. States of matter are the different physical states that matter can be found in, including gas, liquid, and solid. A change of state is a physical change from one state of matter to another.

USING KEY TERMS

For each pair of terms, explain how the meanings of the terms differ.

1. *temperature* and *thermal energy*

2. *conduction* and *heat*

3. *conductor* and *insulator*

4. *states of matter* and *change of state*

5. *heat engine* and *thermal pollution*

UNDERSTANDING KEY IDEAS

Multiple Choice

6. Which of the following temperatures is the lowest?
   a. 100°C
   b. 100°F
   c. 100 K
   d. They are all the same.

7. Which of the following materials would NOT be a good insulator?
   a. wood
   b. cloth
   c. metal
   d. rubber

8. In an air conditioner, thermal energy is
   a. transferred from areas of higher temperatures to areas of lower temperatures.
   b. transferred from areas of lower temperatures to areas of higher temperatures.
   c. used to do work.
   d. transferred into the building.

9. The units of energy that you read on a food label are
   a. Newtons.
   b. Calories.
   c. Joules.
   d. Both (b) and (c)

10. Compared wih the Pacific Ocean, a cup of hot chocolate has
    a. more thermal energy and a higher temperature.
    b. less thermal energy and a higher temperature.
    c. more thermal energy and a lower temperature.
    d. less thermal energy and a lower temperature.

Short Answer

11. How does temperature relate to kinetic energy?

12. What are the differences between conduction, convection, and radiation?

13. Explain how heat affects matter durin a change of state.

Math Skills

14. The weather forecast calls for a temperature of 84°F. What is the corresponding temperature in degrees Celsius? in kelvins?

15. Suppose 1.3 kg of water is heated from 20°C to 100°C. How much energy was transferred to the water? (Water's specific heat is 4,184 J/kg•°C.)

5. A heat engine is an engine that uses thermal energy to do work. Thermal pollution is the raising of the temperature of an environment, particularly a body of water, due to waste thermal energy being put into it.

Understanding Key Ideas

6. c
7. c
8. b
9. b
10. b
11. Temperature is a measure of the average kinetic energy of particles of a substance.

12. Conduction is the direct transfer of thermal energy between objects that are touching. Convection is the transfer of thermal energy by convection currents through a fluid that result when different areas of a substance are heated to different temperatures. Radiation is the transfer of thermal energy through space by electromagnetic waves.

13. During a change of state, heat changes the arrangement of particles within matter without changing its temperature.

14. 5/9 × (84°F − 32) = 29°C
    29°C + 273 = 302 K

CRITICAL THINKING

6 Concept Mapping Create a concept map using the following terms: *thermal energy, temperature, radiation, heat, conduction,* and *convection.*

7 Applying Concepts The metal lid is stuck on a glass jar of jelly. Explain why running hot water over the lid will help you get the lid off.

8 Applying Concepts How does a down jacket keep you warm? (Hint: Think about what insulation does.)

9 Predicting Consequences Would opening the refrigerator cool a room in a house? Explain your answer.

10 Evaluating Assumptions Someone claims that a large bowl of soup has more thermal energy than a small bowl of soup. Is this always true? Explain.

11 Analyzing Processes In a hot-air balloon, air is heated by a flame. Explain how this enables the balloon to float in the air.

22 Analyzing Processes What is different about the two kinds of metal on the bimetallic strip of a thermostat coil?

23 Making Comparisons How is radiation different from both conduction and convection?

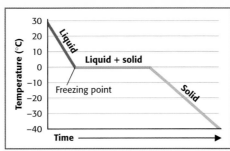

INTERPRETING GRAPHICS

Examine the graph below, and then answer the questions that follow.

24 What physical change does this graph illustrate?

25 What is the freezing point of this liquid?

26 What is happening at the point where the line is horizontal?

19. no; A refrigerator would only expel the warmer air from the room back into the room, plus the thermal energy that results from running the refrigerator. Therefore, keeping the refrigerator door open would actually raise the temperature of the room.

20. This claim is not necessarily true: it depends upon the temperatures of each bowl of soup. If the small bowl of soup has a much higher temperature than the large bowl of soup, it will have more thermal energy than the large bowl.

21. Thermal expansion causes the air in the balloon to expand and to become less dense, which causes a buoyant force on the balloon from the denser air outside the balloon.

22. Each of the two kinds of metal has a different rate of thermal expansion.

23. Radiation transfers thermal energy through space without the need for a medium.

Interpreting Graphics

24. This graph illustrates the process of freezing.

25. 0°C

26. The substance is freezing: the particles are rearranging from a liquid into a solid. The temperature is not changing during this process.

---

15. 1.3 kg × 4,184 J/kg•°C × (100°C − 20°C) = 435,000 J

Critical Thinking

16. An answer to this exercise can be found at the end of this book.

17. Heating the lid will cause thermal expansion, which will make it easier to unscrew.

18. A down jacket has a thick layer of insulation, which prevents thermal energy from your body from escaping into the surrounding air.

CHAPTER RESOURCES

Chapter Resource File

- Chapter Review **GENERAL**
- Chapter Test A **GENERAL**
- Chapter Test B **ADVANCED**
- Chapter Test C **SPECIAL NEEDS**
- Vocabulary Activity **GENERAL**

Workbooks

Study Guide
• Study Guide is also available in Spanish.

Standardized Test Preparation

Teacher's Note

To provide practice under more realistic testing conditions, give students 20 minutes to answer all of the questions in this Standardized Test Preparation.

MISCONCEPTION
/// **ALERT** \\\

Answers to the standardized test preparation can help you identify student misconceptions and misunderstandings.

Passage 1

1. D
2. H
3. A

➕ **TEST DOCTOR**

Question 2: The statement in answer G is not strictly true, because the passage says that at absolute zero, all particle motion should stop. H is the better answer.

Standardized Test Preparation

READING

Read each of the passages below. Then, answer the questions that follow each passage.

Passage 1 All matter is made up of particles. Temperature is a measure of the average kinetic energy of these particles. The colder a substance gets, the less kinetic energy its particles have, and the slower the particles move. In theory, at absolute zero (–273°C), all movement of particles should stop. Scientists are working in laboratories to cool matter so much that the temperature approaches absolute zero.

1. What is the purpose of this text?
   A to entertain
   B to influence
   C to express
   D to inform

2. What does information in the passage suggest?
   F Matter at absolute zero no longer exists.
   G No one knows what would happen to matter at absolute zero.
   H It is currently not possible to cool matter to absolute zero.
   I Scientists have cooled matter to absolute zero.

3. What information does the passage give about the relationship between kinetic energy and temperature?
   A The higher the temperature, the more kinetic energy a substance has.
   B There is no relationship between temperature and kinetic energy.
   C The higher the temperature, the less kinetic energy a substance has.
   D No one knows what the relationship between kinetic energy and temperature is.

Passage 2 Birds and mammals burn fuel to maintain body temperatures that are usually greater than the air temperature of their surroundings. A lot of energy is necessary to maintain a high body temperature. Tiny animals such as shrews and hummingbirds maintain high body temperature only during the day. At night or when the air temperature falls significantly, these tiny creatures go into a state called torpor. When an animal is in torpor, its respiration and heart rate are slow. Circulation continues primarily to major organs. Body temperature drops. Because their body processes are slowed, animals in torpor use much less energy than they usually need.

1. Which of the following would be the **best** summary of this passage?
   A Some animals use less energy than other animals.
   B Some animals use more energy than other animals.
   C Some animals maintain high body temperatures only during the day, going into torpor at night.
   D Going into torpor at night is necessary for some animals to maintain high body temperatures.

2. What happens when an animal goes into torpor?
   F Respiration and heart rate slow, and body temperature drops.
   G Normal respiration and heart rate are maintained, and body temperature drops.
   H Respiration and heart rate increase, and body temperature drops.
   I Respiration and heart rate increase, and body temperature rises.

Passage 2

1. C
2. F

Question 1: Students may be tempted to answer A or B. Although the tiny animals mentioned in the passage do use less energy at night than they do in the daytime, the passage does not say how this compares to energy use of other animals at night, likewise for answer B. Answer C most accurately sums up the passage.

TERPRETING GRAPHICS

e figure below shows a thermometer in
ch of two graduated cylinders holding
ater. Use the figure below to answer the
estions that follow.

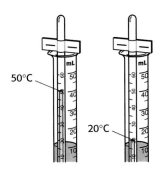

50°C

20°C

Which graduated cylinder contains more
water?

A The cylinder on the left contains more.

B The cylinder on the right contains more.

C The cylinders contain equal amounts.

D There is not enough information to
determine the answer.

If the two cylinders are touching each other,
what will happen to the thermal energy in the
cylinders?

F It will pass from the left cylinder to the
right cylinder.

G It will pass from the right cylinder to the
left cylinder.

H It will pass equally between the two
cylinders.

I Nothing will happen.

If the water in the graduated cylinders is mixed
together, which of the following will most
likely be the temperature of the mixture?

A 25°C

B 35°C

C 50°C

D 70°C

MATH

Read each question below, and choose the
best answer.

1. Elena has a bag containing 4 blue marbles,
   6 red marbles, and 3 green marbles. She picks
   1 marble at random. What is the probability
   of her picking a blue marble?

   A 1 in 13

   B 1 in 4

   C 4 in 13

   D 9 in 13

2. If $8 - 2n = -30$, what is the value of n?

   F 7

   G 19

   H 68

   I 120

3. A rectangle has sides of 4 cm and 10 cm. If
   the lengths of each of its sides are reduced by
   half, what will the change in the area of the
   rectangle be?

   A 1/4 as much area

   B 1/2 as much area

   C 2 times as much area

   D 4 times as much area

4. The specific heat of copper is 387 J/kg•°C. If
   the temperature of 0.05 kg of copper is raised
   from 25°C to 30°C, how much heat was put
   into the copper?

   F 96.8 J

   G 484 J

   H 581 J

   I 96,800 J

5. A change in temperature of 1°C is equal to a
   change in temperature of 1 K. The temperature
   0°C is equal to the temperature 273 K. If the
   temperature is 300 K, what is the temperature
   in degrees Celsius?

   A −27°C

   B 27°C

   C 54°C

   D 73°C

Standardized Test Preparation

INTERPRETING GRAPHICS

1. C

2. F

3. B

✚ TEST DOCTOR

Question 3: To answer this question correctly, students need to realize
that there is the same amount of
water in each graduated cylinder, and
because it is the same substance,
with the same specific heat, they
should intuit that thermal energy will
pass from the 50°C water to the 20°C
water until they are at the same
temperature, which will be halfway
between the two initial temperatures
because of the equal amount of thermal energy lost by the water in the
first cylinder and gained by the water
in the second cylinder.

MATH

1. C

2. G

3. A

4. F

5. B

✚ TEST DOCTOR

Question 3: The correct answer to
this question may be counterintuitive
to some students, who may intuit that
if the length of each of the sides of a
rectangle are halved, the area will
also be halved. The correct answer,
however, is A: the original area is
4 cm × 10 cm = 40 cm², and with the
length of each side halved, the area is
2 cm × 5 cm = 10 cm², which is 1/4 of
the original area.

Scientific Discoveries

Background

Scientists know that as gases approach absolute zero, they condense into a state of matter called a *Bose-Einstein condensate*. This state is named for physicists Satyendra Nath Bose and Albert Einstein. At these very low temperatures, almost all particle motion ceases, and the particles overlap one another. In 1999, scientists used a thick Bose-Einstein condensate of sodium atoms to slow the speed of a beam of light to 61 km/h.

Science, Technology, and Society

Background

DiAPLEX® works on the principles of Brownian motion, the random, zigzag motion of particles in solution. This phenomenon was first observed by the British botanist Robert Brown in 1827. The molecules of this solid fabric are capable of moving and reconfiguring, properties usually believed to occur only in liquids and gases. As the temperature rises, the molecules of DiAPLEX become more excited and move more rapidly.

Science in Action

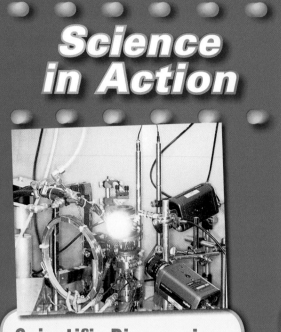

Inside | **DiAPLEX Fabric** | **Outside**

Thermal energy

When your body is cold, DiAPLEX adjusts to prevent the transfer of thermal energy from your body to your surroundings, and you feel warmer.

Moisture

When your body gets too warm, DiAPLEX adjusts to allow your body to transfer excess thermal energy and moisture to your surroundings, and you feel cooler.

Scientific Discoveries

The Deep Freeze

All matter is made up of tiny, constantly vibrating particles. Temperature is a measure of the average kinetic energy of particles. The colder a substance gets, the slower its particles move. Scientists are interested in how matter behaves when it is cooled to almost absolute zero, the absence of all thermal energy, which is about –273°C. In one method, scientists aim lasers at gas particles, holding them so still that their temperature is less than one-millionth of a degree from absolute zero. It's like turning on several garden hoses and pointing each from a different angle at a soccer ball so that the ball won't move in any direction.

Math ACTIVITY

Think of the coldest weather you have ever been in. What was the temperature? Convert this temperature to kelvins. Compare this temperature with absolute zero.

Science, Technology, and Society

DiAPLEX®: The Intelligent Fabric

Wouldn't it be great if you had a winter coat that could automatically adjust to keep you cozy regardless of the outside temperature? Well, scientists have developed a new fabric called DiAPLEX that can be used to make such a coat!

Like most winter coats, DiAPLEX is made from nylon. But whereas most nylon fabrics have thousands of tiny pores, or openings, DiAPLEX doesn't have pores. It is a solid film. This film makes DiAPLEX even more waterproof than other nylon fabrics.

Language Arts ACTIVITY

WRITING SKILL Think of two different items of clothing that you wear when the weather is cool or cold. Write a paragraph explaining how you think each of them works in keeping you warm when it is cold outside. Does one keep you warmer than the other? How does it do so?

Answer to Math Activity

To convert Fahrenheit temperatures to kelvins, students should first use the conversion factor $5/9 \times (°F - 32)$ to convert the temperature to degrees Celsius and should then add 273 to the Celsius temperature to convert it to kelvins. Students should conclude that whatever temperature they gave is still much warmer than absolute zero.

Answer to Language Arts Activity

Students should write about their chosen articles of clothing in relation to thermal energy transfer and how a "warmer" article of clothing keeps them warmer by virtue of its ability to keep more of the body's thermal energy from escaping into the cooler air.

Michael Reynolds

Earthship Architect Would you want to live in a house without a heating system? You could if you lived in an Earthship! Earthships are the brainchild of Michael Reynolds, an architect in Taos, New Mexico. These houses are designed to make the most of our planet's most abundant source of energy, the sun.

Each Earthship takes full advantage of passive solar heating. For example, large windows face south in order to maximize the amount of energy the house receives from the sun. Each home is partially buried in the ground. The soil helps keep the energy that comes in through the windows inside the house.

To absorb the sun's energy, the outer walls of Earthships are massive and thick. The walls may be made with crushed aluminum cans or stacks of old automobile tires filled with dirt. These materials absorb the sun's energy and naturally heat the house. Because an Earthship maintains a temperature around 15°C (about 60°F), it can keep its occupants comfortable through all but the coldest winter nights.

Social Studies ACTIVITY

Find out more about Michael Reynolds and other architects who have invented unique ways of building houses that are energy-efficient. Present your findings.

go.hrw.com

To learn more about these Science in Action topics, visit go.hrw.com and type in the keyword **HP5HOTF.**

Current Science

Check out Current Science® articles related to this chapter by visiting go.hrw.com. Just type in the keyword **HP5CS10.**

Careers

Background

One of the main purposes of housing is to provide shelter from the elements. The inside climate must be kept comfortable when the outside climate is not. Traditional houses accomplish this at high energy costs. The thermal mass of an Earthship's walls is used to store thermal energy and to regulate temperature for the living area. Air pockets between the packed cans and the dirt filling the tires provide extra insulation. As a result, a lot of energy is prevented from leaving the house, even as the sun goes down and the outside air grows cold.

Answer to Social Studies Activity
Answers may vary.

Built for Speed

Teacher's Notes

Time Required
One or two 45-minute class periods

Lab Ratings

EASY ——————————→ HARD

Teacher Prep △
Student Set-Up △
Concept Level △△
Clean Up △

MATERIALS

Students may be able to supply toy vehicles from home. The toy vehicles should be self-propelled, either battery operated or windup.

Preparation Notes

If you are using battery-operated cars, ensure that the batteries are fresh and that spare batteries are available. Discuss the correct units (m/s) before students begin.

Analyze the Results

1. Answers may vary.
2. Answers may vary. Students should analyze their procedure and that of others.
3. Answers may vary. Students may consider factors such as battery life, the age of the spring in wind-up vehicles, the testing surface, or the wheels of the vehicle.

Skills Practice Lab

Built for Speed

Imagine that you are an engineer at GoCarCo, a toy-vehicle company. GoCarCo is trying to beat the competition by building a new toy vehicle. Several new designs are being tested. Your boss has given you one of the new toy vehicles and instructed you to measure its speed as accurately as possible with the tools you have. Other engineers (your classmates) are testing the other designs. Your results could decide the fate of the company!

MATERIALS
- meterstick
- stopwatch
- tape, masking
- toy vehicle

SAFETY

Procedure

1. How will you accomplish your goal? Write a paragraph to describe your goal and your procedure for this experiment. Be sure that your procedure includes several trials.
2. Show your plan to your boss (teacher). Get his or her approval to carry out your procedure.
3. Perform your stated procedure. Record all data. Be sure to express all data in the correct units.

Analyze the Results

1. What was the average speed of your vehicle? How does your result compare with the results of the other engineers?
2. Compare your technique for determining the speed of your vehicle with the techniques of the other engineers. Which technique do you think is the most effective?
3. Was your toy vehicle the fastest? Explain why or why not.

Applying Your Data

Think of several conditions that could affect your vehicle's speed. Design an experiment to test your vehicle under one of those conditions. Write a paragraph to explain your procedure. Be sure to include an explanation of how that condition changes your vehicle's speed.

Applying Your Data
Procedures may vary but should show a clear understanding of how the condition could affect the vehicle's speed.

CHAPTER RESOURCES

Chapter Resource File
- Datasheet for LabBook
- Lab Notes and Answers

Elsie Waynes
Terrell Junior High
Washington, D.C.

Skills Practice Lab

Relating Mass and Weight

Why do objects with more mass weigh more than objects with less mass? All objects have weight on Earth because their mass is affected by Earth's gravitational force. Because the mass of an object on Earth is constant, the relationship between the mass of an object and its weight is also constant. You will measure the mass and weight of several objects to verify the relationship between mass and weight on the surface of Earth.

Procedure

1. Copy the table below.

2. Using the metric balance, find the mass of five or six small classroom objects designated by your teacher. Record the masses.

3. Using the spring scale, find the weight of each object. Record the weights. (You may need to use the string to create a hook with which to hang some objects from the spring scale, as shown at right.)

Analyze the Results

1. Using your data, construct a graph of weight (y-axis) versus mass (x-axis). Draw a line that best fits all your data points.

2. Does the graph confirm the relationship between mass and weight on Earth? Explain your answer.

MATERIALS

- balance, metric
- classroom objects, small
- paper, graph
- scissors
- spring scale (force meter)
- string

SAFETY

CHAPTER RESOURCES

Chapter Resource File

- **Datasheet for LabBook**
- **Lab Notes and Answers**

Analyze the Results

2. Sample answer: Weight is a measure of the gravitational force on an object. Weight depends on mass. Because an object's mass never changes, its weight on Earth never changes. The straight line of the graph illustrates the direct relationship between mass and weight.

Holt Lab Generator CD-ROM

Search for any lab by topic, standard, difficulty level, or time. Edit any lab to fit your needs, or create your own labs. Use the Lab Materials QuickList software to customize your lab materials list.

CLASSROOM TESTED & APPROVED

Barry L. Bishop
San Rafael Junior High
Ferron, Utah

Relating Mass and Weight

Teacher's Notes

Time Required
One 45-minute class period

Lab Ratings

EASY —————————→ HARD

Teacher Prep ▲
Student Set-Up ▲
Concept Level ▲▲
Clean Up ▲

MATERIALS

The materials listed are for each group of 2–3 students. A set of metric masses may be used as objects, but at least one random object should be included. Objects must be measurable with the spring scales and metric balances.

Safety Caution

Remind students to review all safety cautions and icons before beginning this lab activity.

Preparation Notes

If metric masses are used, put a small piece of opaque tape over the stamped value for mass. Ensure all objects are easily picked up with the spring scales. Use string to create a "handle." Choose at least five objects for each group.

Skills Practice Lab

Science Friction

Teacher's Notes

Time Required
One 45-minute class period

Lab Ratings

EASY ——————————————→ HARD

Teacher Prep 🔬
Student Set-Up 🔬
Concept Level 🔬🔬
Clean Up 🔬

MATERIALS
The rollers may be made from ring-stand poles or wooden dowels.

Safety Caution
Remind students to review all safety cautions and icons before beginning this lab activity.

Preparation Notes
If the spring scale is not very sensitive, students may record a force of zero for rolling friction. Encourage students to discuss whether this is realistic and what could be causing them to get such a result. For best results, students should keep the spring scale parallel to the table and should pull gradually. A quick pull will give an incorrect reading.

Skills Practice Lab

Science Friction

In this experiment, you will investigate three types of friction—static, sliding, and rolling—to determine which is the largest force and which is the smallest force.

Ask a Question

1 Which type of friction is the largest force—static, sliding, or rolling? Which is the smallest?

Form a Hypothesis

2 Write a statement or statements that answer the questions above. Explain your reasoning.

Test the Hypothesis

3 Cut a piece of string, and tie it in a loop that fits in the textbook, as shown on the next page. Hook the string to the spring scale.

4 Practice the next three steps several times before you collect data.

5 To measure the static friction between the book and the table, pull the spring scale very slowly. Record the largest force on the scale before the book starts to move.

6 After the book begins to move, you can determine the sliding friction. Record the force required to keep the book sliding at a slow, constant speed.

7 Place two or three rods under the book to act as rollers. Make sure the rollers are evenly spaced. Place another roller in front of the book so that the book will roll onto it. Pull the force meter slowly. Measure the force needed to keep the book rolling at a constant speed.

MATERIALS
- rods, wood or metal (3–4)
- scissors
- spring scale (force meter)
- string
- textbook (covered)

SAFETY

CHAPTER RESOURCES

Chapter Resource File

- • Datasheets for LabBook
- • Lab Notes and Answers

Analyze the Results

1. Which type of friction was the largest? Which was the smallest?

2. Do the results support your hypothesis? If not, how would you revise or retest your hypothesis?

Draw Conclusions

3. Compare your results with those of another group. Are there any differences? Working together, design a way to improve the experiment and resolve possible differences.

Analyze the Results

1. Static friction was the largest. Rolling friction was the smallest.

2. Answers may vary. Students may mention conducting more trials, using different objects or surfaces, or using the spring scale more carefully.

Draw Conclusions

3. Answers may vary but should show consideration of the experimental procedure.

 Holt Lab Generator CD-ROM

Search for any lab by topic, standard, difficulty level, or time. Edit any lab to fit your needs, or create your own labs. Use the Lab Materials QuickList software to customize your lab materials list.

Barry L. Bishop
San Rafael Junior High
Ferron, Utah

Skills Practice Lab

A Marshmallow Catapult

Teacher's Notes

Time Required
One or two 45-minute class periods

Lab Ratings

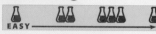

EASY ——————————————→ HARD

Teacher Prep 🧪🧪
Student Set-Up 🧪
Concept Level 🧪🧪
Clean Up 🧪

MATERIALS

The materials listed are for each group of 1–3 students. Marshmallows may be dusted with alum (a harmless but bitter kitchen spice) to discourage students from eating all the materials. You may wish to leave the marshmallows out overnight to harden so they will be easier to launch.

Preparation Notes

Some ceilings may be too low and some classrooms too crowded for this lab. Move to the hallway or outdoors to give students plenty of room.

Analyze the Results

1. The catapult should launch farthest at a 40°–50° angle. Explanations may vary.

Draw Conclusions

2. Sample answer: An angle of about 45° is best because it gives the best combination of distance and height. The evidence is that the marshmallow traveled farthest at a 40°–50° angle.

Using Scientific Methods

Skills Practice Lab

A Marshmallow Catapult

Catapults use projectile motion to launch objects. In this lab, you will build a simple catapult and determine the angle at which the catapult will launch an object the farthest.

Ask a Question

1. At what angle, from 10° to 90°, will a catapult launch a marshmallow the farthest?

Form a Hypothesis

2. Write a hypothesis that is a possible answer to your question.

Angle	Distance 1 (cm)	Distance 2 (cm)	Average distance	Data Collection
10°	DO NOT WRITE IN BOOK			

Test the Hypothesis

3. Copy the table above. In your table, add one row each for 20°, 30°, 40°, 50°, 60°, 70°, 80°, and 90° angles.

4. Using duct tape, attach the plastic spoon to the 1 cm side of the block. Use enough tape to attach the spoon securely.

5. Place one marshmallow in the center of the spoon, and tape it to the spoon. This marshmallow serves as a ledge to hold the marshmallow that will be launched.

6. Line up the bottom corner of the block with the bottom center of the protractor, as shown in the photograph. Start with the block at 10°.

7. Place a marshmallow in the spoon, on top of the taped marshmallow. Pull the spoon back lightly, and let go. Measure and record the distance from the catapult that the marshmallow lands. Repeat the measurement, and calculate an average.

8. Repeat step 7 for each angle up to 90°.

Analyze the Results

1. At what angle did the catapult launch the marshmallow the farthest? Explain any differences from your hypothesis.

Draw Conclusions

2. At what angle should you throw a ball or shoot an arrow so that it will fly the farthest? Why? Support your answer with your data.

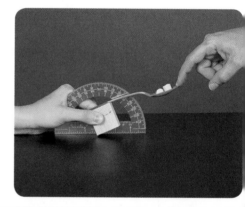

MATERIALS

- marshmallows, miniature (2)
- meterstick
- protractor
- spoon, plastic
- tape, duct
- wood block, 3.5 cm × 3.5 cm × 1 cm

SAFETY

Holt Lab Generator CD-ROM

Search for any lab by topic, standard, difficulty level, or time. Edit any lab to fit your needs, or create your own labs. Use the Lab Materials QuickList software to customize your lab materials list.

CHAPTER RESOURCES

Chapter Resource File

- Datasheet for LabBook
- Lab Notes and Answers

Vicky Farland
Crane Junior High
Yuma, Arizona

Model-Making Lab

Blast Off!

You have been hired as a rocket scientist for NASA. Your job is to design a rocket that will have a controlled flight while carrying a payload. Keep in mind that Newton's laws will have a powerful influence on your rocket.

Procedure

1. When you begin your experiment, your teacher will tape one end of the fishing line to the ceiling.

2. Use a pencil to poke a small hole in each side of the cup near the top. Place a 15 cm piece of string through each hole, and tape down the ends inside.

3. Inflate the balloon, and use the twist tie to hold it closed.

4. Tape the free ends of the strings to the sides of the balloon near the bottom. The cup should hang below the balloon. Your model rocket should look like a hot-air balloon.

5. Thread the fishing line that is hanging from the ceiling through the straw. Tape the balloon securely to the straw. Tape the loose end of the fishing line to the floor.

6. Untie the twist tie while holding the end of the balloon closed. When you are ready, release the end of the balloon. Mark and record the maximum height of the rocket.

7. Repeat the procedure, adding a penny to the cup each time until your rocket cannot lift any more pennies.

Analyze the Results

1. In a paragraph, describe how all three of Newton's laws influenced the flight of your rocket.

Draw Conclusions

2. Draw a diagram of your rocket. Label the action and reaction forces.

Applying Your Data

Brainstorm ways to modify your rocket so that it will carry the most pennies to the maximum height. Select the best design. When your teacher has approved all the designs, build and launch your rocket. Which variable did you modify? How did this variable affect your rocket's flight?

MATERIALS

- balloon, long, thin
- cup, paper, small
- fishing line, 3 m
- meterstick
- pencil
- pennies
- straw, straight plastic
- string, 15 cm (2)
- tape, masking
- twist tie

SAFETY

CHAPTER RESOURCES

Chapter Resource File

- **Datasheet for LabBook**
- **Lab Notes and Answers**

Vicky Farland
Crane Junior High
Yuma, Arizona

Action: downward force of pennies

Reaction: upward force of balloon

Reaction: upward force of released air pushing balloon

Action: downward force of air being squeezed out of balloon

Action: downward gravitational force of the Earth on the rocket (rocket's weight)

Reaction: upward gravitational force of the rocket on Earth.

LabBook

Model-Making Lab

Blast Off!

Teacher's Notes

Time Required

One or two 45-minute class periods

Lab Ratings

EASY ————————————————→ HARD

Teacher Prep 🧪🧪
Student Set-Up 🧪🧪🧪
Concept Level 🧪🧪🧪🧪
Clean Up 🧪

MATERIALS

You need 100 pennies per group. Use 2 balloons for more force.

Analyze the Results

1. Sample answer: Newton's first law: The rocket remains at rest until a force is exerted on it. Newton's second law: The rocket's acceleration depends on the force (which is constant) and the mass (which increases with each penny). Newton's third law: The force of the air leaving the balloon on the rocket is equal and opposite to the force of the balloon on the air.

Draw Conclusions

2. See the sample diagram at left. You may wish to point out the less obvious force pairs.

Applying Your Data

Answers may vary but should show a clear understanding of how the variable affects the rocket's flight.

Quite a Reaction

Teacher's Notes

Time Required

One to two 45-minute class periods

Lab Ratings

EASY ————————→ HARD

Teacher Prep 🧪🧪
Student Set-Up 🧪🧪
Concept Level 🧪🧪🧪
Clean Up 🧪

MATERIALS

The materials listed are for groups of 1–3 students. Thick pieces of poster board work well. One piece of corrugated cardboard will work as a substitute. A large marble will produce more-dramatic results than a small marble. Also, be sure to give students enough time for the glue to dry.

Safety Caution

Remind students to review all safety cautions and icons before beginning this lab activity.

Pick up any marbles, pins, or other materials that fall on uncarpeted floors immediately. This helps prevent slips and falls. Give students plenty of space to do this lab.

Skills Practice Lab

Quite a Reaction

Catapults have been used for centuries to throw objects great distances. According to Newton's third law of motion (whenever one object exerts a force on a second object, the second object exerts an equal and opposite force on the first), when an object is launched, something must also happen to the catapult. In this activity, you will build a kind of catapult that will allow you to observe the effects of Newton's third law of motion and the law of conservation of momentum.

Procedure

1. Glue the cardboard rectangles together to make a stack of three.

2. Push two of the pushpins into the cardboard stack near the corners at one end, as shown below. These pushpins will be the anchors for the rubber band.

3. Make a small loop of string.

4. Put the rubber band through the loop of string, and then place the rubber band over the two pushpin anchors. The rubber band should be stretched between the two anchors with the string loop in the middle.

5. Pull the string loop toward the end of the cardboard stack opposite the end with the anchors, and fasten the loop in place with the third pushpin.

6. Place the six straws about 1 cm apart on a tabletop or on the floor. Then, carefully center the catapult on top of the straws.

7. Put the marble in the closed end of the V formed by the rubber band.

8. Use scissors to cut the string holding the rubber band, and observe what happens. (Be careful not to let the scissors touch the cardboard catapult when you cut the string.)

- cardboard rectangles, 10 cm × 15 cm (3)
- glue
- marble
- meterstick
- pushpins (3)
- rubber band
- scissors
- straws, plastic (6)
- string

SAFETY

CHAPTER RESOURCES

Chapter Resource File

- Datasheets for LabBook
- Lab Notes and Answers

9 Reset the catapult with a new piece of string. Try launching the marble several times to be sure that you have observed everything that happens during a launch. Record all your observations.

Analyze the Results

1 Which has more mass, the marble or the catapult?

2 What happened to the catapult when the marble was launched?

3 How far did the marble fly before it landed?

4 Did the catapult move as far as the marble did?

Draw Conclusions

5 Explain why the catapult moved backward.

6 If the forces that made the marble and the catapult move apart are equal, why didn't the marble and the catapult move apart the same distance? (Hint: The fact that the marble can roll after it lands is not the answer.)

7 The momentum of an object depends on the mass and velocity of the object. What is the momentum of the marble before it is launched? What is the momentum of the catapult? Explain your answers.

8 Using the law of conservation of momentum, explain why the marble and the catapult move in opposite directions after the launch.

Applying Your Data

How would you modify the catapult if you wanted to keep it from moving backward as far as it did? (It still has to rest on the straws.) Using items that you can find in the classroom, design a catapult that will move backward less than the one originally designed.

Holt Lab Generator CD-ROM

Search for any lab by topic, standard, difficulty level, or time. Edit any lab to fit your needs, or create your own labs. Use the Lab Materials QuickList software to customize your lab materials list.

Vicky Farland
Crane Junior High
Yuma, Arizona

Analyze the Results

1. Answers will depend on the type of marble and the type of cardboard. It is likely that the catapult will have more mass.

2. The catapult moved backward.

3. Answers may vary, depending on the mass of the marble, the type of cardboard, and the size of the straws.

4. Answers may vary, but the marble will likely go farther than the catapult.

Draw Conclusions

5. The catapult moved backward as a result of Newton's third law. The catapult exerted a force on the marble that made it move forward. The marble exerted an equal and opposite force on the catapult, making it move backward.

6. More friction acts on the cardboard because it is in contact with the straws. Some students may also note that the marble and the cardboard have different masses. The acceleration of each is different as a result of Newton's second law, $F = m \times a$.

7. The momentum of both the marble and the catapult is 0 kg•m/s because both have a velocity of 0 m/s before the marble is launched.

8. Because the initial momentum of the system is 0 kg•m/s, the catapult has to move backward with a momentum equal to that of the marble moving forward. The momenta of the catapult and marble have to be in opposite directions so they will cancel out.

Applying Your Data

Accept all reasonable designs.

Density Diver

Teacher's Notes

Time Required

One 45-minute class period

Lab Ratings

EASY ——————————→ HARD

Teacher Prep △
Student Set-Up △△
Concept Level △△
Clean Up △

Lab Notes

If there is any air in the bottle, students will have to squeeze harder to make the diver move.

Analyze the Results

1. When the water level inside the diver rises, the diver starts sinking. When the level decreases, the diver floats.

2. Sample answer: Higher water level corresponds to higher density. Adding more water to the diver results in more mass in the same volume, so the density is greater.

Density Diver

Crew members of a submarine can control the submarine's density underwater by allowing water to flow into and out of special tanks. These changes in density affect the submarine's position in the water. In this lab, you'll control a "density diver" to learn for yourself how the density of an object affects its position in a fluid.

MATERIALS

- bottle, plastic, with screw-on cap, 2 L
- dropper, medicine
- water

SAFETY

Ask a Question

1. How does the density of an object determine whether the object floats, sinks, or maintains its position in a fluid?

Form a Hypothesis

2. Write a possible answer to the question above.

Test the Hypothesis

3. Completely fill the 2 L plastic bottle with water.

4. Fill the diver (medicine dropper) approximately halfway with water, and place it in the bottle. The diver should float with only part of the rubber bulb above the surface of the water. If the diver floats too high, carefully remove it from the bottle, and add a small amount of water to the diver. Place the diver back in the bottle. If you add too much water and the diver sinks, empty out the bottle and diver, and go back to step 3.

5. Put the cap on the bottle tightly so that no water leaks out.

6. Apply various pressures to the bottle. Carefully watch the water level inside the diver as you squeeze and release the bottle. Record what happens.

7. Try to make the diver rise, sink, or stop at any level. Record your technique and your results.

Analyze the Results

1. How do the changes inside the diver affect its position in the surrounding fluid?

2. What relationship did you observe between the diver's density and the diver's position in the fluid?

Draw Conclusions

3. Explain how your density diver is like a submarine.

4. Explain how pressure on the bottle is related to the diver's density. Be sure to include Pascal's principle in your explanation.

Draw Conclusions

3. Controlling the water level inside the diver is similar to controlling the water level inside a submarine by using ballast tanks.

4. Sample answer: Squeezing the bottle increases the water pressure. This increase is transmitted equally throughout the bottle to the diver (Pascal's principle). The air inside the diver is compressed, and water enters the diver. This increases the density of the diver.

CHAPTER RESOURCES

Chapter Resource File

- Datasheet for LabBook
- Lab Notes and Answers

CLASSROOM TESTED & APPROVED

C. John Graves
Monforton Middle School
Bozeman, Montana

Skills Practice Lab

Inclined to Move

In this lab, you will examine a simple machine—an inclined plane. Your task is to compare the work done with and without the inclined plane and to analyze the effects of friction.

Ask a Question

1. Write a question that you can test regarding inclined planes.

Form a Hypothesis

2. Write a possible answer to the question you wrote.

Test the Hypothesis

3. Copy the table at right.

4. Tie a piece of string around a book. Attach the spring scale to the string. Use the spring scale to slowly lift the book to a height of 50 cm. Record the output force (the force needed to lift the book). The output force is constant throughout the lab.

5. Use the board and blocks to make a ramp 10 cm high at the highest point. Measure and record the ramp length.

6. Keeping the spring scale parallel to the ramp, as shown, slowly raise the book. Record the input force (the force needed to pull the book up the ramp).

7. Increase the height of the ramp by 10 cm. Repeat step 6. Repeat this step for each ramp height up to 50 cm.

Analyze the Results

1. The real work done includes the work done to overcome friction. Calculate the real work at each height by multiplying the ramp length (converted to meters) by the input force. Graph your results, plotting work (*y*-axis) versus height (*x*-axis).

MATERIALS
- board, wooden
- blocks
- book, small
- meterstick
- paper, graph
- spring scale
- string

SAFETY

Force Versus Height

Ramp height (cm)	Output force (N)	Ramp length (cm)	Input force (N)
10			
20			
30	DO NOT WRITE IN BOOK		
40			
50			

2. The ideal work is the work you would do if there were no friction. Calculate the ideal work at each height by multiplying the ramp height (cm) by the output force. Plot the data on your graph.

Draw Conclusions

3. Does it require more or less force and work to raise the book by using the ramp? Explain, using your calculations.

4. What is the relationship between the height of the inclined plane and the input force?

CHAPTER RESOURCES

Chapter Resource File
- Datasheet for LabBook
- Lab Notes and Answers

Holt Lab Generator CD-ROM
Search for any lab by topic, standard, difficulty level, or time. Edit any lab to fit your needs, or create your own labs. Use the Lab Materials QuickList software to customize your lab materials list.

CLASSROOM TESTED & APPROVED

Jennifer Ford
North Ridge Middle School
North Richland Hills, Texas

Skills Practice Lab

Inclined to Move

Teacher's Notes

Time Required
One 45-minute class period

Lab Ratings

EASY ——————→ HARD

Teacher Prep 🧪🧪
Student Set-Up 🧪🧪
Concept Level 🧪🧪🧪
Clean Up 🧪

Safety Caution
Remind students to review all safety cautions and icons before beginning this lab activity.

Ask a Question
1. Accept all clearly formulated questions.

Form a Hypothesis
2. Accept all testable hypotheses.

Analyze the Results
1. The amount of work done should increase as ramp height increases (line A).

2. The amount of work done should increase as ramp height increases (line B).

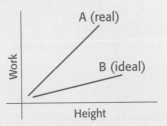

Draw Conclusions
3. It requires less force but more work to raise the book using the ramp. At each height, more work must be done to overcome friction.

4. The greater the height is, the greater the input force is.

Wheeling and Dealing

Teacher's Notes

Time Required

Two 45-minute class periods

Lab Ratings

EASY ———————————→ HARD

Teacher Prep 🧪🧪🧪🧪
Student Set-Up 🧪🧪
Concept Level 🧪🧪🧪🧪
Clean Up 🧪

MATERIALS

The materials listed in this lab are for each group of 2–4 students. The materials listed below are what you will need in order to prepare each wheel-and-axle assembly.

- 30 cm of 1 in. dowel
- 70 cm of 0.5 in. dowel for handles (cut into 4 pieces of 10 cm, 15 cm, 20 cm, and 25 cm)
- wheel
- small screw
- 1.5 in. PVC pipe

Safety Caution

Remind students to review all safety cautions and icons before beginning this lab activity.

Preparation Notes

The wheel-and-axle assembly must be constructed before class.

Wheeling and Dealing

A crank handle, such as that used in pencil sharpeners, ice-cream makers, and water wells, is one kind of wheel and axle. In this lab, you will use a crank handle to find out how a wheel and axle helps you do work. You will also determine what effect the length of the handle has on the operation of the machine.

MATERIALS

- C-clamps (2)
- handles (4)
- mass, large
- meterstick
- spring scale
- string, 0.5 m
- wheel-and-axle assembly

SAFETY

Ask a Question

1 What effect does the length of a handle have on the operation of a crank?

Form a Hypothesis

2 Write a possible answer to the question above.

Test the Hypothesis

3 Copy Table 1.

4 Measure the radius (in meters) of the large dowel in the wheel-and-axle assembly. Record this in Table 1 as the axle radius, which remains constant throughout the lab. (Hint: Measure the diameter, and divide by 2.)

5 Using the spring scale, measure the weight of the large mass. Record this in Table 1 as the output force, which remains constant throughout the lab.

6 Use two C-clamps to secure the wheel-and-axle assembly to the table, as shown.

7 Measure the length (in meters) of handle 1. Record this length as a wheel radius in Table 1.

8 Insert the handle into the hole in the axle. Attach one end of the string to the large mass and the other end to the screw in the axle. The mass should hang down, and the handle should turn freely.

9 Turn the handle to lift the mass off the floor. Hold the spring scale upside down, and attach it to the end of the handle. Measure the force (in newtons) as the handle pulls up on the spring scale. Record this as the input force.

Table 1	Data Collection			
Handle	Axle radius (m)	Output force (N)	Wheel radius (m)	Input force (N)
1				
2				
3	DO NOT WRITE IN BOOK			
4				

Lab Notes

Use a marker to number the handles 1 through 4 (shortest to longest). Drill a 0.5 in. diameter hole halfway through the large dowel near one end. The handles will be inserted into the hole. A small screw should be inserted into the large dowel near the handle attachment point, on the side away from the end. The string will attach to this point. The 1.5 in. PVC pipe should have an inside diameter slightly larger than that of the large dowel. The clamps are the most expensive pieces and are optional. If students work in groups, one student may act as the clamp and hold the PVC pipe firmly against the tabletop. Use a 500 g or 1 kg mass for the large mass. It takes a fair amount of time and materials to build the wheel-and-axle assemblies, but once you have built them, they will be available to use in subsequent years. Students should review the sections on work input, work output, mechanical efficiency, mechanical advantage, and a wheel and axle before beginning this lab. Demonstrate the assembly for students. Remind students that they can measure the axle radius and the wheel radius in centimeters and then convert to meters.

10 Remove the spring scale, and lower the mass to the floor. Remove the handle.

11 Repeat steps 7 through 10 with the other three handles. Record all data in Table 1.

Analyze the Results

1 Copy Table 2.

Table 2 Calculations						
Handle	Axle distance (m)	Wheel distance (m)	Work input (J)	Work output (J)	Mechanical efficiency (%)	Mechanical advantage
1						
2			*DO NOT WRITE IN BOOK*			
3						
4						

2 Calculate the following for each handle, using the equations given. Record your answers in Table 2.

a. *Distance axle rotates =*
   2 × π × axle radius

   Distance wheel rotates =
   2 × π × wheel radius

   (Use 3.14 for the value of π.)

b. *Work input =*
   input force × wheel distance

   Work output =
   output force × axle distance

c. *Mechanical efficiency =*
   $$\frac{work\ output}{work\ input} \times 100$$

d. *Mechanical advantage =*
   $$\frac{wheel\ radius}{axle\ radius}$$

Draw Conclusions

3 What happens to work output and work input as the handle length increases? Why?

4 What happens to mechanical efficiency as the handle length increases? Why?

5 What happens to mechanical advantage as the handle length increases? Why?

6 What will happen to mechanical advantage if the handle length is kept constant and the axle radius gets larger?

7 What factors were controlled in this experiment? What was the variable?

Safety Caution

Remind students not to stand too close to the handle after the string is wound on the axle. If the spring scale comes off the handle, the handle may spin around and hit someone.

Form a Hypothesis

2. Accept all testable hypotheses.

Analyze the Results

2. **a.** Axle distance = 2π × (0.012 m) = 0.075 m
   Wheel distance = 2π × (handle length: 0.10 m, 0.15 m, 0.20 m, 0.25 m) = 0.63 m, 0.94 m, 1.3 m, 1.6 m

   b. Answers will depend on the mass used. Check calculations for accuracy.

   c. Mechanical efficiency will depend on the materials used. Check calculations for accuracy.

   d. Mechanical advantages are 8.3, 12.5, 16.7, and 20.8 for the handles (10 cm, 15 cm, 20 cm, and 25 cm).

Draw Conclusions

3. As the handle length increases, work output stays the same, but work input gets slightly larger because the machine becomes less efficient.

4. The mechanical efficiency decreases as the handle length increases because the large dowel rotates within the PVC pipe more, creating more friction. More friction leads to lower mechanical efficiency.

5. Mechanical advantage increases as handle length increases because the input force for a large handle (wheel) is less.

6. The mechanical advantage will decrease.

7. Controlled factors include the axle radius and the mass used. The variable was the wheel radius (the length of the handle).

Building Machines

Teacher's Notes

Time Required
One or two 45-minute class periods

Lab Ratings

EASY ——————————→ HARD

Teacher Prep 🧪🧪
Student Set-Up 🧪🧪
Concept Level 🧪🧪
Clean Up 🧪

MATERIALS
The materials listed for this lab should be available in quantities sufficient for the entire class. You may provide different materials for students to use. Be sure students work carefully with the supplied materials. Students should work in groups of 2–4. Be sure to approve designs before students begin building their compound machines.

Safety Caution
Remind students to review all safety cautions and icons before beginning this lab activity.

Analyze the Results
1–4. Accept all reasonable answers.
   5. the pair of scissors

Applying Your Data
Accept all reasonable designs. Check all materials for safety and availability.

Building Machines
You are surrounded by machines. Some are simple machines, such as ramps for wheelchair access to a building. Others are compound machines, such as elevators and escalators, that are made of two or more simple machines. In this lab, you will design and build several simple machines and a compound machine.

Ask a Question
❶ How can simple machines be combined to make compound machines?

Form a Hypothesis
❷ Write a possible answer to the question above.

Test the Hypothesis
❸ Use the listed materials to build a model of each simple machine: inclined plane, lever, wheel and axle, pulley, screw, and wedge. Describe and draw each model.

❹ Design a compound machine by using the materials listed. You may design a machine that already exists, or you may invent your own machine. Be creative!

❺ After your teacher approves your design, build your compound machine.

Analyze the Results
❶ List a possible use for each of your simple machines.

❷ How many simple machines are in your compound machine? List them.

❸ Compare your compound machine with those created by your classmates.

❹ What is a possible use for your compound machine? Why did you design it as you did?

❺ A compound machine is listed in the materials list. What is it?

Applying Your Data
Design a compound machine that has all the simple machines in it. Explain what the machine will do and how it will make work easier. With your teacher's approval, build your machine.

MATERIALS
- bottle caps
- cardboard
- clay, modeling
- craft sticks
- glue
- paper
- pencils
- rubber bands
- scissors
- shoe boxes
- stones
- straws
- string
- tape
- thread spools, empty
- other materials available in your classroom that are approved by your teacher

SAFETY

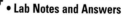

💿 Holt Lab Generator CD-ROM
Search for any lab by topic, standard, difficulty level, or time. Edit any lab to fit your needs, or create your own labs. Use the Lab Materials QuickList software to customize your lab materials list.

CHAPTER RESOURCES
Chapter Resource File
- **Datasheet for LabBook**
- **Lab Notes and Answers**

Norman Holcomb
Marion Elementary School
Maria Stein, Ohio

Skills Practice Lab

Energy of a Pendulum

A pendulum clock is a compound machine that uses stored energy to do work. A spring stores energy, and with each swing of the pendulum, some of that stored energy is used to move the hands of the clock. In this lab, you will take a close look at the energy conversions that occur as a pendulum swings.

MATERIALS

- marker
- mass, hooked, 100 g
- meterstick
- string, 1 m

SAFETY

Procedure

1. Make a pendulum by tying the string around the hook of the mass. Use the marker and the meterstick to mark points on the string that are 50 cm, 70 cm, and 90 cm away from the mass.

2. Hold the string at the 50 cm mark. Gently pull the mass to the side, and release it without pushing it. Observe at least 10 swings of the pendulum.

3. Record your observations. Be sure to note how fast and how high the pendulum swings.

4. Repeat steps 2 and 3 while holding the string at the 70 cm mark and again while holding the string at the 90 cm mark.

4. At which point (or points) of the swing did the pendulum have the greatest kinetic energy? the least kinetic energy? Explain your answers.

5. Describe the relationship between the pendulum's potential energy and its kinetic energy on its way down. Explain.

6. What improvements might reduce the amount of energy used to overcome friction so that the pendulum would swing for a longer period of time?

Analyze the Results

1. List similarities and differences in the motion of the pendulum during all three trials.

2. At which point (or points) of the swing was the pendulum moving the slowest? the fastest?

Draw Conclusions

3. In each trial, at which point (or points) of the swing did the pendulum have the greatest potential energy? the least potential energy? (Hint: Think about your answers to question 2.)

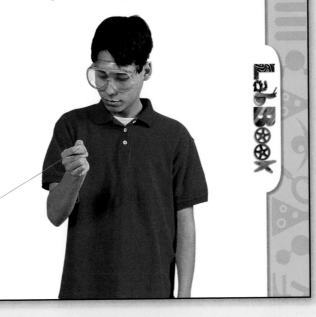

Energy of a Pendulum

Teacher's Notes

Time Required
One 45-minute class period

Lab Ratings
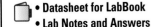
EASY ————————→ HARD

Teacher Prep 🧪
Student Set-Up 🧪
Concept Level 🧪🧪
Clean Up 🧪

MATERIALS
The materials listed are for each student.

Safety Caution
Caution students to swing the pendulum gently. Students should be a reasonable distance from one another and from classroom equipment. Students should wear safety goggles.

Analyze the Results
1. Accept all reasonable answers.
2. slowest when it is first released and when it is at the top of the opposite side; fastest at the bottom of its swing during each trial

Draw Conclusions

3. greatest potential energy at the greatest height on either side; smallest potential energy at the bottom of its swing

4. greatest kinetic energy at the bottom of its swing (moving fastest); smallest kinetic energy at the top of its swing (moving slowest)

5. The pendulum's kinetic energy increases on its way down (as the pendulum speeds up). As the pendulum moves from its highest point to its lowest point, potential energy decreases.

6. Accept all reasonable answers.

Inquiry Lab

Save the Cube!

Teacher's Notes

Time Required

One or two 45-minute class periods

Lab Ratings

🧪	🧪🧪	🧪🧪🧪	🧪🧪🧪🧪
EASY			→ HARD

Teacher Prep 🧪🧪🧪
Student Set-Up 🧪🧪
Concept Level 🧪🧪🧪
Clean Up 🧪

MATERIALS

Use incandescent lights, a hair dryer, or hot plates (low setting) to prepare a "thermal zone." Use the lowest setting on the hot plate so the plastic bags do not melt. Provide a large assortment of materials to protect the ice cubes, including white paper, cotton balls, plastic-foam packing peanuts, bubble wrap, tape, aluminum foil, and rubber bands.

Safety Caution

Caution students to wear heat-resistant gloves if working near a hot plate.

Procedure Notes

Set up the thermal zone before class. Have students find and record the masses of the empty cup and empty bag before they obtain their ice cubes.

Analyze the Results

1. Answers may vary but should provide an accurate assessment of results and reasonable ideas for design improvement.

Inquiry Lab

Save the Cube!

The biggest enemy of an ice cube is the transfer of thermal energy—heat. Energy can be transferred to an ice cube in three ways: conduction (the transfer of energy through direct contact), convection (the transfer of energy by the movement of a liquid or gas), and radiation (the transfer of energy through matter or space). Your challenge in this activity is to design a way to protect an ice cube as much as possible from all three types of energy transfer.

MATERIALS

- bag, plastic, small
- balance, metric
- cup, plastic or paper, small
- ice cube
- milk carton, empty, half-pint
- assorted materials provided by your teacher

Ask a Question

1 What materials prevent energy transfer most efficiently?

Form a Hypothesis

2 Design a system that protects an ice cube against each type of energy transfer. Describe your proposed design.

Test the Hypothesis

3 Use a plastic bag to hold the ice cube and any water if the ice cube melts. You may use any of the materials to protect the ice cube. The whole system must fit inside a milk carton.

4 Find the mass of the empty cup, and record it. Then, find and record the mass of an empty plastic bag.

5 Find and record the mass of the ice cube and cup together.

6 Quickly wrap the bag (and the ice cube inside) in its protection. Remember that the package must fit in the milk carton.

7 Place your ice cube in the "thermal zone" set up by your teacher. After 10 min, remove the ice cube from the zone.

8 Open the bag. Pour any water into the cup. Find and record the mass of the cup and water together.

9 Find and record the mass of the water by subtracting the mass of the empty cup from the mass of the cup and water.

10 Use the same method to determine the mass of the ice cube.

11 Using the following equation, find and record the percentage of the ice cube that melted:

$$\% \text{ melted} = \frac{\text{mass of water}}{\text{mass of ice cube}} \times 100$$

Analyze the Results

1 Compared with other designs in your class, how well did your design protect against each type of energy transfer? How could you improve your design?

💿 Holt Lab Generator CD-ROM

Search for any lab by topic, standard, difficulty level, or time. Edit any lab to fit your needs, or create your own labs. Use the Lab Materials QuickList software to customize your lab materials list.

CHAPTER RESOURCES

Chapter Resource File

- Datasheet for LabBook
- Lab Notes and Answers

David Sparks
Redwater Junior High
Redwater, Texas

Model-Making Lab

Counting Calories

Energy transferred by heat is often expressed in units called *calories*. In this lab, you will build a model of a device called a *calorimeter*. Scientists often use calorimeters to measure the amount of energy that can be transferred by a substance. In this experiment, you will construct your own calorimeter and test it by measuring the energy released by a hot penny.

Procedure

❶ Copy the table below.

Data Collection Table									
Seconds	0	15	30	45	60	75	90	105	120
Water temperature (°C)	DO NOT WRITE IN BOOK								

❷ Place the lid on the small plastic-foam cup, and insert a thermometer through the hole in the top of the lid. (The thermometer should not touch the bottom of the cup.) Place the small cup inside the large cup to complete the calorimeter.

❸ Remove the lid from the small cup, and add 50 mL of room-temperature water to the cup. Measure the water's temperature, and record the value in the first column (0 s) of the table.

❹ Using tongs, heat the penny carefully. Add the penny to the water in the small cup, and replace the lid. Start your stopwatch.

❺ Every 15 s, measure and record the temperature. Gently swirl the large cup to stir the water, and continue recording temperatures for 2 min (120 s).

Analyze the Results

❶ What was the total temperature change of the water after 2 min?

❷ The number of calories absorbed by the water is the mass of the water (in grams) multiplied by the temperature change (in °C) of the water. How many calories were absorbed by the water? (Hint: 1 mL water = 1 g water)

❸ In terms of heat, explain where the calories to change the water temperature came from.

Analyze the Results

1. Answers should be the final temperature (at 120 s) minus the initial temperature (at 0 s).

2. The number of calories absorbed by the water equals temperature change (from question 1) times the mass of the water (50 g).

3. The calories came from the penny. The penny increased the temperature of the water by transferring energy to it.

CHAPTER RESOURCES

Chapter Resource File

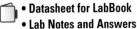

- Datasheet for LabBook
- Lab Notes and Answers

John Zambo
E. Ustach Middle School
Modesto, California

Counting Calories

Teacher's Notes

Time Required
One 45-minute class period

Lab Ratings

EASY ————————————→ HARD

Teacher Prep 🝭🝭
Student Set-Up 🝭
Concept Level 🝭🝭
Clean Up 🝭

MATERIALS
The materials listed are for each group of 2–3 students.

Safety Caution
Caution students to wear goggles and an apron and to use care when working near the heat source. Remind students never to use a thermometer for stirring.

Preparation Notes
You may wish to model the procedure for making the calorimeter and the proper method of heating the penny before students begin the lab. Remind students that a calorie is the amount of energy needed to raise the temperature of 1 g of water by 1°C. All students should heat the penny for the same amount of time.

Contents

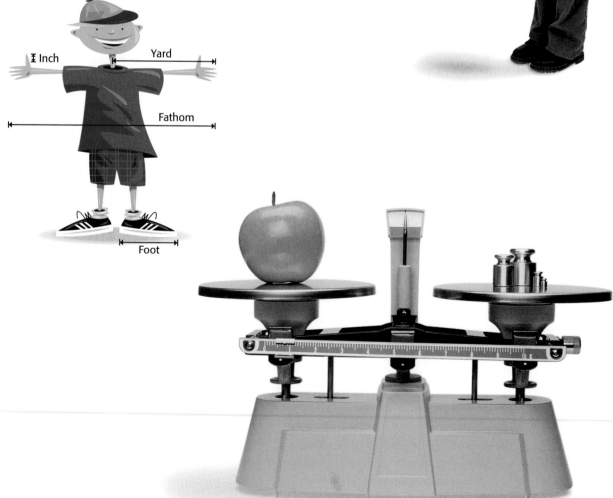

Appendix

✓ *Reading Check* Answers

Chapter 1 Matter in Motion

Section 1
Page 4: A reference point is an object that appears to stay in place.

Page 6: Velocity can change by changing speed or changing direction.

Page 8: The unit for acceleration is meters per second per second (m/s^2).

Section 2
Page 11: If all of the forces act in the same direction, you must add the forces to determine the net force.

Page 12: 2 N north

Section 3
Page 15: Friction is greater between rough surfaces because rough surfaces have more microscopic hills and valleys.

Page 17: *Static* means "not moving."

Page 18: Three common lubricants are oil, grease, and wax.

Section 4
Page 21: You must exert a force to overcome the gravitational force between the object and Earth.

Page 22: Gravitational force increases as mass increases.

Page 24: The weight of an object is a measure of the gravitational force on the object.

Chapter 2 Forces and Motion

Section 1
Page 37: The acceleration due to gravity is 9.8 m/s^2.

Page 38: Air resistance will have more of an effect on the acceleration of a falling leaf.

Page 40: The word *centripetal* means "toward the center."

Page 42: Gravity gives vertical motion to an object in projectile motion.

Section 2
Page 45: When the bus is moving, both you and the bus are in motion. When the bus stops moving, no unbalanced force acts on your body, so your body continues to move forward.

Page 47: The acceleration of an object increases as the force exerted on the object increases.

Page 49: The forces in a force pair are equal in size and opposite in direction.

Page 50: Objects accelerate toward Earth because the force of gravity pulls them toward Earth.

Section 3
Page 53: When two objects collide, some or all of the momentum of each object can be transferred to the other object.

Page 54: After a collision, objects can stick together or can bounce off each other.

Chapter 3 Forces in Fluids

Section 1
Page 67: Two gases in the atmosphere are nitrogen and oxygen.

Page 68: Pressure increases as depth increases.

Page 70: You decrease pressure inside a straw by removing some of the air inside the straw.

Section 2
Page 73: An object is buoyed up if the buoyant force on the object is greater than the object's weight.

Page 74: Helium is less dense than air.

Page 76: Crew members control the density of a submarine by controlling the amount of water in the ballast tanks.

Section 3
Page 79: Lift is an upward force on an object that is moving in a fluid.

Page 81: An irregular or unpredictable flow of fluids is known as *turbulence.*

Page 82: Airplanes can reduce turbulence by changing the shape or area of the wings.

Chapter 4 Work and Machines

Section 1
Page 94: No, work is done on an object only if force causes the object to move in a direction that is parallel to the force.

Page 97: Work is calculated as force times distance.

Page 98: Power is calculated as work done (in joules) divided by the time (in seconds) in which the work was done.

Section 2
Page 101: Machines make work easier by allowing a decreased force to be applied over a greater distance.

Page 102: Machines can change the force or the distance through which force is applied.

Page 104: *mechanical efficiency* = (work output ÷ work input) × 100

Section 3
Page 107: Each class of lever has a different set of mechanical advantage possibilities.

Page 109: the radius of the wheel divided by the radius of the axle

Page 110: a slanted surface that makes the raising of loads easier, such as a ramp

Page 112: They have more moving parts than simple machines do, so they tend to be less efficient than simple machines are.

Chapter 5 Energy and Energy Resources

Section 1

Page 124: Energy is the ability to do work.

Page 127: kinetic energy and potential energy

Page 129: Sound energy consists of vibrations carried through the air.

Page 130: Nuclear energy comes from changes in the nucleus of an atom.

Section 2

Page 133: Elastic potential energy can be stored by stretching a rubber band. Elastic potential energy is released when the rubber band goes back to its original shape.

Page 134: Plants get their energy from the sun.

Page 136: Machines can change the size or direction of the input force.

Section 3

Page 139: Conservation of energy is considered a scientific law because no exception to it has ever been observed.

Page 140: Perpetual motion is impossible because energy conversions always result in the production of waste thermal energy.

Section 4

Page 142: Fossil fuels are nonrenewable resources because they are used up more quickly than they are replaced.

Page 144: Nuclear energy comes from radioactive elements that give off energy during nuclear fission.

Page 146: Geothermal energy comes from the thermal energy given off by underground areas of hot rock.

Chapter 6 Heat and Heat Technology

Section 1

Page 159: Temperature is a measure of the average kinetic energy of the particles of a substance.

Page 160: Thermal expansion makes thermometers work.

Page 163: Expansion joints on a bridge allow the bridge to undergo thermal expansion without breaking.

Section 2

Page 165: If two objects at different temperatures come into contact, thermal energy will be transferred from the higher-temperature object to the lower-temperature object until both objects are at the same temperature.

Page 167: Two objects that are at the same temperature can feel as though they are at different temperatures if one object is a better thermal conductor than the other is. The better conductor will feel colder because it will draw thermal energy away from your hand faster.

Page 168: The greenhouse effect is the trapping of thermal energy from the sun in Earth's atmosphere.

Page 170: Specific heat, mass, and the change in temperature are needed to calculate heat.

Section 3

Page 173: While a substance is undergoing a change of state, the temperature of the substance remains the same.

Page 175: The Calorie is the unit of food energy.

Section 4

Page 177: Insulation helps save energy costs by keeping thermal energy from passing into or escaping from a building.

Page 179: Combustion engines use thermal energy.

Page 181: The inside of a refrigerator is able to stay cooler than the outside because thermal energy inside the refrigerator is continuously being transferred outside of the refrigerator.

Page 182: Sample answer: Thermal pollution can take place when heated water from an electrical generating plant is returned to the river from which the water came. The heated water that is returned to the river raises the temperature of the river water.

Study Skills

FoldNote Instructions

Have you ever tried to study for a test or quiz but didn't know where to start? Or have you read a chapter and found that you can remember only a few ideas? Well, FoldNotes are a fun and exciting way to help you learn and remember the ideas you encounter as you learn science!

FoldNotes are tools that you can use to organize concepts. By focusing on a few main concepts, FoldNotes help you learn and remember how the concepts fit together. They can help you see the "big picture." Below you will find instructions for building 10 different FoldNotes.

Pyramid

1. Place a sheet of paper in front of you. Fold the lower left-hand corner of the paper diagonally to the opposite edge of the paper.

2. Cut off the tab of paper created by the fold (at the top).

3. Open the paper so that it is a square. Fold the lower right-hand corner of the paper diagonally to the opposite corner to form a triangle.

4. Open the paper. The creases of the two folds will have created an X.

5. Using scissors, cut along one of the creases. Start from any corner, and stop at the center point to create two flaps. Use tape or glue to attach one of the flaps on top of the other flap.

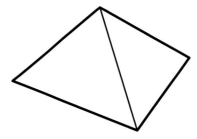

Double Door

1. Fold a sheet of paper in half from the top to the bottom. Then, unfold the paper.

2. Fold the top and bottom edges of the paper to the crease.

Appendix

Booklet

1. Fold a sheet of paper in half from left to right. Then, unfold the paper.

2. Fold the sheet of paper in half again from the top to the bottom. Then, unfold the paper.

3. Refold the sheet of paper in half from left to right.

4. Fold the top and bottom edges to the center crease.

5. Completely unfold the paper.

6. Refold the paper from top to bottom.

7. Using scissors, cut a slit along the center crease of the sheet from the folded edge to the creases made in step 4. Do not cut the entire sheet in half.

8. Fold the sheet of paper in half from left to right. While holding the bottom and top edges of the paper, push the bottom and top edges together so that the center collapses at the center slit. Fold the four flaps to form a four-page book.

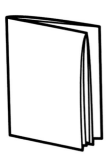

Layered Book

1. Lay one sheet of paper on top of another sheet. Slide the top sheet up so that 2 cm of the bottom sheet is showing.

2. Hold the two sheets together, fold down the top of the two sheets so that you see four 2 cm tabs along the bottom.

3. Using a stapler, staple the top of the FoldNote.

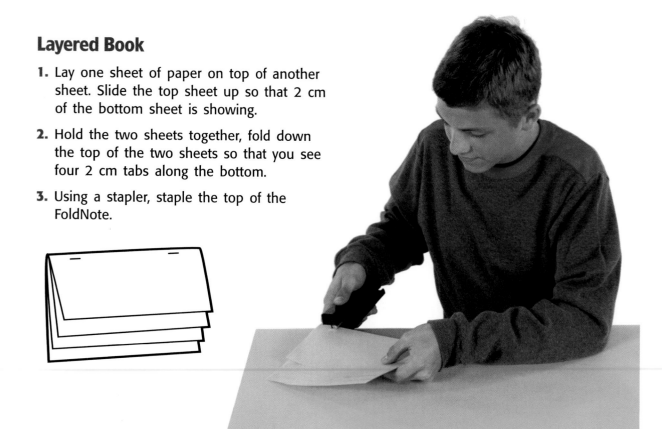

Key-Term Fold

1. Fold a sheet of lined notebook paper in half from left to right.

2. Using scissors, cut along every third line from the right edge of the paper to the center fold to make tabs.

Four-Corner Fold

1. Fold a sheet of paper in half from left to right. Then, unfold the paper.

2. Fold each side of the paper to the crease in the center of the paper.

3. Fold the paper in half from the top to the bottom. Then, unfold the paper.

4. Using scissors, cut the top flap creases made in step 3 to form four flaps.

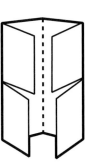

Three-Panel Flip Chart

1. Fold a piece of paper in half from the top to the bottom.

2. Fold the paper in thirds from side to side. Then, unfold the paper so that you can see the three sections.

3. From the top of the paper, cut along each of the vertical fold lines to the fold in the middle of the paper. You will now have three flaps.

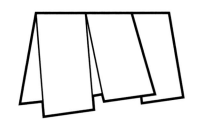

Table Fold

1. Fold a piece of paper in half from the top to the bottom. Then, fold the paper in half again.

2. Fold the paper in thirds from side to side.

3. Unfold the paper completely. Carefully trace the fold lines by using a pen or pencil.

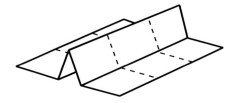

Two-Panel Flip Chart

1. Fold a piece of paper in half from the top to the bottom.

2. Fold the paper in half from side to side. Then, unfold the paper so that you can see the two sections.

3. From the top of the paper, cut along the vertical fold line to the fold in the middle of the paper. You will now have two flaps.

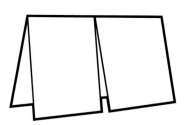

Tri-Fold

1. Fold a piece a paper in thirds from the top to the bottom.

2. Unfold the paper so that you can see the three sections. Then, turn the paper sideways so that the three sections form vertical columns.

3. Trace the fold lines by using a pen or pencil. Label the columns "Know," "Want," and "Learn."

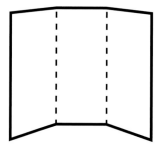

Appendix

Graphic Organizer Instructions

Have you ever wished that you could "draw out" the many concepts you learn in your science class? Sometimes, being able to *see* how concepts are related really helps you remember what you've learned. Graphic Organizers do just that! They give you a way to draw or map out concepts.

All you need to make a Graphic Organizer is a piece of paper and a pencil. Below you will find instructions for four different Graphic Organizers designed to help you organize the concepts you'll learn in this book.

Spider Map

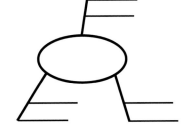

1. Draw a diagram like the one shown. In the circle, write the main topic.

2. From the circle, draw legs to represent different categories of the main topic. You can have as many categories as you want.

3. From the category legs, draw horizontal lines. As you read the chapter, write details about each category on the horizontal lines.

Comparison Table

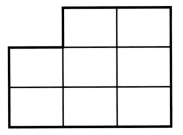

1. Draw a chart like the one shown. Your chart can have as many columns and rows as you want.

2. In the top row, write the topics that you want to compare.

3. In the left column, write characteristics of the topics that you want to compare. As you read the chapter, fill in the characteristics for each topic in the appropriate boxes.

Chain-of-Events-Chart

1. Draw a box. In the box, write the first step of a process or the first event of a timeline.

2. Under the box, draw another box, and use an arrow to connect the two boxes. In the second box, write the next step of the process or the next event in the timeline.

3. Continue adding boxes until the process or timeline is finished.

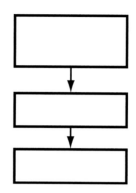

Concept Map

1. Draw a circle in the center of a piece of paper. Write the main idea of the chapter in the center of the circle.

2. From the circle, draw other circles. In those circles, write characteristics of the main idea. Draw arrows from the center circle to the circles that contain the characteristics.

3. From each circle that contains a characteristic, draw other circles. In those circles, write specific details about the characteristic. Draw arrows from each circle that contains a characteristic to the circles that contain specific details. You may draw as many circles as you want.

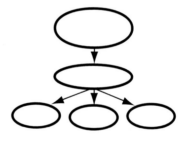

SI Measurement

The International System of Units, or SI, is the standard system of measurement used by many scientists. Using the same standards of measurement makes it easier for scientists to communicate with one another.

SI works by combining prefixes and base units. Each base unit can be used with different prefixes to define smaller and larger quantities. The table below lists common SI prefixes.

SI Prefixes

Prefix	Symbol	Factor	Example
kilo-	k	1,000	kilogram, 1 kg = 1,000 g
hecto-	h	100	hectoliter, 1 hL = 100 L
deka-	da	10	dekameter, 1 dam = 10 m
		1	meter, liter, gram
deci-	d	0.1	decigram, 1 dg = 0.1 g
centi-	c	0.01	centimeter, 1 cm = 0.01 m
milli-	m	0.001	milliliter, 1 mL = 0.001 L
micro-	μ	0.000 001	micrometer, 1 μm = 0.000 001 m

SI Conversion Table

SI units	From SI to English	From English to SI
Length		
kilometer (km) = 1,000 m	1 km = 0.621 mi	1 mi = 1.609 km
meter (m) = 100 cm	1 m = 3.281 ft	1 ft = 0.305 m
centimeter (cm) = 0.01 m	1 cm = 0.394 in.	1 in. = 2.540 cm
millimeter (mm) = 0.001 m	1 mm = 0.039 in.	
micrometer (μm) = 0.000 001 m		
nanometer (nm) = 0.000 000 001 m		
Area		
square kilometer (km^2) = 100 hectares	1 km^2 = 0.386 mi^2	1 mi^2 = 2.590 km^2
hectare (ha) = 10,000 m^2	1 ha = 2.471 acres	1 acre = 0.405 ha
square meter (m^2) = 10,000 cm^2	1 m^2 = 10.764 ft^2	1 ft^2 = 0.093 m^2
square centimeter (cm^2) = 100 mm^2	1 cm^2 = 0.155 in.^{2}	1 in.^{2} = 6.452 cm^2
Volume		
liter (L) = 1,000 mL = 1 dm^3	1 L = 1.057 fl qt	1 fl qt = 0.946 L
milliliter (mL) = 0.001 L = 1 cm^3	1 mL = 0.034 fl oz	1 fl oz = 29.574 mL
microliter (μL) = 0.000 001 L		
Mass		*Equivalent weight at Earth's surface
kilogram (kg) = 1,000 g	1 kg = 2.205 lb*	1 lb* = 0.454 kg
gram (g) = 1,000 mg	1 g = 0.035 oz*	1 oz* = 28.350 g
milligram (mg) = 0.001 g		
microgram (μg) = 0.000 001 g		

Scientific Methods

The ways in which scientists answer questions and solve problems are called **scientific methods.** The same steps are often used by scientists as they look for answers. However, there is more than one way to use these steps. Scientists may use all of the steps or just some of the steps during an investigation. They may even repeat some of the steps. The goal of using scientific methods is to come up with reliable answers and solutions.

Six Steps of Scientific Methods

Ask a Question Good questions come from careful **observations.** You make observations by using your senses to gather information. Sometimes, you may use instruments, such as microscopes and telescopes, to extend the range of your senses. As you observe the natural world, you will discover that you have many more questions than answers. These questions drive investigations.

Questions beginning with *what, why, how,* and *when* are important in focusing an investigation. Here is an example of a question that could lead to an investigation.

Question: How does acid rain affect plant growth?

Form a Hypothesis After you ask a question, you need to form a **hypothesis.** A hypothesis is a clear statement of what you expect the answer to your question to be. Your hypothesis will represent your best "educated guess" based on what you have observed and what you already know. A good hypothesis is testable. Otherwise, the investigation can go no further. Here is a hypothesis based on the question, "How does acid rain affect plant growth?"

Hypothesis: Acid rain slows plant growth.

The hypothesis can lead to predictions. A prediction is what you think the outcome of your experiment or data collection will be. Predictions are usually stated in an if-then format. Here is a sample prediction for the hypothesis that acid rain slows plant growth.

Prediction: If a plant is watered with only acid rain (which has a pH of 4), then the plant will grow at half its normal rate.

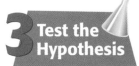

Test the Hypothesis After you have formed a hypothesis and made a prediction, your hypothesis should be tested. One way to test a hypothesis is with a controlled experiment. A **controlled experiment** tests only one factor at a time. In an experiment to test the effect of acid rain on plant growth, the **control group** would be watered with normal rain water. The **experimental group** would be watered with acid rain. All of the plants should receive the same amount of sunlight and water each day. The air temperature should be the same for all groups. However, the acidity of the water will be a variable. In fact, any factor that is different from one group to another is a **variable.** If your hypothesis is correct, then the acidity of the water and plant growth are *dependant variables.* The amount a plant grows is dependent on the acidity of the water. However, the amount of water each plant receives and the amount of sunlight each plant receives are *independent variables.* Either of these factors could change without affecting the other factor.

Sometimes, the nature of an investigation makes a controlled experiment impossible. For example, the Earth's core is surrounded by thousands of meters of rock. Under such circumstances, a hypothesis may be tested by making detailed observations.

Analyze the Results After you have completed your experiments, made your observations, and collected your data, you must analyze all the information you have gathered. Tables and graphs are often used in this step to organize the data.

5 Draw Conclusions

After analyzing your data, you can determine if your results support your hypothesis. If your hypothesis is supported, you (or others) might want to repeat the observations or experiments to verify your results. If your hypothesis is not supported by the data, you may have to check your procedure for errors. You may even have to reject your hypothesis and make a new one. If you cannot draw a conclusion from your results, you may have to try the investigation again or carry out further observations or experiments.

6 Communicate Results

After any scientific investigation, you should report your results. By preparing a written or oral report, you let others know what you have learned. They may repeat your investigation to see if they get the same results. Your report may even lead to another question and then to another investigation.

Scientific Methods in Action

Scientific methods contain loops in which several steps may be repeated over and over again. In some cases, certain steps are unnecessary. Thus, there is not a "straight line" of steps. For example, sometimes scientists find that testing one hypothesis raises new questions and new hypotheses to be tested. And sometimes, testing the hypothesis leads directly to a conclusion. Furthermore, the steps in scientific methods are not always used in the same order. Follow the steps in the diagram, and see how many different directions scientific methods can take you.

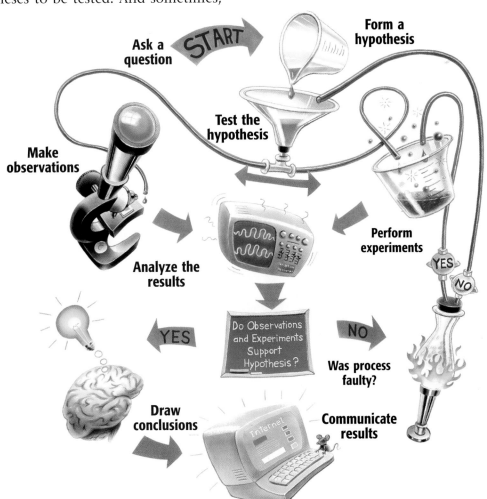

Making Charts and Graphs

Pie Charts

A pie chart shows how each group of data relates to all of the data. Each part of the circle forming the chart represents a category of the data. The entire circle represents all of the data. For example, a biologist studying a hardwood forest in Wisconsin found that there were five different types of trees. The data table at right summarizes the biologist's findings.

Wisconsin Hardwood Trees	
Type of tree	Number found
Oak	600
Maple	750
Beech	300
Birch	1,200
Hickory	150
Total	3,000

How to Make a Pie Chart

1 To make a pie chart of these data, first find the percentage of each type of tree. Divide the number of trees of each type by the total number of trees, and multiply by 100.

$$\frac{600 \text{ oak}}{3,000 \text{ trees}} \times 100 = 20\%$$

$$\frac{750 \text{ maple}}{3,000 \text{ trees}} \times 100 = 25\%$$

$$\frac{300 \text{ beech}}{3,000 \text{ trees}} \times 100 = 10\%$$

$$\frac{1,200 \text{ birch}}{3,000 \text{ trees}} \times 100 = 40\%$$

$$\frac{150 \text{ hickory}}{3,000 \text{ trees}} \times 100 = 5\%$$

2 Now, determine the size of the wedges that make up the pie chart. Multiply each percentage by 360°. Remember that a circle contains 360°.

$20\% \times 360° = 72°$ $25\% \times 360° = 90°$

$10\% \times 360° = 36°$ $40\% \times 360° = 144°$

$5\% \times 360° = 18°$

3 Check that the sum of the percentages is 100 and the sum of the degrees is 360.

$20\% + 25\% + 10\% + 40\% + 5\% = 100\%$

$72° + 90° + 36° + 144° + 18° = 360°$

4 Use a compass to draw a circle and mark the center of the circle.

5 Then, use a protractor to draw angles of 72°, 90°, 36°, 144°, and 18° in the circle.

6 Finally, label each part of the chart, and choose an appropriate title.

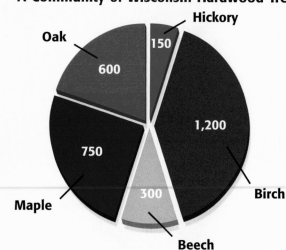

A Community of Wisconsin Hardwood Trees

Line Graphs

Line graphs are most often used to demonstrate continuous change. For example, Mr. Smith's students analyzed the population records for their hometown, Appleton, between 1900 and 2000. Examine the data at right.

Because the year and the population change, they are the *variables*. The population is determined by, or dependent on, the year. Therefore, the population is called the **dependent variable,** and the year is called the **independent variable.** Each set of data is called a **data pair.** To prepare a line graph, you must first organize data pairs into a table like the one at right.

Population of Appleton, 1900–2000	
Year	Population
1900	1,800
1920	2,500
1940	3,200
1960	3,900
1980	4,600
2000	5,300

How to Make a Line Graph

1 Place the independent variable along the horizontal (*x*) axis. Place the dependent variable along the vertical (*y*) axis.

2 Label the *x*-axis "Year" and the *y*-axis "Population." Look at your largest and smallest values for the population. For the *y*-axis, determine a scale that will provide enough space to show these values. You must use the same scale for the entire length of the axis. Next, find an appropriate scale for the *x*-axis.

3 Choose reasonable starting points for each axis.

4 Plot the data pairs as accurately as possible.

5 Choose a title that accurately represents the data.

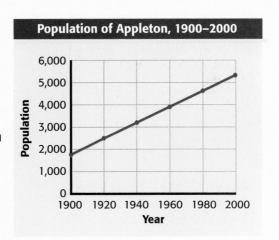

How to Determine Slope

Slope is the ratio of the change in the *y*-value to the change in the *x*-value, or "rise over run."

1 Choose two points on the line graph. For example, the population of Appleton in 2000 was 5,300 people. Therefore, you can define point *a* as (2000, 5,300). In 1900, the population was 1,800 people. You can define point *b* as (1900, 1,800).

2 Find the change in the *y*-value.
(*y* at point *a*) − (*y* at point *b*) =
5,300 people − 1,800 people =
3,500 people

3 Find the change in the *x*-value.
(*x* at point *a*) − (*x* at point *b*) =
2000 − 1900 = 100 years

4 Calculate the slope of the graph by dividing the change in *y* by the change in *x*.

$$slope = \frac{change\ in\ y}{change\ in\ x}$$

$$slope = \frac{3,500\ people}{100\ years}$$

$$slope = 35\ people\ per\ year$$

In this example, the population in Appleton increased by a fixed amount each year. The graph of these data is a straight line. Therefore, the relationship is **linear.** When the graph of a set of data is not a straight line, the relationship is **nonlinear.**

Using Algebra to Determine Slope

The equation in step 4 may also be arranged to be

$$y = kx$$

where y represents the change in the y-value, k represents the slope, and x represents the change in the x-value.

$$slope = \frac{change\ in\ y}{change\ in\ x}$$

$$k = \frac{y}{x}$$

$$k \times x = \frac{y \times x}{x}$$

$$kx = y$$

Bar Graphs

Bar graphs are used to demonstrate change that is not continuous. These graphs can be used to indicate trends when the data cover a long period of time. A meteorologist gathered the precipitation data shown here for Hartford, Connecticut, for April 1–15, 1996, and used a bar graph to represent the data.

Precipitation in Hartford, Connecticut April 1–15, 1996			
Date	Precipitation (cm)	Date	Precipitation (cm)
April 1	0.5	April 9	0.25
April 2	1.25	April 10	0.0
April 3	0.0	April 11	1.0
April 4	0.0	April 12	0.0
April 5	0.0	April 13	0.25
April 6	0.0	April 14	0.0
April 7	0.0	April 15	6.50
April 8	1.75		

How to Make a Bar Graph

1. Use an appropriate scale and a reasonable starting point for each axis.

2. Label the axes, and plot the data.

3. Choose a title that accurately represents the data.

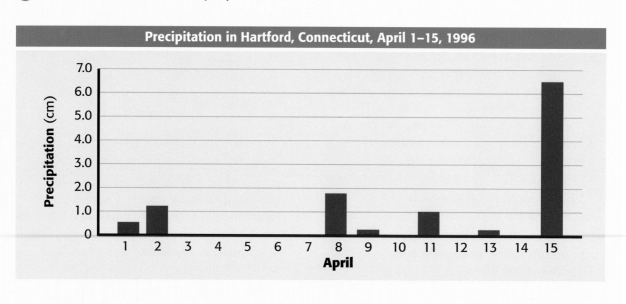

Math Refresher

Science requires an understanding of many math concepts. The following pages will help you review some important math skills.

Averages

An **average**, or **mean**, simplifies a set of numbers into a single number that *approximates* the value of the set.

> **Example:** Find the average of the following set of numbers: 5, 4, 7, and 8.

Step 1: Find the sum.

$$5 + 4 + 7 + 8 = 24$$

Step 2: Divide the sum by the number of numbers in your set. Because there are four numbers in this example, divide the sum by 4.

$$\frac{24}{4} = 6$$

The average, or mean, is **6.**

Ratios

A **ratio** is a comparison between numbers, and it is usually written as a fraction.

> **Example:** Find the ratio of thermometers to students if you have 36 thermometers and 48 students in your class.

Step 1: Make the ratio.

$$\frac{36 \text{ thermometers}}{48 \text{ students}}$$

Step 2: Reduce the fraction to its simplest form.

$$\frac{36}{48} = \frac{36 \div 12}{48 \div 12} = \frac{3}{4}$$

The ratio of thermometers to students is **3 to 4,** or $\frac{3}{4}$. The ratio may also be written in the form 3:4.

Proportions

A **proportion** is an equation that states that two ratios are equal.

$$\frac{3}{1} = \frac{12}{4}$$

To solve a proportion, first multiply across the equal sign. This is called *cross-multiplication*. If you know three of the quantities in a proportion, you can use cross-multiplication to find the fourth.

> **Example:** Imagine that you are making a scale model of the solar system for your science project. The diameter of Jupiter is 11.2 times the diameter of the Earth. If you are using a plastic-foam ball that has a diameter of 2 cm to represent the Earth, what must the diameter of the ball representing Jupiter be?
>
> $$\frac{11.2}{1} = \frac{x}{2 \text{ cm}}$$

Step 1: Cross-multiply.

$$\frac{11.2}{1} \diagdown\!\!\!\!\diagup \frac{x}{2}$$

$$11.2 \times 2 = x \times 1$$

Step 2: Multiply.

$$22.4 = x \times 1$$

Step 3: Isolate the variable by dividing both sides by 1.

$$x = \frac{22.4}{1}$$

$$x = 22.4 \text{ cm}$$

You will need to use a ball that has a diameter of **22.4** cm to represent Jupiter.

Appendix

Percentages

A **percentage** is a ratio of a given number to 100.

> **Example:** What is 85% of 40?

Step 1: Rewrite the percentage by moving the decimal point two places to the left.

$$0.\underset{\smile}{85}$$

Step 2: Multiply the decimal by the number that you are calculating the percentage of.

$$0.85 \times 40 = 34$$

85% of 40 is **34.**

Decimals

To **add** or **subtract decimals,** line up the digits vertically so that the decimal points line up. Then, add or subtract the columns from right to left. Carry or borrow numbers as necessary.

> **Example:** Add the following numbers: 3.1415 and 2.96.

Step 1: Line up the digits vertically so that the decimal points line up.

$$\begin{array}{r} 3.1415 \\ + \ 2.96 \\ \hline \end{array}$$

Step 2: Add the columns from right to left, and carry when necessary.

$$\begin{array}{r} {}^{1}\ {}^{1} \\ 3.1415 \\ + \ 2.96 \\ \hline 6.1015 \end{array}$$

The sum is **6.1015.**

Fractions

Numbers tell you how many; **fractions** tell you *how much of a whole*.

> **Example:** Your class has 24 plants. Your teacher instructs you to put 5 plants in a shady spot. What fraction of the plants in your class will you put in a shady spot?

Step 1: In the denominator, write the total number of parts in the whole.

$$\frac{?}{24}$$

Step 2: In the numerator, write the number of parts of the whole that are being considered.

$$\frac{5}{24}$$

So, $\frac{5}{24}$ of the plants will be in the shade.

Reducing Fractions

It is usually best to express a fraction in its simplest form. Expressing a fraction in its simplest form is called *reducing* a fraction.

> **Example:** Reduce the fraction $\frac{30}{45}$ to its simplest form.

Step 1: Find the largest whole number that will divide evenly into both the numerator and denominator. This number is called the *greatest common factor* (GCF).

Factors of the numerator 30:
  1, 2, 3, 5, 6, 10, **15,** 30

Factors of the denominator 45:
  1, 3, 5, 9, **15,** 45

Step 2: Divide both the numerator and the denominator by the GCF, which in this case is 15.

$$\frac{30}{45} = \frac{30 \div 15}{45 \div 15} = \frac{2}{3}$$

Thus, $\frac{30}{45}$ reduced to its simplest form is $\frac{2}{3}$.

Adding and Subtracting Fractions

To **add** or **subtract fractions** that have the **same denominator,** simply add or subtract the numerators.

Examples:

$$\frac{3}{5} + \frac{1}{5} = ? \text{ and } \frac{3}{4} - \frac{1}{4} = ?$$

Step 1: Add or subtract the numerators.

$$\frac{3}{5} + \frac{1}{5} = \frac{4}{} \text{ and } \frac{3}{4} - \frac{1}{4} = \frac{2}{}$$

Step 2: Write the sum or difference over the denominator.

$$\frac{3}{5} + \frac{1}{5} = \frac{4}{5} \text{ and } \frac{3}{4} - \frac{1}{4} = \frac{2}{4}$$

Step 3: If necessary, reduce the fraction to its simplest form.

$\frac{4}{5}$ cannot be reduced, and $\frac{2}{4} = \frac{1}{2}$.

To **add** or **subtract fractions** that have **different denominators,** first find the least common denominator (LCD).

Examples:

$$\frac{1}{2} + \frac{1}{6} = ? \text{ and } \frac{3}{4} - \frac{2}{3} = ?$$

Step 1: Write the equivalent fractions that have a common denominator.

$$\frac{3}{6} + \frac{1}{6} = ? \text{ and } \frac{9}{12} - \frac{8}{12} = ?$$

Step 2: Add or subtract the fractions.

$$\frac{3}{6} + \frac{1}{6} = \frac{4}{6} \text{ and } \frac{9}{12} - \frac{8}{12} = \frac{1}{12}$$

Step 3: If necessary, reduce the fraction to its simplest form.

The fraction $\frac{4}{6} = \frac{2}{3}$, and $\frac{1}{12}$ cannot be reduced.

Multiplying Fractions

To **multiply fractions,** multiply the numerators and the denominators together, and then reduce the fraction to its simplest form.

Example:

$$\frac{5}{9} \times \frac{7}{10} = ?$$

Step 1: Multiply the numerators and denominators.

$$\frac{5}{9} \times \frac{7}{10} = \frac{5 \times 7}{9 \times 10} = \frac{35}{90}$$

Step 2: Reduce the fraction.

$$\frac{35}{90} = \frac{35 \div 5}{90 \div 5} = \frac{7}{18}$$

Dividing Fractions

To **divide fractions,** first rewrite the divisor (the number you divide by) upside down. This number is called the *reciprocal* of the divisor. Then multiply and reduce if necessary.

Example:

$$\frac{5}{8} \div \frac{3}{2} = ?$$

Step 1: Rewrite the divisor as its reciprocal.

$$\frac{3}{2} \rightarrow \frac{2}{3}$$

Step 2: Multiply the fractions.

$$\frac{5}{8} \times \frac{2}{3} = \frac{5 \times 2}{8 \times 3} = \frac{10}{24}$$

Step 3: Reduce the fraction.

$$\frac{10}{24} = \frac{10 \div 2}{24 \div 2} = \frac{5}{12}$$

Appendix

Scientific Notation

Scientific notation is a short way of representing very large and very small numbers without writing all of the place-holding zeros.

Example: Write 653,000,000 in scientific notation.

Step 1: Write the number without the place-holding zeros.

653

Step 2: Place the decimal point after the first digit.

6.53

Step 3: Find the exponent by counting the number of places that you moved the decimal point.

6.53000000

The decimal point was moved eight places to the left. Therefore, the exponent of 10 is positive 8. If you had moved the decimal point to the right, the exponent would be negative.

Step 4: Write the number in scientific notation.

$$6.53 \times 10^8$$

Area

Area is the number of square units needed to cover the surface of an object.

Formulas:

area of a square = side × side
area of a rectangle = length × width
area of a triangle = $\frac{1}{2}$ × base × height

Examples: Find the areas.

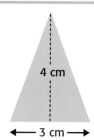

Triangle

area = $\frac{1}{2}$ × base × height

area = $\frac{1}{2}$ × 3 cm × 4 cm

area = **6 cm²**

4 cm

3 cm

Rectangle

area = length × width
area = 6 cm × 3 cm
area = **18 cm²**

3 cm

6 cm

Square

area = side × side
area = 3 cm × 3 cm
area = **9 cm²**

3 cm

3 cm

Volume

Volume is the amount of space that something occupies.

Formulas:

volume of a cube =
side × side × side

volume of a prism =
area of base × height

Examples:

Find the volume of the solids.

Cube

volume = side × side × side
volume = 4 cm × 4 cm × 4 cm
volume = **64 cm³**

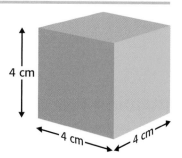

4 cm

4 cm

4 cm

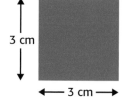

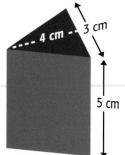

4 cm

3 cm

5 cm

Prism

volume = area of base × height
volume = (area of triangle) × height
volume = ($\frac{1}{2}$ × 3 cm × 4 cm) × 5 cm
volume = 6 cm² × 5 cm
volume = **30 cm³**

Physical Science Laws and Principles

Law of Conservation of Mass

Mass cannot be created or destroyed during ordinary chemical or physical changes.

The total mass in a closed system is always the same no matter how many physical changes or chemical reactions occur.

Law of Conservation of Energy

Energy can be neither created nor destroyed.

The total amount of energy in a closed system is always the same. Energy can be changed from one form to another, but all of the different forms of energy in a system always add up to the same total amount of energy no matter how many energy conversions occur.

Law of Universal Gravitation

All objects in the universe attract each other by a force called *gravity*. The size of the force depends on the masses of the objects and the distance between the objects.

The first part of the law explains why lifting a bowling ball is much harder than lifting a marble. Because the bowling ball has a much larger mass than the marble does, the amount of gravity between the Earth and the bowling ball is greater than the amount of gravity between the Earth and the marble.

The second part of the law explains why a satellite can remain in orbit around the Earth. The satellite is carefully placed at a distance great enough to prevent the Earth's gravity from immediately pulling the satellite down but small enough to prevent the satellite from completely escaping the Earth's gravity and wandering off into space.

Newton's Laws of Motion

Newton's first law of motion states that an object at rest remains at rest and an object in motion remains in motion at constant speed and in a straight line unless acted on by an unbalanced force.

The first part of the law explains why a football will remain on a tee until it is kicked off or until a gust of wind blows it off.

The second part of the law explains why a bike rider will continue moving forward after the bike comes to an abrupt stop. Gravity and the friction of the sidewalk will eventually stop the rider.

Newton's second law of motion states that the acceleration of an object depends on the mass of the object and the amount of force applied.

The first part of the law explains why the acceleration of a 4 kg bowling ball will be greater than the acceleration of a 6 kg bowling ball if the same force is applied to both balls.

The second part of the law explains why the acceleration of a bowling ball will be larger if a larger force is applied to the bowling ball.

The relationship of acceleration (*a*) to mass (*m*) and force (*F*) can be expressed mathematically by the following equation:

$$acceleration = \frac{force}{mass}, \text{ or } a = \frac{F}{m}$$

This equation is often rearranged to the form

$$force = mass \times acceleration, \text{ or } F = m \times a$$

Newton's third law of motion states that whenever one object exerts a force on a second object, the second object exerts an equal and opposite force on the first.

This law explains that a runner is able to move forward because of the equal and opposite force that the ground exerts on the runner's foot after each step.

Law of Reflection

The law of reflection states that the angle of incidence is equal to the angle of reflection. This law explains why light reflects off a surface at the same angle that the light strikes the surface.

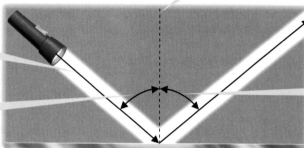

The beam of light traveling toward the mirror is called the *incident beam.*

A line perpendicular to the mirror's surface is called the *normal.*

The beam of light reflected off the mirror is called the *reflected beam.*

The angle between the incident beam and the normal is called the *angle of incidence.*

The angle between the reflected beam and the normal is called the *angle of reflection.*

Charles's Law

Charles's law states that for a fixed amount of gas at a constant pressure, the volume of the gas increases as the temperature of the gas increases. Likewise, the volume of the gas decreases as the temperature of the gas decreases.

If a basketball that was inflated indoors is left outside on a cold winter day, the air particles inside the ball will move more slowly. They will hit the sides of the basketball less often and with less force. The ball will get smaller as the volume of the air decreases.

Boyle's Law

Boyle's law states that for a fixed amount of gas at a constant temperature, the volume of a gas increases as the pressure of the gas decreases. Likewise, the volume of a gas decreases as its pressure increases.

If an inflated balloon is pulled down to the bottom of a swimming pool, the pressure of the water on the balloon increases. The pressure of the air particles inside the balloon must increase to match that of the water outside, so the volume of the air inside the balloon decreases.

Pascal's Principle

Pascal's principle states that a change in pressure at any point in an enclosed fluid will be transmitted equally to all parts of that fluid.

When a mechanic uses a hydraulic jack to raise an automobile off the ground, he or she increases the pressure on the fluid in the jack by pushing on the jack handle. The pressure is transmitted equally to all parts of the fluid-filled jacking system. As fluid presses the jack plate against the frame of the car, the car is lifed off the ground.

Archimedes' Principle

Archimedes' principle states that the buoyant force on an object in a fluid is equal to the weight of the volume of fluid that the object displaces.

A person floating in a swimming pool displaces 20 L of water. The weight of that volume of water is about 200 N. Therefore, the buoyant force on the person is 200 N.

Bernoulli's Principle

Bernoulli's principle states that as the speed of a moving fluid increases, the fluid's pressure decreases.

The lift on an airplane wing or on a Frisbee® can be explained in part by using Bernoulli's principle. Because of the shape of the Frisbee, the air moving over the top of the Frisbee must travel farther than the air below the Frisbee in the same amount of time. In other words, the air above the Frisbee is moving faster than the air below it. This faster-moving air above the Frisbee exerts less pressure than the slower-moving air below it does. The resulting increased pressure below exerts an upward force and pushes the Frisbee up.

Useful Equations

Average speed

$$average\ speed = \frac{total\ distance}{total\ time}$$

Example: A bicycle messenger traveled a distance of 136 km in 8 h. What was the messenger's average speed?

$$\frac{136\ km}{8\ h} = 17\ km/h$$

The messenger's average speed was **17 km/h.**

Average acceleration

$$\frac{average}{acceleration} = \frac{final\ velocity - starting\ velocity}{time\ it\ takes\ to\ change\ velocity}$$

Example: Calculate the average acceleration of an Olympic 100 m dash sprinter who reaches a velocity of 20 m/s south at the finish line. The race was in a straight line and lasted 10 s.

$$\frac{20\ m/s - 0\ m/s}{10s} = 2\ m/s/s$$

The sprinter's average acceleration is **2 m/s/s south.**

Net force

Forces in the Same Direction
When forces are in the same direction, add the forces together to determine the net force.

Example: Calculate the net force on a stalled car that is being pushed by two people. One person is pushing with a force of 13 N northwest, and the other person is pushing with a force of 8 N in the same direction.

$$13\ N + 8\ N = 21\ N$$

The net force is **21 N northwest.**

Forces in Opposite Directions
When forces are in opposite directions, subtract the smaller force from the larger force to determine the net force. The net force will be in the direction of the larger force.

Example: Calculate the net force on a rope that is being pulled on each end. One person is pulling on one end of the rope with a force of 12 N south. Another person is pulling on the opposite end of the rope with a force of 7 N north.

$$12\ N - 7\ N = 5\ N$$

The net force is **5 N south.**

Work

Work is done by exerting a force through a distance. Work has units of joules (J), which are equivalent to Newton-meters.

$$Work = F \times d$$

Example: Calculate the amount of work done by a man who lifts a 100 N toddler 1.5 m off the floor.

$Work = 100 \text{ N} \times 1.5 \text{ m} = 150 \text{ N} \cdot \text{m} = 150 \text{ J}$

The man did **150 J** of work.

Power

Power is the rate at which work is done. Power is measured in watts (W), which are equivalent to joules per second.

$$P = \frac{Work}{t}$$

Example: Calculate the power of a weightlifter who raises a 300 N barbell 2.1 m off the floor in 1.25 s.

$Work = 300 \text{ N} \times 2.1 \text{ m} = 630 \text{ N} \cdot \text{m} = 630 \text{ J}$

$$P = \frac{630 \text{ J}}{1.25 \text{ s}} = \frac{504 \text{ J}}{\text{s}} = 504 \text{ W}$$

The weightlifter has **504 W** of power.

Pressure

Pressure is the force exerted over a given area. The SI unit for pressure is the pascal (Pa).

$$pressure = \frac{force}{area}$$

Example: Calculate the pressure of the air in a soccer ball if the air exerts a force of 25,000 N over an area of 0.15 m².

$$pressure = \frac{25,000 \text{ N}}{0.15 \text{ m}^2} = \frac{167,000 \text{ N}}{\text{m}^2} = 167,000 \text{ Pa}$$

The pressure of the air inside the soccer ball is **167,000 Pa.**

Density

$$density = \frac{mass}{volume}$$

Example: Calculate the density of a sponge that has a mass of 10 g and a volume of 40 cm³.

$$\frac{10 \text{ g}}{40 \text{ cm}^3} = \frac{0.25 \text{ g}}{\text{cm}^3}$$

The density of the sponge is $\frac{0.25 \text{ g}}{\text{cm}^3}$.

Concentration

$$concentration = \frac{mass \ of \ solute}{volume \ of \ solvent}$$

Example: Calculate the concentration of a solution in which 10 g of sugar is dissolved in 125 mL of water.

$$\frac{10 \text{ g of sugar}}{125 \text{ mL of water}} = \frac{0.08 \text{ g}}{\text{mL}}$$

The concentration of this solution is $\frac{0.08 \text{ g}}{\text{mL}}$.

Glossary

A

absolute zero the temperature at which molecular energy is at a minimum (0 K on the Kelvin scale or -273.16°C on the Celsius scale) (161)

acceleration (ak SEL uhr AY shuhn) the rate at which velocity changes over time; an object accelerates if its speed, direction, or both change (7)

Archimedes' principle (AHR kuh MEE DEEZ PRIN suh puhl) the principle that states that the buoyant force on an object in a fluid is an upward force equal to the weight of the volume of fluid that the object displaces (72)

atmospheric pressure the pressure caused by the weight of the atmosphere (67)

B

Bernoulli's principle (ber NOO leez PRIN suh puhl) the principle that states that the pressure in a fluid decreases as the fluid's velocity increases (78)

buoyant force (BOY uhnt FAWRS) the upward force that keeps an object immersed in or floating on a liquid (72)

C

change of state the change of a substance from one physical state to another (173)

compound machine a machine made of more than one simple machine (112)

convection the transfer of thermal energy by the circulation or movement of a liquid or gas (167)

D

drag a force parallel to the velocity of the flow; it opposes the direction of an aircraft and, in combination with thrust, determines the speed (81)

E

energy the capacity to do work (10)

energy conversion a change from one form of energy to another (132)

F

fluid a nonsolid state of matter in which the atoms or molecules are free to move past each other, as in a gas or liquid (66)

force a push or a pull exerted on an object in order to change the motion of the object; force has size and direction (10)

fossil fuel a nonrenewable energy resource formed from the remains of organisms that lived long ago (142)

free fall the motion of a body when only the force of gravity is acting on the body (39)

friction a force that opposes motion between two surfaces that are in contact (14)

G

gravity a force of attraction between objects that is due to their masses (20)

H

heat the energy transferred between objects that are at different temperatures (164)

heat engine a machine that transforms heat into mechanical energy, or work (179)

I

inclined plane a simple machine that is a straight, slanted surface, which facilitates the raising of loads; a ramp (110)

inertia (in UHR shuh) the tendency of an object to resist being moved or, if the object is moving, to resist a change in speed or direction until an outside force acts on the object (46)

insulation a substance that reduces the transfer of electricity, heat, or sound (177)

J

joule the unit used to express energy; equivalent to the amount of work done by a force of 1 N acting through a distance of 1 m in the direction of the force (symbol, J) (97)

K

kinetic energy (ki NET ik EN uhr jee) the energy of an object that is due to the object's motion (11)

L

law of conservation of energy the law that states that energy cannot be created or destroyed but can be changed from one form to another (139)

lever a simple machine that consists of a bar that pivots at a fixed point called a *fulcrum* (106)

lift an upward force on an object that moves in a fluid (79)

M

machine a device that helps do work by either overcoming a force or changing the direction of the applied force (100)

mass a measure of the amount of matter in an object (24)

mechanical advantage a number that tells how many times a machine multiplies force (103)

mechanical efficiency (muh KAN i kuhl e FISH uhn see) the ratio of output to input of energy or of power; it can be calculated by dividing work output by work input (104)

mechanical energy the amount of work an object can do because of the object's kinetic and potential energies (127)

momentum (moh MEN tuhm) a quantity defined as the product of the mass and velocity of an object (52)

motion an object's change in position relative to a reference point (4)

N

net force the combination of all of the forces acting on an object (11)

newton the SI unit for force (symbol, N) (10)

nonrenewable resource a resource that forms at a rate that is much slower than the rate at which it is consumed (142)

P

pascal the SI unit of pressure (symbol, Pa) (66)

Pascal's principle the principle that states that a fluid in equilibrium contained in a vessel exerts a pressure of equal intensity in all directions (82)

potential energy the energy that an object has because of the position, shape, or condition of the object (126)

power the rate at which work is done or energy is transformed (98)

pressure the amount of force exerted per unit area of a surface (66)

projectile motion (proh JEK tuhl MOH shuhn) the curved path that an object follows when thrown, launched, or otherwise projected near the surface of Earth (41)

pulley a simple machine that consists of a wheel over which a rope, chain, or wire passes (108)

R

radiation the transfer of energy as electromagnetic waves (168)

renewable resource a natural resource that can be replaced at the same rate at which the resource is consumed (145)

S

screw a simple machine that consists of an inclined plane wrapped around a cylinder (111)

specific heat the quantity of heat required to raise a unit mass of homogeneous material 1 K or 1°C in a specified way given constant pressure and volume (169)

speed the distance traveled divided by the time interval during which the motion occurred (5)

states of matter the physical forms of matter, which include solid, liquid, and gas (172)

T

temperature a measure of how hot (or cold) something is; specifically, a measure of the average kinetic energy of the particles in an object (158)

terminal velocity the constant velocity of a falling object when the force of air resistance is equal in magnitude and opposite in direction to the force of gravity (38)

thermal conduction the transfer of energy as heat through a material (282)

thermal conductor a material through which energy can be transferred as heat (167)

thermal energy the kinetic energy of a substance's atoms (165)

thermal expansion an increase in the size of a substance in response to an increase in the temperature of the substance (46)

thermal insulator a material that reduces or prevents the transfer of heat (167)

thermal pollution a temperature increase in a body of water that is caused by human activity and that has a harmful effect on water quality and on the ability of that body of water to support life (182)

thrust the pushing or pulling force exerted by the engine of an aircraft or rocket (80)

Glossary

V

velocity (vuh LAHS uh tee) the speed of an object in a particular direction (6)

W

watt the unit used to express power; equivalent to joules per second (symbol, W) (98)

wedge a simple machine that is made up of two inclined planes and that moves; often used for cutting (111)

weight a measure of the gravitational force exerted on an object; its value can change with the location of the object in the universe (24)

wheel and axle a simple machine consisting of two circular objects of different sizes; the wheel is the larger of the two circular objects (109)

work the transfer of energy to an object by using a force that causes the object to move in the direction of the force (94)

work input the work done on a machine; the product of the input force and the distance through which the force is exerted (101)

work output the work done by a machine; the product of the output force and the distance through which the force is exerted (101)

Spanish Glossary

A

absolute zero/cero absoluto la temperatura a la que la energía molecular es mínima (0 K en la escala de Kelvin ó −273.16°C en la escala de Celsius) (161)

acceleration/aceleración la tasa a la que la velocidad cambia con el tiempo; un objeto acelera si su rapidez cambia, si su dirección cambia, o si tanto su rapidez como su dirección cambian (7)

Archimedes' principle/principio de Arquímedes el principio que establece que la fuerza flotante de un objeto que está en un fluido es una fuerza ascendente cuya magnitud es igual al peso del volumen del fluido que el objeto desplaza (72)

atmospheric pressure/presión atmosférica la presión producida por el peso de la atmósfera (67)

B

Bernoulli's principle/principio de Bernoulli el principio que establece que la presión de un fluido disminuye a medida que la velocidad del fluido aumenta (78)

buoyant force/fuerza boyante la fuerza ascendente que hace que un objeto se mantenga sumergido en un líquido o flotando en él (72)

C

change of state/cambio de estado el cambio de una substancia de un estado físico a otro (173)

compound machine/máquina compuesta una máquina hecha de más de una máquina simple (112)

convection/convección la transferencia de energía térmica mediante la circulación o el movimiento de un líquido o gas (167)

D

drag/resistencia aerodinámica una fuerza paralela a la velocidad del flujo; se opone a la dirección de un avión y, en combinación con el empuje, determina la velocidad del avión (81)

E

energy/energía la capacidad de realizar un trabajo (10)

energy conversion/transformación de energía un cambio de un tipo de energía a otro (132)

F

fluid/fluido un estado no sólido de la materia en el que los átomos o moléculas tienen libertad de movimiento, como en el caso de un gas o un líquido (66)

force/fuerza una acción de empuje o atracción que se ejerce sobre un objeto con el fin de cambiar su movimiento; la fuerza tiene magnitud y dirección (10)

fossil fuel/combustible fósil un recurso energético no renovable formado a partir de los restos de organismos que vivieron hace mucho tiempo (142)

free fall/caída libre el movimiento de un cuerpo cuando la única fuerza que actúa sobre él es la fuerza de gravedad (39)

friction/fricción una fuerza que se opone al movimiento entre dos superficies que están en contacto (14)

G

gravity/gravedad una fuerza de atracción entre dos objetos debido a sus masas (20)

H

heat/calor la transferencia de energía entre objetos que están a temperaturas diferentes (164)

heat engine/motor térmico una máquina que transforma el calor en energía mecánica, o trabajo (179)

I

inclined plane/plano inclinado una máquina simple que es una superficie recta e inclinada, que facilita el levantamiento de cargas; una rampa (110)

inertia/inercia la tendencia de un objeto a no moverse o, si el objeto se está moviendo, la tendencia a resistir un cambio en su rapidez o dirección hasta que una fuerza externa actúe en el objeto (46)

insulation/aislante una substancia que reduce la transferencia de electricidad, calor o sonido (177)

J

joule/joule la unidad que se usa para expresar energía; equivale a la cantidad de trabajo realizada por una fuerza de 1 N que actúa a través de una distancia de 1 m en la dirección de la fuerza (símbolo: J) (97)

K

kinetic energy/energía cinética la energía de un objeto debido al movimiento del objeto (11)

L

law of conservation of energy/ley de la conservación de la energía la ley que establece que la energía ni se crea ni se destruye, sólo se transforma de una forma a otra (139)

lever/palanca una máquina simple formada por una barra que gira en un punto fijo llamado fulcro (106)

lift/propulsión una fuerza hacia arriba en un objeto que se mueve en un fluido (79)

M

machine/máquina un aparato que ayuda a realizar un trabajo, ya sea venciendo una fuerza o cambiando la dirección de la fuerza aplicada (100)

mass/masa una medida de la cantidad de materia que tiene un objeto (24)

mechanical advantage/ventaja mecánica un número que dice cuántas veces una máquina multiplica una fuerza (103)

mechanical efficiency/eficiencia mecánica la relación entre la entrada y la salida de energía o potencia; se calcula dividiendo la salida de trabajo por la entrada de trabajo (104)

mechanical energy/energía mecánica la cantidad de trabajo que un objeto realiza debido a las energías cinética y potencial del objeto (127)

momentum/momento una cantidad que se define como el producto de la masa de un objeto por su velocidad (52)

motion/movimiento el cambio en la posición de un objeto respecto a un punto de referencia (4)

N

net force/fuerza neta la combinación de todas las fuerzas que actúan sobre un objeto (11)

newton/newton la unidad de fuerza del sistema internacional de unidades (símbolo: N) (10)

nonrenewable resource/recurso no renovable un recurso que se forma a una tasa que es mucho más lenta que la tasa a la que se consume (142)

P

pascal/pascal la unidad de presión del sistema internacional de unidades (símbolo: Pa) (66)

Pascal's principle/principio de Pascal el principio que establece que un fluido en equilibro que esté contenido en un recipiente ejerce una presión de igual intensidad en todas las direcciones (82)

potential energy/energía potencial la energía que tiene un objeto debido a su posición, forma o condición (126)

power/potencia la tasa a la que se realiza un trabajo o a la que se transforma la energía (98)

pressure/presión la cantidad de fuerza ejercida en una superficie por unidad de área (66)

projectile motion/movimiento proyectil la trayectoria curva que sigue un objeto cuando es aventado, lanzado o proyectado de cualquier otra manera cerca de la superficie de la Tierra (41)

pulley/polea una máquina simple formada por una rueda sobre la cual pasa una cuerda, cadena o cable (108)

R

radiation/radiación la transferencia de energía en forma de ondas electromagnéticas (168)

renewable resource/recurso renovable un recurso natural que puede reemplazarse a la misma tasa a la que se consume (145)

S

screw/tornillo una máquina simple formada por un plano inclinado enrollado a un cilindro (111)

specific heat/calor específico la cantidad de calor que se requiere para aumentar una unidad de masa de un material homogéneo 1 K ó 1°C de una manera especificada, dados un volumen y una presión constantes (169)

speed/rapidez la distancia que un objeto se desplaza dividida entre el intervalo de tiempo durante el cual ocurrió el movimiento (5)

states of matter/estados de la material las formas físicas de la materia, que son sólida, líquida y gaseosa (172)

T

temperature/temperatura una medida de qué tan caliente (o frío) está algo; específicamente, una medida de la energía cinética promedio de las partículas de un objeto (158)

terminal velocity/velocidad terminal la velocidad constante de un objeto en caída cuando la fuerza de resistencia del aire es igual en magnitud y opuesta en dirección a la fuerza de gravedad (38)

thermal conduction/conducción térmica la transferencia de energía en forma de calor a través de un material (282)

thermal conductor/conductor térmico un material a través del cual es posible transferir energía en forma de calor (167)

thermal energy/energía térmica la energía cinética de los átomos de una sustancia (165)

thermal expansion/expansión térmica un aumento en el tamaño de una sustancia en respuesta a un aumento en la temperatura de la sustancia (46)

thermal insulator/aislante térmico un material que reduce o evita la transferencia de calor (167)

thermal pollution/contaminación térmica un aumento en la temperatura de una masa de agua, producido por las actividades humanas y que tieneun efecto dañino en la calidad del agua y en la capacidad de esa masa de agua para permitir que se desarrolle la vida (182)

thrust/empuje la fuerza de empuje o arrastre ejercida por el motor de un avión o cohete (80)

V

velocity/velocidad la rapidez de un objeto en una dirección dada (6)

W

watt/watt (o vatio) la unidad que se usa para expresar potencia; es equivalente a un joule por segundo (símbolo: W) (98)

wedge/cuña una máquina simple que está formada por dos planos inclinados y que se mueve; normalmente se usa para cortar (111)

weight/peso una medida de la fuerza gravitacional ejercida sobre un objeto; su valor puede cambiar en función de la ubicación del objeto en el universo (24)

wheel and axle/eje y rueda una máquina simple que está formada por dos objetos circulares de diferente tamaño; la rueda es el mayor de los dos objetos circulares (109)

work/trabajo la transferencia de energía a un objeto mediante una fuerza que hace que el objeto se mueva en la dirección de la fuerza (94)

work input/trabajo de entrada el trabajo realizado en una máquina; el producto de la fuerza de entrada por la distancia a través de la que se ejerce la fuerza (101)

work output/trabajo producido el trabajo realizado por una máquina; el producto de la fuerza de salida por la distancia a través de la que se ejerce la fuerza (101)

Spanish Glossary

Index

Boldface page numbers refer to illustrative material, such as figures, tables, margin elements, photographs, and illustrations.

Index

Index

Index

Index   241

Index

Credits

Abbreviations used: (t) top, (c) center, (b) bottom, (l) left, (r) right, (bkgd) background

PHOTOGRAPHY

Front Cover Daryl Benson/Masterfile

Skills Practice Lab Teens Sam Dudgeon/HRW

Connection to Astronomy Corbis Images; **Connection to Biology** David M. Phillips/Visuals Unlimited; **Connection to Chemistry** Digital Image copyright © 2005 PhotoDisc; **Connection to Environment** Digital Image copyright © 2005 PhotoDisc; **Connection to Geology** Letraset Phototone; **Connection to Language Arts** Digital Image copyright © 2005 PhotoDisc; **Connection to Meteorology** Digital Image copyright © 2005 PhotoDisc; **Connection to Oceanography** © ICONOTEC; **Connection to Physics** Digital Image copyright © 2005 PhotoDisc

Table of Contents iv (cl), age fotostock/Fabio Cardoso; v (tl), Larry L. Miller/Photo Researchers, Inc.; v (tr), CORBIS Images/HRW; v (cl), © Galen Rowell/CORBIS; vi, Victoria Smith/HRW; x (bl), Sam Dudgeon/HRW; xi (tl), John Langford/HRW; xi (b), Sam Dudgeon/HRW; xii (tl), Victoria Smith/HRW; xii (bl), Stephanie Morris/HRW; xii (br), Sam Dudgeon/HRW; xiii (tl), Patti Murray/Animals, Animals; xiii (tr), Jana Birchum/HRW; xiii (b), Peter Van Steen/HRW

Chapter One 2–3 (all), © AFP/CORBIS; 4 (all), © SuperStock; 6 (bl), Robert Ginn/PhotoEdit; 8 (t), Sergio Purtell/Foca; 9 (tr), Digital Image copyright © 2005 PhotoDisc; 10 (b), Michelle Bridwell/HRW; 11 (b), Michelle Bridwell/HRW; 11 (t), © Roger Ressmeyer/CORBIS; 12 (t), Daniel Schaefer/HRW; 12 (bl), Sam Dudgeon/HRW; 13 (tr), age fotostock/Fabio Cardoso; 16 (bl, br), Michelle Bridwell/HRW; 16 (inset), Stephanie Morris/HRW; 18 (br), © Annie Griffiths Belt/CORBIS; 19 (tr), Sam Dudgeon/HRW; 19 (cr), Victoria Smith/HRW; 20 (tr), NASA; 25 (tr), Digital Image copyright © 2005 PhotoDisc; 26 (bl), Sam Dudgeon/HRW; 27 (b), Sam Dudgeon/HRW; 28 (tr), © Roger Ressmeyer/CORBIS; 28 (tl), Digital Image copyright © 2005 PhotoDisc; 29 (br), Sam Dudgeon/HRW; 32 (tl, c), Sam Dudgeon/HRW; 32 (tr), Justin Sullivan/Getty Images; 33 (bl), Allsport Concepts/Getty Images; 33 (cr), Courtesy Dartmouth University

Chapter Two 34–35 (all), NASA; 35 (br), NASA; 36 (bl), Richard Megna/Fundamental Photographs; 38 (tl), Toby Rankin/Masterfile; 39 (tr), James Sugar/Black Star; 39 (bl), NASA; 41 (bl), Michelle Bridwell/Frontera Fotos; 41 (br), Image copyright © 2005 PhotoDisc, Inc.; 42 (tc), Richard Megna/Fundamental Photographs; 43 (tr), Toby Rankin/Masterfile; 44 (b), John Langford/HRW; 46 (br), Mavournea Hay/HRW; 46 (bc), Michelle Bridwell/Frontera Fotos; 47 (all), Victoria Smith/HRW; 48 (all), Image copyright © 2005 PhotoDisc, Inc.; 49 (b), David Madison; 50 (tc), Gerard Lacz/Animals Animals/Earth Scenes; 50 (tr), Sam Dudgeon/HRW; 50 (r), Image copyright © 2005 PhotoDisc, Inc.; 50 (tl), NASA; 51 (br), Lance Schriner/HRW; 51 (tr), Victoria Smith/HRW; 53 (all), Michelle Bridwell/HRW; 54 (br), Zigy Kaluzny/Getty Images; 54 (bl), © SuperStock; 55 (cl), Michelle Bridwell/HRW; 56 (bl), Image ©2001 PhotoDisc, Inc.; 57 (all), Sam Dudgeon/HRW; 58 (tc), Gerard Lacz/Animals Animals/Earth Scenes; 59 (all), Sam Dudgeon/HRW; 62 (tl), AP Photo/Martyn Hayhow; 62 (tr), Junko Kimura/Getty Images/NewsCom; 63 (tr), Steve Okamoto; 63 (br), Lee Schwabe

Chapter Three 64–65 (all), © Nicholas Pinturas/Getty Images; 68 (tl), © Royalty Free/CORBIS; 68 (tcl), David R. Frazier Photolibrary; 68 (cl), Dieter and Mary Plage/Bruce Coleman, Inc.; 68 (bcl), Wolfgang Kaehler/CORBIS; 68 (bl), © Martin Barraud/Getty Images; 69 (tr), © SuperStock; 69 (tcr), Daniel A. Nord; 69 (cr), © Ken Marschall/Madison Press Books; 69 (bcr), Dr. Paul A. Zahl/Photo Researchers, Inc.; 69 (br), CORBIS/Bettman; 71 (tr), © Charles Doswell III/Getty Images; 74 (tl), Bruno P. Zehnder/Peter Arnold, Inc.; 78 (br), Richard Megna/Fundamental Photographs/HRW Photo; 80 (tl), Larry L. Miller/Photo Researchers, Inc.; 80 (tr), Richard Neville/Check Six; 82 (tr), John Neubauer/PhotoEdit; 83 (br), Check Six; 85 (b), Sam Dudgeon/HRW; 86 (tr), © SuperStock; 90 (tc), © Victor Malafronte; 90 (tl), Sam Dudgeon/HRW; 91 (bl), Corbis Images; 91 (tr), Courtesy of Alisha Bracken

Chapter Four 92–93 (all), age fotostock/Photographer, Year; 94 (bl), John Langford/HRW; 95 (all), John Langford/HRW; 96 (all), © Galen Rowell/CORBIS; 97 (all), Sam Dudgeon/HRW; 98 (all), John Langford/HRW; 100 (cr), Scott Van Osdol/HRW; 100 (br), Robert Wolf/HRW; 100 (bc), Digital Image copyright © 2005 Artville; 101 (br), Sam Dudgeon/HRW; 102 (all), Scott Van Osdol/HRW; 103 (tr, cr), Sam Dudgeon/HRW; 103 (tl), John Langford/HRW; 104 (br), CC Studio/Science Photo Library/Photo Researchers, Inc.; 105 (tr), © Reuters NewMedia Inc./CORBIS; 106 (bc), Victoria Smith/HRW; 106 (br), Robert Wolf/HRW; 107 (tr), Robert Wolf/HRW; 107 (br), Scott Van Osdol/HRW; 107 (bc), Sam Dudgeon/HRW; 107 (tc), John Langford/HRW; 109 (t), Robert Wolf/HRW; 110 (tr), Lisa Davis/HRW; 111 (tl, cr), Sam Dudgeon/HRW; 111 (br), Robert Wolf/HRW ; 112 (b), Robert Wolf/HRW; 113 (tr), Robert Wolf/HRW; 113 (br), John Langford/HRW; 114 (bl), Stephanie Morris/HRW; 115 (br), Paul Dance/Getty Images; 116 (tl), John Langford/HRW; 117 (cl), Helmut Gritscher/Peter Arnold, Inc.; 117 (tr), Robert Wolf/HRW; 117 (cr), John Langford/HRW; 117 (br), Stephanie Morris/HRW; 120 (tr), © Visuals Unlimited; 120 (tl), Wayne Sorce; 121 (cr), A.W. Stegmeyer/Upstream; 121 (bl), Digital Image copyright © 2005 PhotoDisc

Chapter Five 122–123 (all), © AFP/CORBIS; 124 (br), Tim Kiusalaas/Masterfile; 125 (cr), Sam Dudgeon/HRW; 126 (tl), Earl Kowall/CORBIS; 127 (br), Sam Dudgeon/HRW; 128 (tl), John Langford/HRW; 128 (tc), Corbis Images; 128 (tr), David Phillips/HRW; 129 (br), Sam Dudgeon/HRW; 129 (cr), Peter Van Steen/HRW; 130 (tr), John Langford/HRW; 130 (bl), NASA; 131 (cr), Peter Van Steen/HRW; 132 (br), © Duomo/CORBIS; 133(bl, br), John Langford/HRW; 133 (tr), Peter Van Steen/HRW; 136 (all), John Langford/HRW; 137 (tr), © Martin Bond/Photo Researchers, Inc.; 140 (bl), Sam Dudgeon/HRW; 141 (all), Courtesy of Honda; 143 (tl), Robert Brook/Photo Researchers, Inc.; 143 (cl), Sam Dudgeon/HRW; 143 (bl), John Langford/HRW; 144 (bl), D.O.E./Science Source/Photo Researchers, Inc.; 145 (tr), © John D. Cunningham/Visuals Unlimited; 145 (b), CORBIS Images/HRW; 146 (tl), Digital Image copyright © 2005 PhotoDisc; 150 (tl), Courtesy of Honda; 150 (bc), Digital Image copyright © 2005 PhotoDisc; 151 (bl), © Patrik Glardino/CORBIS; 154 (bl), Courtesy Pursuit Dynamics; 154 (tr), © Bettman/CORBIS; 155 (all), Robert Wolf/HRW

Chapter Six 156–157 (all), © Vandystadt/Allsport/Getty Images; 159 (br), John Langford/HRW; 161 (br), Michelle Bridwell/HRW; 162 (tl), Mark Burnett/Photo Researchers, Inc.; 163 (tr), AP Photo/Joe Giblin; 164 (all), Sam Dudgeon/HRW; 165 (all), John Langford/HRW; 166 (b), John Langford/HRW; 168 (cl), John Langford/HRW; 169 (tr), John Langford/HRW; 170 (tl), John Langford/HRW; 171 (cr), © Simon Watson/FoodPix/Getty Images; 172 (bc), Sam Dudgeon/HRW; 173 (all), John Langford/HRW; 174 (cl), John Langford/HRW; 175 (tr), Peter Van Steen/HRW; 177 (br), John Langford/HRW; 180 (tr), Dorling Kindersley Ltd.; 180 (bl), © COMSTOCK; 183 (tr), John Langford/HRW; 185 (br), Victoria Smith/HRW; 186 (tl), John Langford/HRW; 187 (bl), AP Photo/Joe Giblin; 190 (tl), Dan Winters/Discover Magazine; 191 (b), Solar Survival Architecture; 191 (tr), Singeli Agnew/Taos News

Lab Book/Appendix "LabBook Header", "L", Corbis Images; "a", Letraset Phototone; "b", and "B", HRW; "o", and "k", images ©2006 PhotoDisc/HRW; 192 (all), Sam Dudgeon/HRW; 193 (br), Sam Dudgeon/HRW; 195 (c), Sam Dudgeon/HRW; 200 (br), Sam Dudgeon/HRW; 201 (b), Sam Dudgeon/HRW; 202 (br), John Langford/HRW; 204 (tr, cr), Robert Wolf; 204 (br), Sam Dudgeon/HRW; 205 (br), Victoria Smith/HRW; 207 (br), Sam Dudgeon/HRW; 212 (br), Victoria Smith; 213 (br), Victoria Smith; 229 (tr), Sam Dudgeon/HRW

TEACHER EDITION CREDITS

1E (br), © Roger Ressmeyer/CORBIS; 1E (tr), Sergio Purtell/Foca; 1F (cl), © Annie Griffiths Belt/CORBIS; 1F (tr), NASA; 33E (br), Toby Rankin/Masterfile; 33F (br), © Zigy Kaluzny/Getty Images/Stone; 33F (tr), Index Stock Imagery, Inc.; 33F (cl), John Langford/HRW; 63F (tr), Larry L. Miller/Photo Researchers, Inc.; 63F (cl), © Charles Doswell III/Getty Images; 91E (cl), John Langford/HRW; 91E (tr), Robert Wolf/HRW; 91F (cr), John Langford/HRW; 91F (tl), © Reuters NewMedia Inc./CORBIS; 121E (cl), Tim Kiusalaas/Masterfile; 121E (bl), David Phillips/HRW; 121F (bl), Courtesy of Honda; 121F (tr), Robert Brook/Photo Researchers, Inc.; 155E (cr, br), Sam Dudgeon/HRW; 155F (tr), Dorling Kindersley Ltd.

Answers to Concept Mapping Questions

The following pages contain sample answers to all of the concept mapping questions that appear in the Chapter Reviews. Because there is more than one way to do a concept map, your students' answers may vary.

CHAPTER 1   Matter in Motion

15.

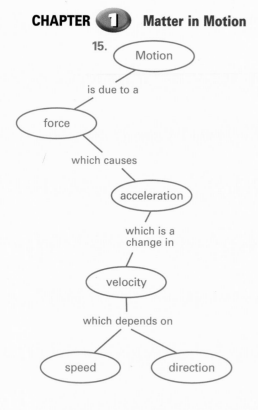

CHAPTER 2   Forces and Motion

15.

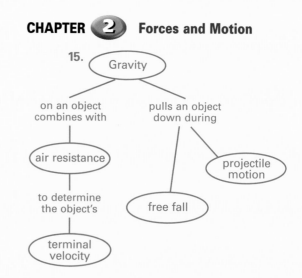

CHAPTER 3   Forces in Fluids

16.

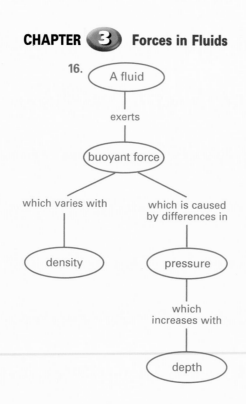

CHAPTER **4** Work and Machines

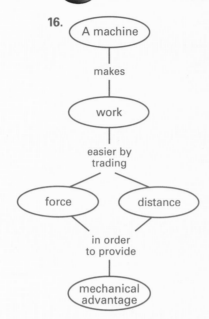

16.

```
A machine
    │
  makes
    │
  work
    │
easier by
 trading
   ╱  ╲
force   distance
   ╲  ╱
 in order
to provide
    │
mechanical
 advantage
```

CHAPTER **5** Energy and Energy Resources

CHAPTER **6** Heat and Heat Technology

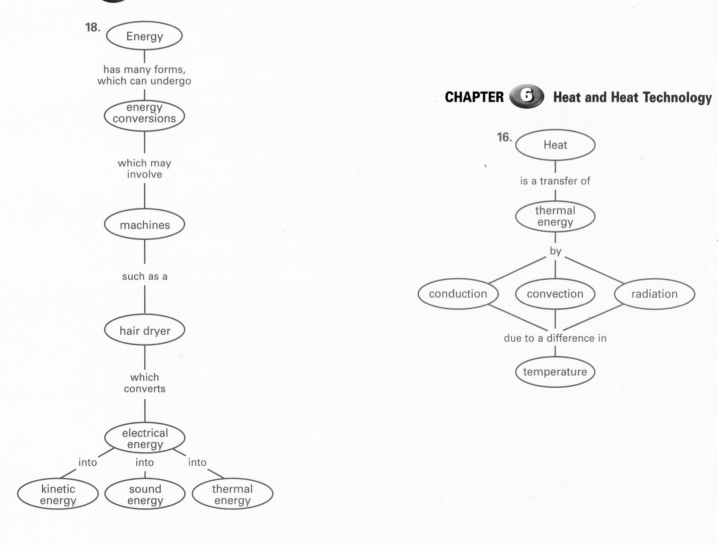

18.

```
Energy
   │
has many forms,
which can undergo
   │
energy
conversions
   │
which may
 involve
   │
machines
   │
such as a
   │
hair dryer
   │
which
converts
   │
electrical
 energy
 ╱  │  ╲
into into into
 ╱   │   ╲
kinetic  sound  thermal
energy   energy  energy
```

16.

```
Heat
   │
is a transfer of
   │
thermal
energy
   │
  by
 ╱ │ ╲
conduction  convection  radiation
 ╲    │    ╱
due to a difference in
       │
  temperature
```